CAROL BERTRAND

SECOND EDITION

DIGITAL SIGNAL PROCESSING

WILLIAM D. STANLEY
Old Dominion University

GARY R. DOUGHERTY
The New School

RAY DOUGHERTY
New York University

RESTON PUBLISHING COMPANY, INC.
A Prentice-Hall Company
Reston, Virginia

Library of Congress Cataloging in Publication Data

Stanley, William D.
   Digital signal processing.

   Includes bibliographical references and index.
   1. Signal processing—Digital techniques.
I. Dougherty, Gary R. II. Dougherty, Ray. III. Title.
TK5102.5.S69   1984   621.38'043   83–4412
ISBN 0–8359–1321–X

*Editorial/production supervision and
interior design by* NORMA M. KARLIN

© 1984 by
Reston Publishing Company, Inc.
A Prentice-Hall Company
Reston, Virginia 22090

10 9 8 7 6 5

PRINTED IN THE UNITED STATES OF AMERICA

Dedicated to
Karen Louise Stanley

CONTENTS

━━━━━ PREFACE ━━━━━

The use of digital techniques for various signal processing applications has increased tremendously in the last few years, and this trend is expected to continue in the years ahead. Systems that previously consisted only of analog circuits now have incorporated digital circuits to do many of the functions required. Engineering personnel at all levels are now required to deal with such systems, and the impact on electronic hardware development and design is most significant.

A major objective of this book is to provide an introductory treatment of the concepts of digital signal processing, with suitable supporting work in linear system concepts and filter design. A further objective is to present a survey of many of the current applications of these techniques, including a consideration of available hardware and software. The project was motivated by the authors' recognition that there was a need for such a book at the introductory level. Most of the journal articles and textbooks having direct application to digital processing are written at a higher level, with strong assumptions about the reader's mathematical background. Thus, this book will have served one of its purposes if it presents enough of a basis to prepare readers with little or no background in discrete system theory to understand some of the many fine references in this field. However, sufficient information is also given to enable the reader to actually specify, implement, or utilize digital signal processing operations.

The first chapter provides a qualitative discussion of digital signal processing and a very brief introduction to the applications. A review of some of the important fundamentals of continuous-time linear system theory is given in Chapter 2. The techniques of Fourier series and spectral analysis are discussed in Chapter 3, and the concept of the sampled signal and its spectrum are developed. The basic theory of discrete-time systems is developed in Chapter 4, while Chapter 5 presents the realization process for such systems and their frequency responses. A survey of the major types of analog filters is given in Chapter 6. Chapter 7 presents a comprehensive treatment of infinite-duration impulse response digital filter design, and the treatment of finite-duration impulse response digital filter design is given in Chapter 8. The properties of the fast Fourier transform are presented in Chapter 9, and various applications of this concept are discussed in Chapter 10.

While the first ten chapters are concerned with the foundations of digital signal processing and the basic principles involved, the last five chapters emphasize a broad survey of the applications in various disciplines. Chapter 11 covers a general overview of these applications; topics covered in Chapters 12 through 15 include industrial signal processing, medical signal processing, speech synthesis, and digital signal processing chips.

Digital Signal Processing can be used as either (a) a textbook for formal college courses in digital signal processing at either the advanced undergraduate or beginning graduate levels, (b) a textbook or reference book for noncredit professional courses in the same area, and (c) a self-study book for practicing engineers who wish to learn the fundamentals of digital signal processing. The large number of example problems and exercises should enhance its value in the third category.

The material has been organized toward a gradual development of the concepts of digital signal processing, on the assumption that many readers will need to review and strengthen their understanding of continuous-time system theory as they progress. However, the reader who has a reasonable background in these fundamentals should be able to advance to any appropriate section of the book without any significant difficulty.

William D. Stanley
Gary R. Dougherty
Ray Dougherty

ACKNOWLEDGMENTS

In addition to acknowledgments within the text, the authors would like to thank the following for their contribution to Chapters 11 to 15.

Paul T. Cody, Eastern Regional Sales Manager of EG & G Reticon, Sunnyvale, California. Intel Corporation.

Stephen J. Durham, Cermetek Microelectronics Inc., Sunnyvale, California.

Fred Williams, TRW, LSI Products Division, La Jolla, California. Tektronix, Inc., Beaverton, Oregon.

Paul E. Mengers, CEO and Chairman of the Board of Quantex Corporation, Sunnyvale, California.

Frank J. Oswald, Specialist, Marketing Communication of General Electric Medical Systems, Milwaukee, Wisconsin.

Joseph Yovar, Director of SPIE, Bellingham, Washington.

Scott Foote, Director of Advertising, National Semiconductor Corporation, Santa Clara, California.

Mr. David Gelbon, Sales Manager, Telesensory Speech Systems, Palo Alto, California.

Jorlin E. Moon, Vice President, Corporate Planning, Votan, Hayward, California.

Richard M. Perdue, Director of Corporate Public Relations, Texas Instruments, Incorporated, Dallas, Texas.

Elliott Blackman, Project Manager, Digital Signal Processing, NEC Electronics, U.S.A., Natick, Massachusetts.

Robert S. Clark, The Optical Publishing Company, Inc., Pittsfield, Massachusetts.

Lynell D. Camron, Marketing Planning Manager, LogEtronics Inc., Springfield, Massachusetts.

Ruth Palaszewski, Boston College.

Robotic Age, Inc., Peterborough, N.H.

Finally, the second edition of *Digital Signal Processing* would never have gotten off the ground floor without the efforts of Mr. David Dusthimer, Mr. Greg Michael, Mrs. Linda MacInnes, and Ms. Norma Karlin of Reston Publishing Company.

—ONE—

THEORY AND PRINCIPLES OF DIGITAL SIGNAL PROCESSING

BY

WILLIAM D. STANLEY

1

GENERAL CONCEPTS OF DIGITAL SIGNAL PROCESSING

1-0 INTRODUCTION

In recent years, there has been a tremendous increase in the use of digital computers and special-purpose digital circuitry for performing varied signal processing functions that were originally achieved with analog equipment. The continued evolution of relatively inexpensive integrated circuits has led to a variety of microcomputers and minicomputers that can be used for various signal processing functions. It is now possible to build special-purpose digital processors within the same size and cost constraints of systems previously all analog in nature.

　　This chapter will provide a general discussion of a few of the basic concepts associated with digital signal processing. The major intent is to provide the reader with a brief overview of the subject before developing the concepts in detail in later chapters.

1-1 GENERAL DISCUSSION

At the beginning of this work, it is appropriate to discuss a few of the common terms that will be used and some of the assumptions that will be made. Wherever possible, the definitions and terminology will be

3

established in accordance with the recommendations of the IEEE Group on Audio and Electroacoustics.

An *analog* signal is a function that is defined over a continuous range of time and in which the amplitude may assume a continuous range of values. Common examples are the sinusoidal function, the step function, the output of a microphone, etc. The term "analog" apparently originated from the field of analog computation, in which voltages and currents are used to represent physical variables, but it has been extended in usage.

A *continuous-time* signal is a function that is defined over a continuous range of time, but in which the amplitude may either have a continuous range of values or a finite number of possible values. In this context, an analog signal could be considered as a special case of a continuous-time signal. In practice, however, the terms "analog" and "continuous-time" are interchanged casually in usage and are often used to mean the same thing. Because of the association of the term "analog" with physical analogies, preference has been established for the term "continuous-time," and this practice will be followed for the most part in this text. Nevertheless, there will be places in which the term "analog" will be used for clarity, particularly where it relates to the term "digital."

The term *quantization* describes the process of representing a variable by a set of distinct values. A *quantized variable* is one that may assume only distinct values.

A *discrete-time* signal is a function that is defined only at a particular set of values of time. This means that the independent variable, time, is quantized. If the amplitude of a discrete-time signal is permitted to assume a continuous range of values, the function is said to be a *sampled-data* signal. A sampled-data signal could arise from sampling an analog signal at discrete values of time.

A *digital* signal is a function in which both time and amplitude are quantized. A digital signal may always be represented by a sequence of numbers in which each number has a finite number of digits.

The terms "discrete-time" and "digital" are often interchanged in practice and are often used to mean the same thing. A great deal of the theory underlying discrete-time signals is applicable to purely digital signals, so it is not always necessary to make rigid distinctions. The term "discrete-time" will more often be used in pursuing theoretical developments, and the term "digital" will more often be used in describing hardware or software realizations.

A system can be described by any of the preceding terms according to the type of hardware or software employed and the type of signals present. Thus, reference can be made to "analog systems," "continuous-time systems," "discrete-time systems," "digital systems," etc.

A *linear* system is one in which the parameters of the system are not dependent on the nature or the level of the input excitation. This statement is equivalent to the statement that the principle of super-position applies. A linear system can be described by linear differential or difference equations. A *time-invariant* linear system is one in which the parameters are fixed and do not vary with time.

A *lumped* system is one that is composed of finite nonzero elements satisfying ordinary differential or difference equation relation-ships (as opposed to a distributed system, satisfying partial differential equation relationships). Very little reference will be made in this text to distributed systems; the implication is that all systems considered will be lumped unless otherwise noted.

In carrying out various theoretical developments, it will fre-quently be necessary to refer to systems that are either (a) continuous-time, linear, and time-invariant, or (b) discrete-time, linear, and time-invariant. For conciseness, we will designate (a) as a CTLTI sys-tem and (b) as a DTLTI system.

The standard form for numerical processing of a digital signal is the binary number system. The binary number system makes use only of the values 0 and 1 to represent all possible numbers. The number of levels m that can be represented by a number having n *binary* dig*its* (bits) is given by

$$m = 2^n \qquad\qquad (1\text{-}1)$$

Conversely, if m is the number of possible levels required, the number of bits required is the smallest integer greater than or equal to $\log_2 m$.

The process by which digital signal processing is achieved will be illustrated by a simplified system in which the signal is assumed to vary from 0 to 7 volts and in which 8 possible levels (at 1 V increments) are used for the binary numbers. A block diagram is shown in Fig. 1-1, and some waveforms of interest are shown in Fig. 1-2. The signal is first passed through a continuous-time presampling filter whose function

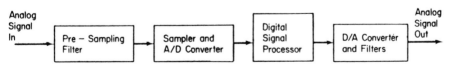

Figure 1-1 Block diagram of a possible digital processing system.

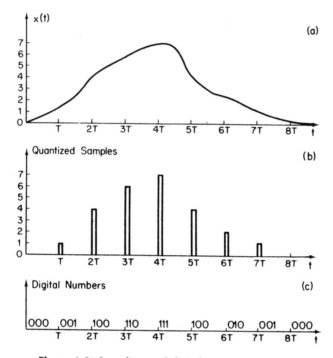

Figure 1-2 Sampling and digital conversion process.

will be discussed later. The signal is then read at intervals of T seconds by a sampler. These samples must then be quantized to one of the standard levels. Although there are different strategies employed in the quantization process, one common approach, which will be assumed here, is that a sample is assigned to the *nearest* level. Thus, a sample of value 4.2 V would be quantized to 4 V, and a sample of value 4.6 V would be quantized to 5 V.

This process for the signal given is illustrated in Fig. 1-2, (a) and (b). The pulses representing the signal have been made very narrow to illustrate the fact that other signals may be inserted, or *multiplexed,* in the empty space. These pulses may then be represented as binary numbers as illustrated in (c). In order that these numbers could be seen on the figure, each has been shown over much of the space in a given interval. In practice, if other signals are to be inserted, the pulses representing the bits of the binary numbers could be made very short. A given binary number could then be read in a very short interval at the beginning of a sampling period, thus leaving most of the time available for other signals.

The process by which an analog sample is quantized and converted to a binary number is called *analog-to-digital (A/D) conversion.* In general, the dynamic range of the signal must be compatible with that of the A/D converter employed, and the number of bits employed must be sufficient for the required accuracy.

The signal can now be processed by the type of unit appropriate for the application intended. This unit may be a general-purpose computer or minicomputer, or it may be a special unit designed specifically for this purpose. At any rate, it is composed of some combination of standard digital circuits capable of performing the various arithmetic functions of addition, subtraction, multiplication, etc. In addition, it has logic and storage capability.

At the output of the processor, the digital signal can be converted to analog form again. This is achieved by the process of *digital-to-analog (D/A) conversion.* In this step, the binary numbers are first successively converted back to continuous-time pulses. The "gaps" between the pulses are then filled in by a *reconstruction filter.* This filter may consist of a holding circuit, which is a special circuit designed to hold the value of a pulse between successive sample values. In some cases, the holding circuit may be designed to extrapolate the output signal between successive points according to some prescribed curve-fitting strategy. In addition to a holding circuit, a basic continuous-time filter may be employed to provide additional smoothing between points.

A fundamental question that may arise is whether or not some information has been lost in the process. After all, the signal has been sampled only at discrete intervals of time; is there something that might be missed in the intervening time intervals? Furthermore, in the process of quantization, the actual amplitude is replaced by the nearest standard level, which means that there is a possible error in amplitude.

In regard to the sampling question, it will be shown in Chapt. 3 that if the signal is bandlimited, and if the sampling rate is greater than or equal to twice the highest frequency, the signal can theoretically be recovered from its discrete samples. This corresponds to a minimum of two samples per cycle at the highest frequency. In practice, this sampling rate is usually chosen to be somewhat higher than the minimum rate (say, three or four times the highest frequency) in order to ensure practical implementation. For example, if the highest frequency of the analog signal is 5 kHz, the theoretical minimum sampling rate is 10,000 samples per second, and a practical system would employ a rate somewhat higher. The input continuous-time signal is often passed through a low-pass analog *presampling filter* to ensure that the highest frequency is within the bounds for which the signal can be recovered.

    If a signal is not sampled at a sufficiently high rate, a phenomenon known as *aliasing* results. This concept results in a frequency's being mistaken for an entirely different frequency upon recovery. For example, suppose a signal with frequencies ranging from dc to 5 kHz is sampled at a rate of 6 kHz, which is clearly too low to ensure recovery. If recovery is attempted, a component of the original signal at 5 kHz now appears to be at 1 kHz, resulting in an erroneous signal. A common example of this phenomenon is one we will call the "wagon wheel effect," probably noticed by the reader in western movies as the phenomenon in which the wheels appear to be rotating backwards. Since each individual frame of a film is equivalent to a discrete sampling operation, if the rate of spokes passing a given angle is too large for a given movie frame rate, the wheels appear to be turning either backwards or at a very slow speed. The effect of a presampling filter removes the possibility that a spurious signal whose frequency is too high for the system will be mistaken for one in the proper frequency range.

    With respect to the quantization error, it can be seen that the error can be made as small as one chooses if the number of bits can be made arbitrarily large. Of course, there is a practical maximum limit, so it is necessary to tolerate some error from this phenomenon. Even in continuous-time systems, there may be noise present which would introduce uncertainty in the actual magnitude. In fact, the uncertainty present in the digital sampling process is called *quantization noise.*

    Let E_{max} and E_{min} represent the maximum and minimum values of the signal, and let q represent the vertical distance between successive quantum levels. Using n and m as previously defined, we have

$$q = \frac{E_{max} - E_{min}}{2^n} = \frac{E_{max} - E_{min}}{m} \qquad (1\text{-}2)$$

Assuming that a sample between two successive quantum levels is assigned to the nearest quantum level, the peak quantization noise and peak percentage quantization noise values are

$$\text{Peak Quantization Noise} = \frac{q}{2} \qquad (1\text{-}3)$$

$$\text{Peak Percentage Quantization Noise} = \frac{100\%}{2m} \qquad (1\text{-}4)$$

    In many cases, the *variance* of the quantization noise is more important than the maximum value. The variance is directly proportional to the *average power* associated with the noise. If the signal is assumed to be uniformly distributed between quantum levels, it can be shown by statistical analysis that the noise variance σ^2 is

$$\sigma^2 = \frac{q^2}{12} \qquad (1\text{-}5)$$

The *root-mean-square (RMS)* (or *standard deviation*) value of this noise component is

$$\sigma = \frac{q}{2\sqrt{3}} \qquad (1\text{-}6)$$

Comparing (1-6) with (1-3), it is seen that the RMS noise component is $1/\sqrt{3}$ times the peak noise component.

In view of the preceding discussion, it appears that no information is lost in the sampling operation provided that the sampling rate is high enough, and the quantization error can be reduced to an insignificantly small level by choosing a sufficient number of bits to represent each binary number. These concepts then permit us to represent a continuous-time signal in terms of a series of discrete binary numbers, which may be processed directly with digital circuits.

The rather involved procedure of A/D conversion, processing, and final D/A conversion may seem like a lot of effort in order to handle one signal channel. Indeed, in many cases such a complex process may not be economically feasible for a single signal. One of the great advantages of the digital concept is the possibility of processing a number of channels with the same arithmetic unit. This process can be achieved by a process called *time-division multiplexing (TDM)*. It was observed in the sampled signal shown in Fig. 1-2 that there was a relatively long period between successive samples of the signal. During this period, samples of additional signals are fed into the processor.

This concept is illustrated in Fig. 1-3. Each channel is read in a sequential order, and the corresponding values are converted into bi-

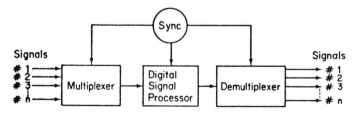

Figure 1-3 Multiplexed digital processing system.

nary numbers in the same sequence. These numbers enter into the processing unit and, after suitable processing, appear at the output in the appropriate order. This composite digital signal must first be separated into the original different channels by means of a *demultiplexer,* which is synchronized with the input sampling signal. The channels then undergo the D/A conversion required for output.

In the preceding discussions, we have assumed that both the starting and final signals in the system are in continuous-time form. Actually, there are many systems in which one or both are already digital in form. In such cases the A/D conversion and/or the D/A conversion may not be required, thus simplifying the system. For example, assume that a number of continuous-time telemetry signals is to be processed by a digital unit, but the output data is to be kept in digital form for scientific data reduction and computation. In this case, the A/D unit at the input is required, but no conversion is needed at the output.

1-2 TYPES OF PROCESSING

Much of this textbook will be devoted to the development and applications of two important tools for modern digital signal processing: *digital filters* and *fast Fourier transforms (FFTs).*

A digital filter is a computational process in which the sequence of input numbers is converted into a sequence of output numbers representing the alteration of the data in some prescribed manner. A common example is the process of filtering out a certain range of frequencies in a signal while rejecting all other frequencies, which is one of the foremost classical approaches to analog filter design. In the classical continuous-time case, this filtering is achieved by a suitable choice of inductors, capacitors, and resistors arranged to provide the required transmission characteristics. However, in the digital case, this can be achieved completely by the process of digital addition, multiplication by constants, and delay.

To present an example which the reader is not expected to understand at this point, but which is shown for motivation, consider the circuits in Fig. 1-4. A certain low-pass analog filter having a 3 dB cutoff frequency of 50 Hz is shown in (a). A digital filter having approximately the same frequency response from dc to five times cutoff (250 kHz) is shown in (b). The various units in the filter correspond to addition, multiplication, and delay, as indicated on the figure.

The second method that we will consider is that of the fast Fourier transform (FFT) concept. The techniques of spectral analysis employing Fourier transforms and series have long represented an important

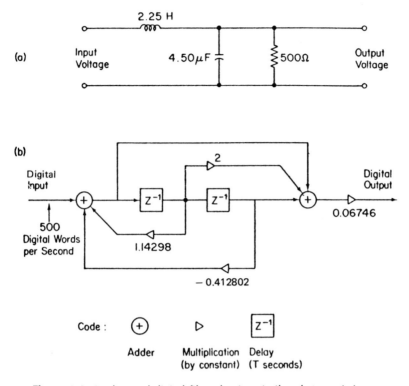

Figure 1-4 Analog and digital filters having similar characteristics.

area of application in continuous-time signal processing. The development in 1965 of the Cooley-Tukey algorithms for rapid computation of the approximate spectrum paved the way for new and varied applications of spectral analysis. With this approach, the spectrum of signals containing many thousands of sample points can be achieved in a matter of milliseconds. In fact, it has become quite feasible to filter signals by FFT transformation, numerical alteration of the spectrum, and inverse FFT computation.

There are many varied scientific disciplines that utilize spectral analysis in one form or another and in which the FFT has opened new potential applications. Among these are communications signal analysis, solution of boundary value problems in heat and electricity, statistical analysis, oceanographic wave analysis, spectroscopy, and vibrations. There are available special FFT processors which may be used for real-time processing in many applications. In addition, many computers have FFT subroutines available in their libraries.

2

CONTINUOUS-TIME
SYSTEM ANALYSIS

2-0 INTRODUCTION

As a basis for developing the concepts of digital signal processing and simulation, it is highly desirable that the fundamentals of classical continuous-time linear system theory be understood and utilized extensively in the development process. This body of material has been widely used in the analysis of electric circuits, communications systems, control systems, vibration systems, and many other areas of scientific endeavor.

   The treatment of continuous-time linear system theory given in this chapter is intended to summarize only some of the more basic concepts essential to our primary goal, since many complete textbooks have been written on the subject. It is assumed that most readers will have been previously exposed to the subject in one form or another, so that many of the concepts presented are necessarily abbreviated.

2-1 TIME-DOMAIN DESCRIPTION

Consider a continuous-time, linear, time-invariant (CTLTI) system with a single input $x(t)$ and a single output (response) $y(t)$ as illustrated in block form in Fig. 2-1. The output-input relationship of such a system can always be described by a differential equation of the form

$$b_k \frac{d^k y}{dt^k} + b_{k-1} \frac{d^{k-1} y}{dt^{k-1}} + \cdots + b_0 y =$$

$$a_\ell \frac{d^\ell x}{dt^\ell} + a_{\ell-1} \frac{d^{\ell-1} x}{dt^{\ell-1}} + \cdots + a_0 x$$

(2-1)

In most cases of interest here, $k \geqslant \ell$, and we will assume this inequality unless otherwise stated. In this case, the integer k specifies the *order* of the system. For any arbitrary input $x(t)$, the solution of the resulting kth order differential equation will yield the output $y(t)$. Various classical procedures for solving differential equations are available, and they may be found in both linear system and differential equation textbooks.

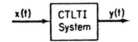

Figure 2-1 Input-output form for CTLTI system.

The output may also be expressed in terms of the *convolution integral* and the impulse response. The impulse response $g(t)$ is the response of the system when the input is a unit impulse function $\delta(t)$. Assuming that the impulse response is known, the response due to any input $x(t)$ can be expressed as

$$y(t) = x(t)*g(t) = \int_{-\infty}^{\infty} x(\tau)g(t-\tau)\,d\tau \qquad (2\text{-}2)$$

or

$$y(t) = \int_{-\infty}^{\infty} g(\tau)x(t-\tau)\,d\tau \qquad (2\text{-}3)$$

where τ is a dummy variable of integration, and the symbol $*$ denotes convolution. Some examples will now be given to illustrate the relationships of this section.

Example 2-1

Obtain a differential equation of the form of (2-1) for the circuit of Fig. 2-2). The input is v_1 and the output is v_2.

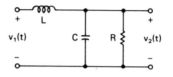

Figure 2-2 Circuit of Ex. 2-1.

Solution

A node voltage equation written at the output node will accomplish the goal. This equation results from the application of Kirchhoff's Current Law at this node, which states that the sum of the currents leaving the node is zero. We have

$$i_L + i_C + i_R = 0$$

or

$$\frac{1}{L}\int_{-\infty}^{t}(v_2 - v_1)\,dt + C\frac{dv_2}{dt} + \frac{v_2}{R} = 0 \qquad (2\text{-}4)$$

Differentiation of all terms of (2-4) and rearrangement yield

$$\frac{d^2v_2}{dt^2} + \frac{1}{RC}\frac{dv_2}{dt} + \frac{1}{LC}v_2 = \frac{1}{LC}v_1 \qquad (2\text{-}5)$$

The form of (2-5) indicates that the circuit represents a second-order system. Note that there are no derivative terms on the right in this particular case.

Example 2-2

Obtain a differential equation of the form of (2-1) for the circuit of Fig. 2-3. The input is v_1 and the output is v_2.

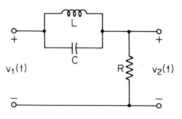

Figure 2-3 Circuit of Ex. 2-2.

Solution

Proceeding as in Ex. 2-1, we sum the currents leaving the output node to obtain

$$C\frac{d}{dt}(v_2 - v_1) + \frac{1}{L}\int_{-\infty}^{t}(v_2 - v_1)dt + \frac{v_2}{R} = 0 \qquad (2\text{-}6)$$

Differentiation of all terms and rearrangement yield

$$\frac{d^2v_2}{dt^2} + \frac{1}{RC}\frac{dv_2}{dt} + \frac{1}{LC}v_2 = \frac{d^2v_1}{dt^2} + \frac{1}{LC}v_1 \qquad (2\text{-}7)$$

Note that the order of the highest derivative on the right is the same as the order of the highest derivative on the left in this case.

Example 2-3

The impulse response of a certain CTLTI system is given by

$$g(t) = 0 \quad \text{for } t < 0$$
$$= \epsilon^{-2t} \text{ for } t \geq 0 \qquad (2\text{-}8)$$

By means of the convolution integral, determine the response $y(t)$ due to the ramp input

$$x(t) = 0 \text{ for } t < 0$$
$$= 4t \text{ for } t \geq 0 \qquad (2\text{-}9)$$

Solution

Although the form of either (2-2) or (2-3) could be used, we will arbitrarily select (2-3) in this case. It is highly recommended that a series of sketches depicting the various quantities within the integrand be made before actually performing any convolution integration. Such sketches serve to precisely define the actual integration limits required in the integral. The determination of these limits is often a source of difficulty in applying the convolution process, particularly for functions having different forms over different intervals.

Referring to Fig. 2-4, the functions $g(t)$ and $x(t)$ are first shown in (a) and (b) with the actual time variable t replaced by the dummy variable τ. Hence, the functions shown are $g(\tau)$ and $x(\tau)$. The dummy variable τ in $x(\tau)$ is replaced by $-\tau$ in (c). This results in a new function,

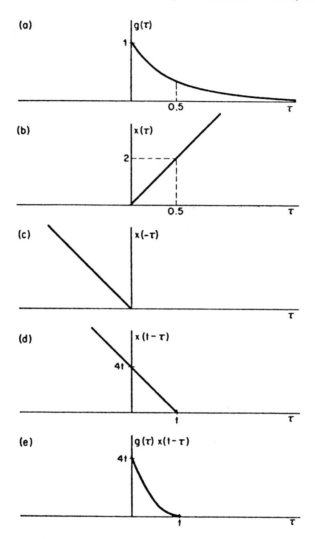

Figure 2-4 Convolution operations for Ex. 2-3.

which is the mirror image of the original function about the vertical axis. When $-\tau$ is replaced by $t - \tau$, where t is any arbitrary positive value of time, the function shifts to the right by an amount t as shown in (d). Note that for integration purposes, t is considered to be a parameter rather than a variable. The form of the product of $g(\tau)$ and $x(t - \tau)$ is shown in (e). This is the integrand of the convolution integral, so the area under this curve must be determined as a function of the parameter t.

In this problem, we will use analytical methods for the integration due to the nature of the functions involved. For problems in which one or both of the functions have constant values over specific intervals, the convolution integral is often easier to evaluate by direct graphical methods. (See Prob. 2-4.) In the present case, the actual limits of integration are seen to be from 0 to t. Substitution of these limits and the appropriate functions in (2-3) results in

$$y(t) = \int_0^t \epsilon^{-2\tau} 4(t-\tau)d\tau = 4t \int_0^t \epsilon^{-2\tau} d\tau - 4 \int_0^t \tau\epsilon^{-2\tau} d\tau$$

$$= \epsilon^{-2t} + 2t - 1 \text{ for } t \geqslant 0$$

(2-10)

2-2   LAPLACE TRANSFORM METHODS

The techniques of the Laplace transform provide certain powerful conceptual and analytical methods having direct application to the analysis and synthesis of linear systems. In this section, we will review some of the fundamentals of this approach as a basis for the linear system developments that follow.

Classically, the Laplace transform is regarded as an operational method for solving a linear differential equation with constant coefficients such as was described in (2-1), with $x(t)$ usually specified. Both sides of the differential equation are transformed by means of certain function and operation pairs. This results in an algebraic equation, which may be manipulated by standard algebraic operations. The transform solution must then be inverted (or inversely transformed) to obtain the desired solution. For systems such as (2-1) in which time is the independent variable, the original differential equation is said to be a representation in the *time domain*, whereas the transformed equation is said to be a representation in the *transform*, or *complex frequency*, *domain*.

The general response $y(t)$ due to any arbitrary input $x(t)$ can be represented as the sum of a *natural response* $y_n(t)$ and a *forced response* $y_f(t)$, i.e.,

$$y(t) = y_n(t) + y_f(t)$$

(2-11)

The *form of the natural response depends only on the parameters* of the system, but its magnitude depends both on the initial energy stored in the system and on the form of the excitation. The form of the forced response depends only on the type of excitation, and in general will exhibit the same form as the excitation. Its magnitude, however, will be a function of the system parameters.

There are several different terms used in the literature to denote these quantities. The terms *free response, complementary solution*, and *transient response* are used synonymously with *natural response*. Likewise, the terms *particular solution* and *steady-state* are used synonymously with *forced response*. Strictly speaking, the terms *transient* and *steady-state* in this context are descriptively correct only when the system is stable. In this case, these latter terms are widely used in engineering problems to describe the system behavior. (More will be said about these points later.)

The treatment of the Laplace transform in this text will be limited to the *one-sided* form, which is the most widely employed form in engineering applications. The actual definition of the one-sided Laplace transform is given by

$$X(s) = \mathcal{L}\left[x(t)\right] = \int_0^\infty x(t)\,\epsilon^{-st}\,dt \qquad (2\text{-}12)$$

subject to certain mathematical restrictions on $x(t)$. (These restrictions rarely cause difficulty in most engineering applications and will not be discussed here.) The inverse Laplace transform is given by the complex inversion integral

$$x(t) = \mathcal{L}^{-1}[X(s)] = \frac{1}{2\pi j} \int_C X(s)\,\epsilon^{st}\,ds \qquad (2\text{-}13)$$

where C is a contour chosen to include all singularities of $X(s)$. Many transforms can be inverted with the aid of a few standard pairs, so it is not often necessary to employ (2-13) in routine transform problems.

Using the transform definition, various pairs can be derived and tabulated. A list of the most common transform pairs encountered in CTLTI system analysis is given in Table 2-1. It is also convenient to employ certain operation pairs in manipulating transforms. A list of some of the most common operation pairs is given in Table 2-2. Many of the more complex function and operation pairs can be derived by application of these basic pairs.

The actual transforms of most desired response waveforms will normally be more complex than the functions given in the tables. However, such transforms can usually be decomposed into a sum of terms of the forms given in the tables by means of partial fraction expansion methods.

Table 2-1
Some common Laplace transform function pairs.

x(t)	X(s) = $\mathcal{L}[x(t)]$	
$\delta(t)$	1	(LT-1)
1 or u(t)	$\dfrac{1}{s}$	(LT-2)
t	$\dfrac{1}{s^2}$	(LT-3)
$\epsilon^{-\alpha t}$	$\dfrac{1}{s+\alpha}$	(LT-4)
$\sin \omega t$	$\dfrac{\omega}{s^2+\omega^2}$	(LT-5)
$\cos \omega t$	$\dfrac{s}{s^2+\omega^2}$	(LT-6)
$\epsilon^{-\alpha t}\sin \omega t$	$\dfrac{\omega}{(s+\alpha)^2+\omega^2}$	(LT-7)
$\epsilon^{-\alpha t}\cos \omega t$	$\dfrac{s+\alpha}{(s+\alpha)^2+\omega^2}$	(LT-8)
t^n	$\dfrac{n!}{s^{n+1}}$	(LT-9)
$\epsilon^{-\alpha t} t^n$	$\dfrac{n!}{(s+\alpha)^{n+1}}$	(LT-10)

Example 2-4

The input-output relationship of a certain system is described by the differential equation

$$\frac{d^2y}{dt^2} + 3\frac{dy}{dt} + 2y = x \qquad (2\text{-}14)$$

Find the response when $x(t)$ is a step function of 10 units applied at $t = 0$, i.e., $x(t) = u(t)$. The initial conditions are $y(0) = 2, y'(0) = -10$.

Table 2-2

Some common Laplace transform operation pairs.

$x(t)$	$X(s) = \mathcal{L}[x(t)]$	
$ax_1(t) + bx_2(t)$	$aX_1(s) + bX_2(s)$	(LO-1)
$\dfrac{d^n x(t)}{dt^n}$	$s^n X(s) - \sum\limits_{i=0}^{n-1} s^{n-1-i}\, \dfrac{d^i x(0)}{dt^i}$	(LO-2)
$\displaystyle\int_{-\infty}^{t} x(\tau)\,d\tau$	$\dfrac{X(s)}{s} + \dfrac{1}{s}\displaystyle\int_{-\infty}^{0} x(\tau)\,d\tau$	(LO-3)
$x(t-a)\,u(t-a)$	$\epsilon^{-as}\,X(s)$	(LO-4)
$\epsilon^{-at}\,x(t)$	$X(s+a)$	(LO-5)
$x(at)$	$\dfrac{1}{a}\,X\left(\dfrac{s}{a}\right)$	(LO-6)
$tx(t)$	$-\dfrac{dX(s)}{ds}$	(LO-7)
$x(0^+)$	$\lim\limits_{s\to\infty} sX(s)$	(LO-8)
$x(\infty)$	$^{1}\lim\limits_{s\to 0} sX(s)$	(LO-9)
$\displaystyle\int_{-\infty}^{\infty} x_1(\tau)x_2(t-\tau)\,d\tau$	$X_1(s)X_2(s)$	(LO-10)

[1]This theorem is valid only if the poles of $sX(s)$ are located in the left-hand half-plane

Solution

Application of the Laplace transformation to both sides of the equation and utilization of pairs (LT-2), (LO-1), and (LO-2) yield

$$s^2 Y(s) - 2s - (-10) + 3[sY(s) - 2] + 2Y(s) = \frac{10}{s} \qquad (2\text{-}15)$$

$$(s^2 + 3s + 2)Y(s) = \frac{10}{s} + 2s - 4 \qquad (2\text{-}16)$$

$$Y(s) = \frac{10}{s(s^2 + 3s + 2)} + \frac{2s - 4}{s^2 + 3s + 2} \qquad (2\text{-}17)$$

$$= \frac{10}{s(s+1)(s+2)} + \frac{2s - 4}{(s+1)(s+2)}$$

Individual partial fraction expansion of the preceding terms yields

$$Y(s) = \frac{5}{s} - \frac{10}{s+1} + \frac{5}{s+2} - \frac{6}{s+1} + \frac{8}{s+2} \qquad (2\text{-}18)$$

Inversion yields

$$y(t) = 5 - 16\epsilon^{-t} + 13\epsilon^{-2t} \qquad (2\text{-}19)$$

The reader is invited to verify that the initial conditions are satisfied.

2-3   TRANSFER FUNCTION _____

Consider a CTLTI system as described by (2-1), and assume that the system is initially *relaxed*, i.e., no energy is stored in the system. Under these conditions, it can be shown that all initial condition terms resulting from application of the Laplace transform to (2-1) cancel on both sides of the equation. Making use of this fact, the transformed equation is

$$(b_k s^k + b_{k-1} s^{k-1} + \cdots + b_0) Y(s) =$$
$$(a_\ell s^\ell + a_{\ell-1} s^{\ell-1} + \cdots + a_0) X(s) \qquad (2\text{-}20)$$

Solving for $Y(s)$, we obtain

$$Y(s) = \frac{(a_\ell s^\ell + a_{\ell-1} s^{\ell-1} + \cdots + a_0)}{(b_k s^k + b_{k-1} s^{k-1} + \cdots + b_0)} X(s) \qquad (2\text{-}21)$$

We may now define a *transfer function* (or *system function*) $G(s)$ as

$$G(s) = \frac{N(s)}{D(s)} = \frac{a_\ell s^\ell + a_{\ell-1} s^{\ell-1} + \cdots + a_0}{b_k s^k + b_{k-1} s^{k-1} + \cdots + b_0} \qquad (2\text{-}22)$$

where $N(s)$ is the numerator polynomial and $D(s)$ is the denominator polynomial. Using the transfer function, the input-output relationship simply becomes

$$Y(s) = G(s) X(s) \qquad (2\text{-}23)$$

The time--domain response $y(t)$ can then be determined by inversion of $Y(s)$.

The impulse response can now be readily determined by letting $x(t) = \delta(t)$ or $X(s) = 1$. In this case the output transform is identical with the transfer function, so we have for the impulse response

$$g(t) = \mathcal{L}^{-1}[G(s)] \qquad (2\text{-}24)$$

In later chapters, we will deal with transfer functions of discrete-time systems as well as those of continuous-time systems. When it is necessary to distinguish between these different functions, a transfer function of a CTLTI system as described by (2-22) will be denoted simply as a *continuous transfer function*.

Example 2-5

(a) Determine the transfer function of the circuit in Ex. 2-1. (b) Determine the impulse response for $L = 2$ H, $C = 1/10$ F, and $R = 5$ Ω.

Solution

(a) We may transform (2-4) directly and obtain

$$\left(\frac{1}{sL} + sC + \frac{1}{R}\right) V_2(s) = \frac{1}{sL} V_1(s) \qquad (2\text{-}25)$$

or

$$\frac{V_2(s)}{V_1(s)} = G(s) = \frac{\dfrac{1}{LC}}{s^2 + \dfrac{s}{RC} + \dfrac{1}{LC}} \qquad (2\text{-}26)$$

As an alternate approach, we may replace the resistor, inductor, and capacitor by their *transform impedances* as shown in Fig. 2-5. This circuit may now be manipulated by any standard circuit method without going through the differential equation at all. (Note that if a system is not initially relaxed, a transform circuit model would have to contain one or more fictitious generators to take care of the initial energy stored.)

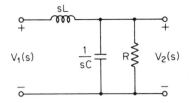

Figure 2-5 Transform impedance circuit for Ex. 2-5.

(b) For the choice of parameters given, the transfer function is

$$G(s) = \frac{5}{s^2 + 2s + 5} = \frac{2.5(2)}{(s+1)^2 + (2)^2} \qquad (2\text{-}27)$$

which has been put in the form of (LT-7) in Table 2-1 due to the presence of complex roots. The impulse response is then

$$g(t) = 2.5\epsilon^{-t}\sin 2t \qquad (2\text{-}28)$$

Example 2-6

Determine the response of the system considered in Ex. 2-5 when the input is a sinusoidal function $x(t) = 40 \sin t$.

Solution

The transform of the input signal is

$$X(s) = \frac{40}{s^2 + 1} \qquad (2\text{-}29)$$

The output transform is

$$Y(s) = \frac{200}{(s^2 + 2s + 5)(s^2 + 1)} \qquad (2\text{-}30)$$

Although there are various approaches to inverting (2-30), we will use a standard partial fraction expansion with the quadratic polynomials factored in the forms displaying their natural roots. (We will also choose to express the angles of complex exponentials in degrees for convenience.) We have

$$\frac{200}{(s+1-j2)(s+1+j2)(s-j)(s+j)} =$$

$$\frac{11.18\epsilon^{j\,26.565°}}{s+1-j2} + \frac{11.18\epsilon^{-j\,26.565°}}{s+1+j2} + \frac{22.361\epsilon^{-j\,116.565°}}{s-j} + \frac{22.361\epsilon^{j\,116.565°}}{s+j}$$

$$(2\text{-}31)$$

Inversion of the terms in (2-31) and conversion of the two complex exponential pairs to real functions yield

$$
\begin{aligned}
y(t) &= 22.361\epsilon^{-t}\,\cos\,(2t + 26.565°) + 44.721\,\cos\,(t-116.565°) \\
&= 22.361\epsilon^{-t}\,\sin\,(2t + 116.565°) + 44.721\,\sin\,(t-26.565°)
\end{aligned}
$$

$$(2\text{-}32)$$

2-4   POLES, ZEROS, AND STABILITY

Consider the transfer function

$$G(s) = \frac{N(s)}{D(s)} \qquad (2\text{-}33)$$

The following definitions are given:

(a) *Poles (finite)*. The k roots of $D(s)$ are called the *finite poles* of the transfer function.

(b) *Zeros (finite)*. The ℓ roots of $N(s)$ are called the *finite zeros* of the transfer function.

(c) *Critical Frequencies*. All the poles and zeros are said to be the complex critical frequencies of the function.

The finite poles and zeros of a transfer function may be plotted in the *complex s-plane* as illustrated in Fig. 2-6 for a particular case. The zeros are represented as O's and the poles as X's.

In the analysis of filter responses, it is desirable to refer to *zeros at* ∞, (as contrasted from finite zeros). Assuming that the degree of the denominator polynomial k is larger than the degree of the numerator polynomial ℓ, we define an integer r to represent the *number of zeros at* ∞. The quantity r is given by

$$r = k - \ell \qquad (2\text{-}34)$$

It can be shown that for large s, the function $G(s)$ becomes asymptotic to

$$G(s) \approx \frac{a_\ell}{b_k s^{k-\ell}} = \frac{a_\ell}{b_k s^r} \text{ for } |s| \gg 1 \qquad (2\text{-}35)$$

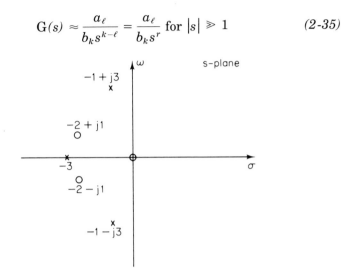

Figure 2-6 Pole-zero plot for a typical CTLTI transfer function.

In the analysis of certain special types of functions, the degree of $N(s)$ may exceed the degree of $D(s)$. In this case, it is convenient to define an integer r_1 to represent the *number of poles at* ∞. It is given by

$$r_1 = \ell - k \qquad (2\text{-}36)$$

In this case, for large s, $G(s)$ becomes asymptotic to

$$G(s) \approx \frac{a_\ell s^{\ell-k}}{b_k} = \frac{a_\ell s^{r_1}}{b_k} \text{ for } |s| \gg 1 \qquad (2\text{-}37)$$

Using these definitions, the number of poles will always equal the number of zeros as long as we include critical frequencies at $s = \infty$.

Assume now that all the finite zeros and poles of a transfer function are known. Let us denote the ℓ finite zeros as $z_1, z_2, \cdots, z_\ell$ and the k finite poles as $p_1, p_2, \cdots, p_k$. $G(s)$ can then be expressed as

$$G(s) = \frac{A(s - z_1)(s - z_2) \cdots (s - z_\ell)}{(s - p_1)(s - p_2) \cdots (s - p_k)} \qquad (2\text{-}38)$$

where $A = a_\ell / b_k$ is equivalent to a single constant. Thus, a transfer function may be determined within a constant multiplier from a knowledge of its poles and zeros.

When a system is excited by an aribtrary input $x(t)$, the transform of the output $Y(s)$ is obtained by multiplying $G(s)$ by $X(s)$. For simplicity in discussion, assume for the moment that there are no multiple-order poles in $Y(s)$ and that the denominator degree is higher than the numerator degree. $Y(s)$ may then be expanded to a partial fraction expansion of the form

$$Y(s) = \sum_{r=1}^{M} \frac{K_r}{s - p_r} \qquad (2\text{-}39)$$

A given K_r represents the coefficient corresponding to the pole p_r in the partial fraction expansion. (It is also the *residue* of $Y(s)$ at $s = p_r$.) The integer M is the sum of the order of $G(s)$ and the number of poles of $X(s)$. The time response resulting from inversion of (2-39) is of the form

$$y(t) = \sum_{r=1}^{M} K_r \epsilon^{p_r t} \qquad (2\text{-}40)$$

In general, a given pole p_r is complex and can be expressed as

$$p_r = \sigma_r + j\omega_r \qquad (2\text{-}41)$$

where σ_r is the real part and ω_r is the imaginary part. The poles in (2-39) correspond to complex natural frequencies in the exponential terms of (2-40). A given σ_r quantity represents the damping factor for an exponential (if it is negative), and a given ω_r quantity represents the radian frequency of a sinusoidal oscillation.

The poles present in $Y(s)$ may result from two sources: poles due to the transfer function $G(s)$, and poles due to the input $X(s)$. The *natural response* is defined as that portion of the response due to the poles of $G(s)$. The *forced response* is defined as that portion of the response due to the poles of $X(s)$. The critical frequencies appearing in the natural response are identical with the critical frequencies appearing in the impulse response $g(t)$. For this reason, the impulse response provides a convenient means to characterize the natural response of a system without obscuring its behavior by some arbitrary forcing function.

If the *natural response* vanishes after a sufficiently long time, it is often called the *transient response*. In this case, only the *forced response* remains, and it is then often referred to as the *steady-state response*.

A system is said to be stable if every finite input produces a finite output. The properties of stability for a CTLTI system may be readily expressed by conditions relating to the impulse response $g(t)$. These conditions are:

(a) *Stable system*. A system is stable if $g(t)$ vanishes after a sufficiently long time.

(b) *Unstable system*. A system is unstable if $g(t)$ grows without bound, i.e., approaches ∞ after a sufficiently long time.

(c) *Marginally stable system*. A system is marginally stable if $g(t)$ approaches a constant nonzero value or a bounded oscillation after a sufficiently long time.

Examples of the three cases are shown in Fig. 2-7.

A stable system will have a bounded output for any bounded input. At the other extreme, an unstable system will have an unbounded output for almost any input signal. A marginally stable system may have either a bounded or an unbounded output, depending on the excitation.

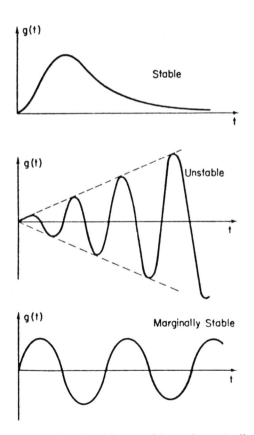

Figure 2-7 Examples of stable, unstable, and marginally stable impulse responses.

   Stability is best determined from the transfer function if the poles are known. A given complex pole $p_r = \sigma_r + j\omega_r$, which may be of multiple order, can be considered to produce terms of the form

$$y_r(t) = A t^i \epsilon^{\sigma_r t} \epsilon^{j\omega_r t} \qquad (2\text{-}42)$$

It can be shown that the only condition required for $y_r(t)$ to eventually vanish is that $\sigma_r < 0$. Likewise, if $\sigma_r = 0$ and $i = 0$ (corresponding to a first-order pole), $y_r(t)$ will be either a constant ($\omega_r = 0$) or a constant amplitude oscillation. However, if $\sigma_r = 0$ and $i > 0$ (corresponding to a multiple-order pole on the $j\omega$-axis), $y_r(t)$ will grow without bound.

   A summary of the preceding points and a few other inferences follow:

(a) Poles of a transfer function in the left-hand half-plane (LHHP) represent stable terms regardless of their order.

(b) Poles of a transfer function in the right-hand half-plane (RHHP) represent unstable terms regardless of their order.

(c) First-order poles on the $j\omega$-axis represent marginally stable terms, but multiple-order poles represent unstable terms.

(d) A system is only as stable as its least stable term. Thus, all poles of a perfectly stable system must lie in the LHHP.

(e) Zeros are permitted in the RHHP and/or the $j\omega$-axis of most transfer functions.

Example 2-7

Write the transfer function corresponding to the pole-zero plot of Fig. 2-6. As an additional fact, it is known that $G(\infty) = 5$.

Solution

Using the form (2-38), we have

$$G(s) = \frac{A(s-0)[s-(-2+j1)][s-(-2-j1)]}{[s-(-3)][s-(-1+j3)][s-(-1-j3)]} \qquad (2\text{-}43)$$

or

$$G(s) = \frac{As(s^2 + 4s + 5)}{(s+3)(s^2 + 2s + 10)} \qquad (2\text{-}44)$$

Alternately, $G(s)$ could be expressed as

$$G(s) = \frac{A(s^3 + 4s^2 + 5s)}{s^3 + 5s^2 + 16s + 30} \tag{2-45}$$

As $s \to \infty$, $G(s) \approx A$. Since $G(\infty) = 5$, then $A = 5$. Thus,

$$G(s) = \frac{5s(s^2 + 4s + 5)}{(s + 3)(s^2 + 2s + 10)} \tag{2-46}$$

Example 2-8

Discuss the stability, natural response, and forced response of the system of Examples 2-5 and 2-6.

Solution

The system has a pair of complex poles at $s = -1 \pm j2$ and a zero of second order at $s = \infty$. This means that the system is stable, and the natural response due to any input will be transient in nature. Hence, the forced response will be of a steady-state nature. This can be observed in Ex. 2-6. From (2-32), it can be seen that the first term, representing the poles of $G(s)$, vanishes after a few seconds, whereas the second term continues indefinitely. Note that the critical frequencies of the transient response are the same as in $g(t)$ of Ex. 2-5, but the amplitude and phase are different. Observe also that the steady-state response is a sinusoid with the same frequency as the input sinusoid, but with a different amplitude and phase.

2-5 STEADY-STATE FREQUENCY RESPONSE CONCEPTS

A very important special case of a CTLTI system is the steady-state response due to a sinusoidal input. This type of situation is probably the most widely used condition employed in analytical and experimental studies of linear systems.

In order for the steady-state sinusoidal response to have meaning, it is necessary that the system be perfectly stable, i.e., all poles must lie in the left-hand half-plane. In this case, the steady-state response will be a sinusoid. Only two quantities are necessary to specify the steady-state output: amplitude and phase.

Assume that the input is of the form

$$x(t) = X\epsilon^{j(\omega t + \phi_x)} \tag{2-47}$$

where ω is the *radian frequency* (rad/s), f is the *cyclic frequency* (Hz), and $\omega = 2\pi f$. We may specify either the real or the imaginary part in (2-47) depending on whether we desire a cosine or a sine input. Letting $y(t)$ represent the *steady-state* response in this case, it will be of the form

$$y(t) = Y\epsilon^{j(\omega t + \phi_y)} \tag{2-48}$$

We need only determine Y and ϕ_y in terms of X and ϕ_x to characterize the solution.

Taking the Laplace transforms of both sides of (2-47) and using the transfer function definition of (2-23), we have

$$Y(s) = \frac{X\epsilon^{j\phi_x}}{s - j\omega} G(s) \tag{2-49}$$

Inversion of only the steady-state portion of (2-49) yields

$$y(t) = G(j\omega) X\epsilon^{j(\omega t + \phi_x)} \tag{2-50}$$

Substitution of (2-48) in (2-50) and cancellation of exponential factors yield

$$Y\epsilon^{j\phi_y} = G(j\omega) X\epsilon^{j\phi_x} \tag{2-51}$$

The input and output variables may now be expressed as phasors.

$$\overline{X} = X\epsilon^{j\phi_x} \overset{\Delta}{=} X \underline{/\phi_x} \tag{2-52}$$

$$\overline{Y} = Y\epsilon^{j\phi_y} \overset{\Delta}{=} Y \underline{/\phi_y} \tag{2-53}$$

We then have

$$\overline{Y} = G(j\omega) \overline{X} \tag{2-54}$$

We may now define the *steady-state* or *Fourier transfer function* as

$$\frac{\overline{Y}}{\overline{X}} = G(j\omega) \tag{2-55}$$

While this development has been carried out at a single frequency, it should be readily observed that the quantity $G(j\omega)$ may be interpreted to include the behavior as a function of a variable frequency if ω is considered as a variable. In so doing, the frequency-dependent behavior of the system is readily determined.

At this point, we will pause briefly to discuss some notational procedures that will be followed throughout the remainder of the book. In many analytical developments involving the steady-state frequency behavior of linear systems, the radian frequency ω appears frequently, often due to its direct link with the Laplace variable s ($s = j\omega$). On the other hand, the cyclic frequency f is almost always the variable specified in a practical situation. Of course, the only difference is the scale factor 2π, i.e., $\omega = 2\pi f$. Nevertheless, there are times when confusion arises because of this difference.

There are certain functions that are best expressed in terms of the argument $j\omega$ (or simply ω in some cases), and there are other functions that are best expressed in terms of the argument f. In fact, some expressions may be encountered in which both the arguments ω and f appear. These should not be thought of as separate variables; rather, they are different ways of expressing the same variable. The choice as to which argument is used will depend on the form of the function and its ultimate use. For example, a function like $G(j\omega)$ in (2-55) is best represented in that form since it is more easily related to the Laplace transfer function. On the other hand, some functions that will be introduced shortly are best represented as functions of the argument f, since the ultimate goal is to display their behavior as a function of frequency, and the most common way this is done in practical applications is in terms of cyclic frequency.

A related point is that we may frequently express a function on the left in terms of the argument f, while the expression on the right involving a series of calculations may remain expressed in terms of ω. This need not cause any concern, since $\omega = 2\pi f$ could be easily inserted in the equation on the right, but the expression is often less awkward if it remains in terms of ω.

Returning to the problem at hand, and with consideration of the notational policy just discussed, the complex transfer function of (2-55) can be expressed in the form

$$G(j\omega) = A(f)\,\epsilon^{j\beta(f)} = A(f)\,\underline{/\beta(f)} \qquad (2\text{-}56)$$

The function $A(f)$ is called the *amplitude* or *magnitude response*, and $\beta(f)$ is called the *phase response*. Normally, $A(f)$ is simply the magnitude of the complex function $G(j\omega)$, but there are a few situations in which the amplitude response is permitted to assume negative values. (Some cases will appear later in the book.) Both $A(f)$ and $\beta(f)$ are real functions of frequency.

Although the simplest procedure for computing the amplitude response $A(f)$ is usually that of converting all factors in $G(j\omega)$ from rectangular to polar form, there is an alternate representation which will be used later in the text for deriving the transfer functions of filters. In general, the square of the magnitude of a complex number can be expressed as the product of the number and its complex conjugate. Using $\sim$ to represent the complex conjugate, we can write

$$A^2(f) = |G(j\omega)|^2 = G(j\omega)\,\widetilde{G}(j\omega) \tag{2-57}$$

For rational functions (ratios of polynomials) with real coefficients, the conjugate of a function of a complex variable can be shown to be equivalent to the function evaluated for the conjugate of the original argument. (The interested reader may wish to verify this point.) Since $\widetilde{j\omega} = -j\omega$, (2-57) is equivalent to

$$A^2(f) = G(j\omega)G(-j\omega) \tag{2-58}$$

Since $G(j\omega)$ can be considered as $G(s)$ evaluated for $s = j\omega$, (2-58) can finally be expressed as

$$A^2(f) = G(s)\,(G(-s)]_{s=j\omega} \tag{2-59}$$

The result given by (2-59) is used extensively in deriving transfer functions from specified amplitude response functions, and developments of this nature will be given in Chapt. 6. In the meantime, we do not necessarily propose that the reader use this relationship for computing $A^2(f)$ from $G(s)$, since the usual sequence of basic complex number operations is normally simpler. This form has been developed here so that we may refer to it when required later in the text.

Two additional definitions related to the phase response will now be given. They are the *phase delay* $T_p(f)$ and the *group* or *envelope delay* $T_g(f)$. The definitions are

$$T_p(f) = \frac{-\beta(f)}{\omega} = \frac{-\beta(f)}{2\pi f} \tag{2-60}$$

$$T_g(f) = \frac{-d\beta(f)}{d\omega} = \frac{-1}{2\pi}\frac{d\beta(f)}{df} \tag{2-61}$$

The significance of these definitions will be discussed in Chapt. 6.

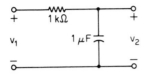

Figure 2-8 Circuit of Ex. 2-9.

Example 2-9

(a) For the circuit shown in Fig. 2-8, determine the following functions: $A(f)$, $\beta(f)$, $T_p(f)$, and $T_g(f)$. The input is $v_1(t)$ and the output is $v_2(t)$. (b) Determine the steady-state output $v_2(t)$ when the input is $v_1(t) = 10 \sin 1000t$.

Solution

(a) The Laplace transfer function is

$$G(s) = \frac{1/10^{-6}s}{10^3 + 1/10^{-6}s} = \frac{1}{1 + 10^{-3}s} \qquad (2\text{-}62)$$

The steady-state transfer function is

$$G(j\omega) = \frac{1}{1 + j\,10^{-3}\omega} = \frac{1}{1 + j(\omega/1000)} \qquad (2\text{-}63)$$

The various functions required are readily calculated from the definitions of this section.

$$A(f) = \frac{1}{\sqrt{1 + (\omega/1000)^2}} \qquad (2\text{-}64)$$

$$\beta(f) = -\tan^{-1}\frac{\omega}{1000} \qquad (2\text{-}65)$$

$$T_p(f) = \frac{1}{\omega}\tan^{-1}\frac{\omega}{1000} \qquad (2\text{-}66)$$

$$T_g(f) = \frac{10^{-3}}{1 + (\omega/1000)^2} \qquad (2\text{-}67)$$

(b) At the specific frequency $\omega = 1000$ rad/s ($f \approx 159$ Hz), the amplitude and phase are determined from (2-64) and (2-65) as

$$A(159) = 1/\sqrt{2} \approx 0.7071$$

$$\beta(159) = -45°$$

(2-68)

The output steady-state sinusoid $v_2(t)$ is then given by

$$v_2(t) = 7.071 \sin(1000t - 45°)$$

(2-69)

_____ **PROBLEMS** _____

2-1 Obtain a differential equation relating v_1 and v_2 in the circuit of Fig. P2-1. The input is v_1 and the output is v_2.

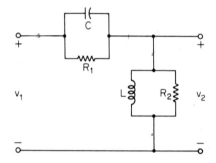

Figure P2-1

2-2 Obtain a differential equation relating v_1 and v_2 in the circuit of Fig. P2-2. The input is v_1 and the output is v_2. (Hint: Write a set of integro-differential equations and eliminate the undesired variable(s).)

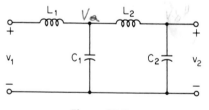

Figure P2-2

2-3 The impulse response of a certain CTLTI system is given by

$$g(t) = 0 \text{ for } t < 0$$

$$= \epsilon^{-t} - \epsilon^{-2t} \text{ for } t \geq 0$$

Using the convolution integral, determine the response $y(t)$ due to each of the following inputs applied at $t = 0$: (a) $x(t) = 10\,\delta(t)$, (b) $x(t) = 10$, (c) $x(t) = 10\epsilon^{-3t}$, (d) $x(t) = 10\epsilon^{-t}$.

2-4 The impulse response $g(t)$ and excitation $x(t)$ for a certain CTLTI system are shown in Fig. P2-4. Find the output $y(t)$ by use of the convolution integral. (Hint: Graphical techniques are suggested.)

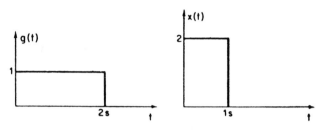

Figure P2-4

2-5 Solve the differential equation

$$4\frac{d^2y}{dt^2} + 24\frac{dy}{dt} + 32y = 800$$

with initial conditions $y(0) = 10$, $y'(0) = -20$.

2-6 Solve the integro-differential equation

$$2\frac{dy}{dt} + 8y + 26\int_0^t y\,dt = 200\cos t$$

with the initial condition that $y(0) = 0$.

2-7 For the system described by the differential equation in Prob. 2-5, determine what values of $y(0)$ and $y'(0)$ would result in no transient response, i.e., the system should immediately reach its steady-state condition.

2-8 Determine the transfer function of the circuit of Prob. 2-1 two ways: (a) by transforming the differential equation, and (b) by transforming the circuit and manipulating it directly in transform form.

2-9 Determine the transfer function of the circuit of Prob. 2-2 by the two procedures stated in Prob. 2-8.

2-10 A transfer function is given by

$$G(s) = \frac{s}{s^2 + 3s + 2}$$

Determine the impulse response $g(t)$.

2-11 Using the transfer function concept, determine the response of the system of Prob. 2-10 when the input is the sinusoid

$$x(t) = 10 \sin t$$

2-12 Determine the response of the system of Ex. 2-5 (b) to the step input $x(t) = 10\,u(t)$.

2-13 Discuss the stability of the system of Prob. 2-10, and identify the natural and forced responses in Prob. 2-11.

2-14 Show that for a second-order polynomial, necessary and sufficient conditions that all roots lie in the LHHP are that (a) all coefficients be nonzero and (b) all coefficients have the same sign.

2-15 Show that the circuit of Fig. P2-15 is unstable. Assume that the amplifier has infinite input impedance and that it performs the amplification of the differential input signal, i.e., $v_0 = A(v_2 - v_1)$, where $A > 1$.

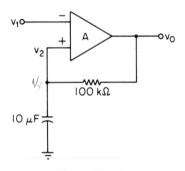

Figure P2-15

2-16 Determine the range of A in the circuit of Fig. P2-16 for which the system is stable. Assume that the amplifier has infinite input impedance and zero output impedance. (This circuit can function as an active high-pass filter.)

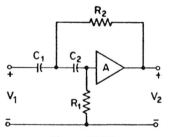

Figure P2-16

2-17 For the transfer function of Prob. 2-10, determine (a) $A(f)$, (b) $\beta(f)$, (c) $T_p(f)$, and (d) $T_g(f)$.

2-18 Determine $A(f)$ and $\beta(f)$ for the series resonant circuit shown in Fig. P2-18.

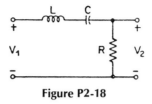

Figure P2-18

2-19 Determine $A(f)$ and $\beta(f)$ for the lead network shown in Fig. P2-19.

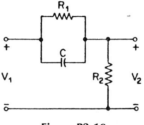

Figure P2-19

2-20 Prove that for a kth order transfer function with *all zeros at infinity*, the high-frequency amplitude response will become asymptotic to a curve with slope $-6k$ dB/octave.

2-21 Prove that for a kth order transfer function with *all zeros at the origin*, the low-frequency amplitude response will become asymptotic to a curve with slope $+6k$ dB/octave.

FOURIER ANALYSIS AND SAMPLED-DATA SIGNALS

3-0 INTRODUCTION

The primary purpose of this chapter is to introduce the concept of a sampled signal as considered from the continuous-time system or analog point of view. This approach enables us to establish a link between the domain of continuous-time signals and the domain of discrete-time or digital signals. Fourier analysis methods are very significant in this process. These techniques enable the concept of the spectrum, a powerful mechanism for analyzing continuous-time systems, to be extended to discrete-time or digital systems.

Because of the importance of spectral analysis in this development, the first portion of the chapter will be devoted to a review and strenghening of Fourier series and transform relationships. The concept of a sampled-data signal will then be introduced by considering it as a continuous-time signal modulated by a pulse train. The Fourier techniques will then be applied to the sampled-data signal, and some powerful interpretations will be developed. A very important relationship that will be deduced from this approach is Shannon's Sampling Theorem, which provides the basic sampling requirements for all sampled-data systems.

3-1 FOURIER SERIES

Some of the most important relationships of Fourier analysis will be reviewed in this section. Full mathematical details of the derivations of the Fourier equations and additional properties can be found in various mathematical and engineering textbooks. It can be shown that a *periodic* function satisfying certain restrictions (usually causing no great limitations in engineering applications) can be expanded into the sum of an infinite number of harmonically related sine and cosine terms of the form

$$x(t) = \frac{a_0}{2} + \sum_{m=1}^{\infty} (a_m \cos m\omega_1 t + b_m \sin m\omega_1 t) \qquad (3\text{-}1)$$

where

$$a_m = \frac{2}{T} \int_{-T/2}^{T/2} x(t) \cos m\omega_1 t \, dt \qquad (3\text{-}2)$$

and

$$b_m = \frac{2}{T} \int_{-T/2}^{T/2} x(t) \sin m\omega_1 t \, dt \qquad (3\text{-}3)$$

Various terms associated with the expansion are defined as follows:

T = period of waveform
f_1 = fundamental cyclic frequency = $1/T$
ω_1 = fundamental radian frequency = $2\pi f_1$
m = integer defining order of harmonic

Although the forms given in (3-1), (3-2), and (3-3) are probably the most widely employed results for practical problems, the development of many analytical and theoretical concepts is enhanced by use of the exponential Fourier series. This form reads

$$x(t) = \sum_{m=-\infty}^{\infty} c_m \epsilon^{jm\omega_1 t} \qquad (3\text{-}4)$$

where

$$c_m = \frac{1}{T} \int_{-T/2}^{T/2} x(t) \epsilon^{-jm\omega_1 t} \, dt \qquad (3\text{-}5)$$

It can be shown (Prob. 3-1) that the coefficients of the two forms are related by

$$c_m = \frac{a_m - jb_m}{2} \tag{3-6}$$

$$a_m = 2 \, \mathrm{R}_e[c_m] = c_m + \widetilde{c}_m \tag{3-7}$$

$$b_m = -2 \, \mathrm{I}_m[c_m] = j(c_m - \widetilde{c}_m) \tag{3-8}$$

where $\mathrm{R}_e[\ ]$ represents the *real* part of the quantity in brackets, $\mathrm{I}_m[\ ]$ represents the *imaginary* part of the same quantity, and $\sim$ represents the complex conjugate.

It can be seen that c_m is, in general, a complex value. As such, it may be written as

$$c_m = |c_m| \, \epsilon^{j\phi_m} \tag{3-9}$$

For a given periodic signal, the complex set c_m is called the *frequency spectrum of the signal. The set* $|c_m|$ specifies the *amplitude* or *magnitude spectrum,* and the set ϕ_m specifies the *phase spectrum.* A typical amplitude spectrum is shown in Fig. 3-1. Note that the horizontal axis is labeled in terms of cyclic frequency f.

In some cases, it is desirable to allow the amplitude spectrum to assume both positive and negative real values rather than purely positive values. This interpretation will be made in Examples 3-1 and 3-2.

A significant point to observe for the *periodic* signal is that its spectrum is *discrete,* consisting only of components at *dc,* the fundamental frequency $f_1 = 1/T$, and integer multiples of the fundamental.

Assume now that a periodic signal excites a CTLTI stable system with transfer function $G(s)$. From work covered in the previous chapter, it can be deduced that the steady-state response due to any single component of the Fourier spectrum can be obtained by weighing the amplitude and phase of that particular frequency component with the steady-state transfer function $G(j\omega)$ evaluated at the frequency in

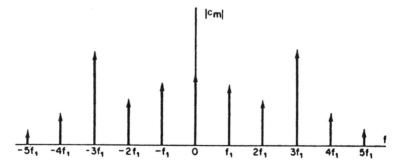

Figure 3-1 Typical discrete amplitude spectrum for a periodic signal.

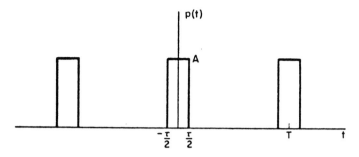

Figure 3-2 Periodic pulse train of Ex. 3-1.

question. By superposition, the total *steady-state response* $y(t)$ can be expressed as

$$y(t) = \sum_{m=-\infty}^{\infty} c_m G(jm\omega_1)\epsilon^{jm\omega_1 t}$$

$$(3\text{-}10)$$

$$= \sum_{m=-\infty}^{\infty} |c_m| A(mf_1)\epsilon^{j[m\omega_1 t + \phi_m + \beta(mf_1)]}$$

where $A(mf_1)$ represents the steady-state amplitude response evaluated at the mth harmonic and $\beta(mf_1)$ is the phase shift produced by the system at the same frequency.

Example 3-1

Determine the frequency spectrum of the periodic pulse train shown in Fig. 3-2.

Solution

Application of (3-5) to the given function yields the following sequence of steps:

$$c_m = \frac{1}{T} \int_{-\tau/2}^{\tau/2} A\epsilon^{-jm\omega_1 t} dt$$

$$= \frac{A}{-jm\omega_1 T} [\epsilon^{-jm\omega_1 t}]_{-\tau/2}^{\tau/2}$$

$$(3\text{-}11)$$

$$= \frac{A}{jm\omega_1 T} [\epsilon^{jm\omega_1\tau/2} - \epsilon^{-jm\omega_1\tau/2}]$$

$$= \frac{2A}{m\omega_1 T} \sin\frac{m\omega_1\tau}{2} = \frac{A\tau}{T}\frac{\sin m\omega_1\tau/2}{m\omega_1\tau/2}$$

Finally, this result can be expressed as

$$c_m = Ad \, \frac{\sin m\pi d}{m\pi d} \qquad\qquad (3\text{-}12)$$

where the quantity d is called the *duty cycle* and is defined as $d = \tau/T$.

For this example, the values of c_m are all real. To avoid phase discontinuities of $\pm 180°$, we will interpret the amplitude spectral components to be both positive and negative, yielding $\phi_m = 0$. Hence, the amplitude spectrum is equivalent to c_m, and a sketch of this function for the particular value $d = 0.2$ is shown in Fig. 3-3.

3-2 FOURIER TRANSFORM

In the last section, we saw that the spectrum of a periodic signal could be represented in terms of a Fourier series. Assume now that it is desired to define the spectrum of a *nonperiodic* signal. For this purpose, the class of signals under consideration will be limited to those containing finite energy. We may think of the nonperiodic signal as arising from a periodic signal in which the period is allowed to increase without limit. Following this logic, it can be deduced that the difference f_1 between successive components decreases as the period increases. In the limit, the difference between successive components approaches

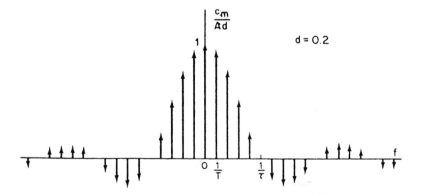

Figure 3-3 Amplitude spectrum of periodic pulse train of Ex. 3-1 with $d = 0.2$.

zero, and the curve becomes a continuous function of frequency. In this case, the Fourier integral transform pair is defined as

$$x(t) = \int_{-\infty}^{\infty} X(f) e^{j\omega t} \, df \qquad (3\text{-}13)$$

$$X(f) = \int_{-\infty}^{\infty} x(t) e^{-j\omega t} \, dt \qquad (3\text{-}14)$$

where $X(f)$ is defined as the Fourier transform of $x(t)$.

A significant point to observe for the *nonperiodic* signal is that its spectrum is *continuous*, consisting of components at all frequencies over the range for which it is nonzero.

Assume now that a nonperiodic signal excites a CTLTI stable system with transfer function $G(s)$. As in the case of a single frequency or for a particular component of a discrete spectrum, the response due to a given frequency in the continuous spectrum can be determined by weighting the input with the transfer function. In this case, the Fourier transform of the output $Y(f)$ is obtained by weighting the spectrum of the input $X(f)$ by the Fourier transfer function $G(j\omega)$.

$$Y(f) = G(j\omega) X(f) = A(f) X(f) e^{j\beta(f)} \qquad (3\text{-}15)$$

The output time response can then be written as

$$y(t) = \int_{-\infty}^{\infty} A(f) X(f) e^{j[\omega t + \beta(f)]} df \qquad (3\text{-}16)$$

It can be observed from the preceding work that there are certain close similarities between the Laplace and Fourier transform relationships. One of the most important is the relationship between the Laplace transfer function $G(s)$ and the Fourier (or steady-state) transfer function $G(j\omega)$. The simple substitution $s = j\omega$ is all that is required to relate the two functions. Note that the Fourier transfer function is the same as the steady-state transfer function for a single frequency excitation. In the case of a complex Fourier spectrum, the excitation is assumed to be represented by an infinite number of sinusoids, but the transfer function evaluated at a given frequency is the same as for a single sinusoid of that particular frequency.

In spite of the strong similarities between the Laplace and Fourier definitions and in the transfer functions, there are some important differences, particularly in regard to the transforms of various waveforms. Some of these differences arise from existence conditions and from the fact that the most widely employed form of the Laplace transform is defined only with respect to positive time (one-sided Laplace transform), while the Fourier transform is defined for both negative and positive time.

As in the case of a discrete spectrum, the Fourier transform is a complex function and may be expressed as

$$X(f) = |X(f)| \epsilon^{j\phi(f)} \qquad (3\text{-}17)$$

where $|X(f)|$ is the *amplitude* or *magnitude spectrum* and $\phi(f)$ is the *phase spectrum*. As in the case of nonperiodic functions, the amplitude spectrum may be allowed to assume negative values in some cases. Some of the most common Fourier transform operation pairs are given in Table 3-1.

Example 3-2

Determine the Fourier transform of the nonperiodic pulse $p(t)$ shown in Fig. 3-4.

Table 3-1
Some common Fourier transform operation pairs.

$x(t)$	$X(f) = F\left[x(t)\right]$	
$ax_1(t) + bx_2(t)$	$aX_1(f) + bX_2(f)$	(FO-1)
$\dfrac{d^n x(t)}{dt^n}$	$(j\omega)^n X(f)$	(FO-2)
$\displaystyle\int_{-\infty}^{t} x(\tau)d\tau$	$\dfrac{X(f)}{j\omega}$	(FO-3)
$x(t-a)$	$\epsilon^{-j\omega a} X(f)$	(FO-4)
$\epsilon^{j2\pi f_o t} x(t)$	$X(f-f_o)$	(FO-5)
$x(at)$	$\dfrac{1}{a} X(\dfrac{f}{a})$	(FO-6)
$\displaystyle\int_{-\infty}^{\infty} x_1(\tau)x_2(t-\tau)d\tau$	$X_1(f) X_2(f)$	(FO-7)
$x_1(t) x_2(t)$	$\displaystyle\int_{-\infty}^{\infty} X_1(\bar{f}) X_2(f-\bar{f})d\bar{f}$	(FO-8)

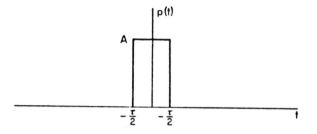

Figure 3-4 Nonperiodic pulse of Ex. 3-2.

Solution

Using the basic definition given by (3-14), the sequence of steps follows:

$$P(f) = \int_{-\tau/2}^{\tau/2} A\epsilon^{-j\omega t}\,dt$$

$$= \frac{A}{-j\omega}\left[\epsilon^{-j\omega t}\right]_{-\tau/2}^{\tau/2}$$

$$= \frac{A}{j\omega}\left[\epsilon^{j\omega\tau/2} - \epsilon^{-j\omega\tau/2}\right] \qquad (3\text{-}18)$$

$$= \frac{2A}{\omega}\sin\frac{\omega\tau}{2}$$

This result can be expressed as

$$P(f) = A\tau\,\frac{\sin\pi f\tau}{\pi f\tau} \qquad (3\text{-}19)$$

As in the case of Ex. 3-1, by choosing the amplitude spectrum to be both positive and negative, the phase spectrum in this case is simply $\phi(f) = 0$. The form of $P(f)$ is shown in Fig. 3-5.

3-3 SAMPLED-DATA SIGNALS

At this point, we will introduce an important class of signals whose properties serve as a link between continuous-time signals and discrete-time or digital signals. A *sampled-data signal* can be considered as arising from sampling a continuous-time signal at periodic

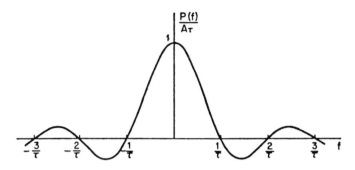

Figure 3-5 Amplitude spectrum of nonperiodic pulse of Ex. 3-2.

intervals of time T as illustrated in Fig. 3-6. The *sampling rate* or *sampling frequency* is $f_s = 1/T$.

Initially, we will assume that each sample has a width τ, so that the resulting signal consists of a series of relatively narrow pulses whose amplitudes are modulated by the original continuous-time signal. This particular form of a sampled-data signal is designated in communications systems as a pulse amplitude modulated (PAM) signal.

Let $x^*(t)$ represent the sampled-data signal, and let $x(t)$ represent the original continuous-time signal. We may consider $x^*(t)$ as the product of $x(t)$ and a hypothetical pulse train $p(t)$ as illustrated in Fig. 3-6. Thus,

$$x^*(t) = x(t)p(t) \qquad (3\text{-}20)$$

An important property of the sampled-data signal is its spectrum $X^*(f)$. This can be derived by first expressing $p(t)$ in the Fourier series form

$$p(t) = \sum_{-\infty}^{\infty} c_m \epsilon^{jm\,\omega_s t} \qquad (3\text{-}21)$$

where $\omega_s = 2\pi f_s = 2\pi/T$. The coefficients c_m in (3-21) follow a (sin $m\pi d/m\pi d$) frequency variation. (See Ex. 3-1.) However, it is not necessary at this point to actually introduce the values for c_m into (3-21) as long as we understand their general behavior.

Substitution of (3-21) in (3-20) results in the expression

$$x^*(t) = \sum_{-\infty}^{\infty} c_m x(t)\,\epsilon^{jm\,\omega_s t} \qquad (3\text{-}22)$$

The spectrum may now be determined by taking the Fourier transforms of both sides of (3-22). Each term of the series on the right may be transformed with the help of operation (FO-5) of Table 2-1. The result is

$$X^*(f) = \sum_{-\infty}^{\infty} c_m X(f - mf_s) \tag{3-23}$$

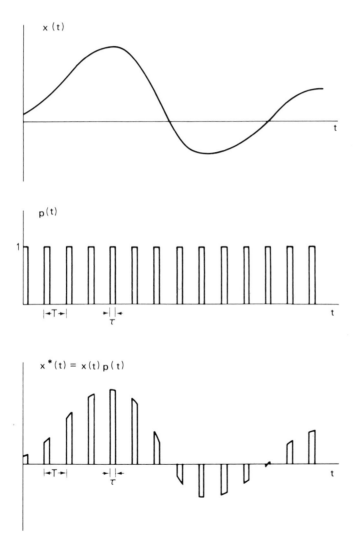

Figure 3-6 Development of sampled-data signal using nonzero width pulse sampling.

Typical sketches of $|X(f)|$ and $|X^*(f)|$ are shown in Fig. 3-7. Due to lack of space, only a small section of the negative frequency range of $|X^*(f)|$ is shown, but since it is an even function of frequency, its behavior in the negative frequency range is readily understood.

It can be observed that the spectrum of a sampled-data signal consists of the original spectrum plus an infinite number of translated versions of the original spectrum. These various translated functions are shifted in frequency by amounts equal to the sampling frequency and its harmonics. The magnitudes are multiplied by the c_m coefficients, so that they diminish with frequency. However, for a very short duty cycle ($\tau \ll T$), the components drop off very slowly, so the spectrum would be extremely wide in this case.

Assume that the spectrum of $x(t)$ is bandlimited to $0 \leq f \leq f_h$ in the positive frequency sense as illustrated in Fig. 3-7, where f_h is the highest possible frequency. In order to be able to eventually recover the original signal from the sampled-data form, it is necessary that none of the shifted spectral components overlap each other. If portions of any of the shifted functions overlap, certain frequencies appear to be different from their actual values, and it becomes impossible to separate or recover these particular components. This process of spectral overlap is called *aliasing*, and it can occur if either of the following conditions exist: (a) the signal is not bandlimited to a finite range, or (b) the sampling rate is too low.

Theoretically, if the signal is not bandlimited, there is no way of avoiding the aliasing problem with the basic sampling scheme employed. However, the spectra of most real-life signals are such that they

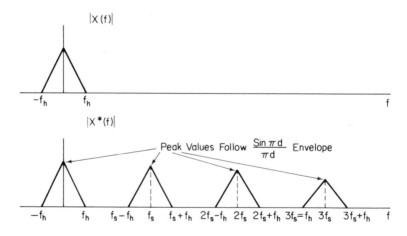

Figure 3-7 Spectrum of sampled-data signal using nonzero width pulse sampling.

may be assumed to be bandlimited. Furthermore, a common practice employed in many sampled-data systems is to filter the continuous-time signal before sampling to ensure that it does meet the bandlimited criterion closely enough for all practical purposes.

Let us now turn to the concept of the sampling rate. In order to avoid aliasing in Fig. 3-7, it is necessary that $f_s - f_h \geqslant f_h$. This leads to the important inequality

$$f_s \geqslant 2f_h \qquad (3\text{-}24)$$

Equation (3-24) is a statement of *Shannon's Sampling Theorem,* which states that a signal must be sampled at a rate at least as high as twice the highest frequency in the spectrum. In practice, the sampling rate must be chosen to be somewhat greater than $2f_h$ to ensure recovery with practical hardware limitations.

If no aliasing occurs, the original signal can be recovered by passing the sampled-data signal through a low-pass filter having a cutoff frequency somewhere between f_h and $f_s - f_h$. It is impossible to build filters having an infinite sharpness of cutoff, so that a *guard band* between f_h and $f_s - f_h$ is desired. This illustrates the need for a sampling rate somewhat greater than the theoretical minimum.

A convenient definition that is useful in sampling analysis is the *folding frequency* f_0. It is given by

$$f_0 = \frac{f_s}{2} = \frac{1}{2T} \qquad (3\text{-}25)$$

The folding frequency is simply the highest frequency that can be processed by a given discrete-time system with sampling rate f_s. Any frequency greater than f_0 will be "folded" and cannot be recovered. In addition, it will obscure data within the correct frequency range; so it is important to clearly limit the frequency content of a signal before sampling.

A word about terminology should be mentioned here. The highest frequency f_h in the signal is called the *Nyquist frequency*, and the minimum sampling rate $2f_h$ at which the signal could theoretically be recovered is called the *Nyquist rate*.

A point of ambiguity is that the frequency $f_0 = f_s/2$ is also referred to as the Nyquist frequency in some references. To avoid confusion in terminology, we will use the term *folding frequency* in reference to $f_0 = f_s/2$, as previously discussed in this chapter.

3-4 IDEAL IMPULSE SAMPLING

The sampled-data signal of the last section was derived on the assumption that each of the samples had a nonzero width τ. We now wish to consider the limiting case that results when the width τ is assumed to approach zero. In this case, the samples will be represented as a sequence of impulse functions.

While the analog samples of any real sampled-data signal derived directly from a continuous-time signal could never reach the extreme limit of zero width, the limiting concept serves two important functions: (a) If the widths of the actual pulse samples are quite small compared with the various time constants of the system under consideration, the impulse function assumption is a good approximation, and it leads to simplified analysis. (b) When a signal is sampled, converted from analog to digital form, and subsequently processed with digital circuitry, it may be considered simply as a number occurring at a specific instant of time. A very convenient way of modeling a digital signal of this form is through the impulse sampling representation. This second concept is the most important one for our purposes, as it will be utilized extensively in the analysis of digital signals throughout the text.

The form of the ideal impulse sampled-data signal is illustrated in Fig. 3-8. As in the previous section, $x^*(t)$ will be used to represent the sampled-data signal, and $x(t)$ will represent the original continuous-time signal. The pulse function is designated as $p_\delta(t)$ and is assumed to be a train of impulse functions of the form

$$p_\delta(t) = \sum_{-\infty}^{\infty} \delta(t - nT) \qquad (3\text{-}26)$$

The sampled-data signal $x^*(t)$ can be expressed as

$$x^*(t) = x(t)p_\delta(t) = x(t) \sum_{-\infty}^{\infty} \delta(t - nT) \qquad (3\text{-}27)$$

The only values of $x(t)$ having significance in (3-27) are those at $t = nT$. Hence, an alternate form for the sampled-data signal is

$$x^*(t) = \sum_{-\infty}^{\infty} x(nT)\delta(t - nT) \qquad (3\text{-}28)$$

Both the forms (3-27) and (3-28) will be used in subsequent work. The first expression is useful in deriving spectral relationships, due to

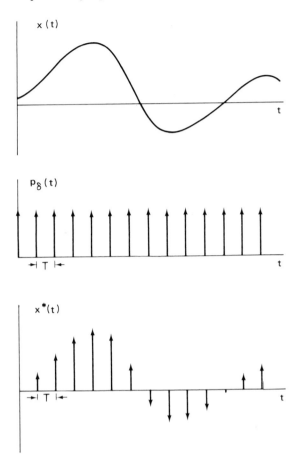

Figure 3-8 Development of sampled-data signal using ideal impulse sampling.

the product form given. The second form provides the interpretation that the sampled-data signal is composed of a series of equally spaced impulses whose weights represent the values of the original signal at sampling instants.

In making these interpretations, the reader is urged to accept the use of the impulse function without too much concern about some of the common "mysteries" associated with this function in CTLTI systems. It turns out that a sequence of numbers that appears in a computer can be conveniently represented as weights of an impulse train for purposes of mathematical analysis, so the concept is very useful. The main point to remember is that the weight of a given impulse represents the value (or digital number) at the instant of time that the impulse occurs.

The spectrum of the ideal impulse train can be derived by utilizing the integration property of an ideal impulse function, which states

$$\int_{-\infty}^{\infty} \delta(t-a)dt = 1 \tag{3-29}$$

Since the impulse train is periodic, it may be expanded in a Fourier series. The coefficients c_m may be determined from the application of (3-5) to (3-26) with the help of (3-29). This yields

$$c_m = \frac{1}{T} \tag{3-30}$$

This result indicates that all of the spectral components have equal weights, and there is no convergence at all for the spectral components! The function $p_\delta(t)$ may then be written as

$$p_\delta(t) = \sum_{-\infty}^{\infty} \frac{1}{T} \epsilon^{jm\omega_s t} \tag{3-31}$$

Substitution of (3-31) in (3-27) yields

$$x^*(t) = \frac{1}{T} \sum_{-\infty}^{\infty} x(t) \epsilon^{jm\omega_s t} \tag{3-32}$$

The Fourier transform may now be applied to both sides of (3-32), and transform operation (FO-5) can be applied to each of the terms on the right. The result is

$$X^*(f) = \frac{1}{T} \sum_{-\infty}^{\infty} X(f - mf_s) \tag{3-33}$$

The form of the spectrum of the ideal impulse sampled-data signal is shown in Fig. 3-9. The general form is similar to that of the sampled-data signal derived from the nonzero sampling process shown in Fig. 3-7, and the basic sampling requirements developed in the last section apply here. Comparison of Figs. 3-7 and 3-9 and equations (3-23) and (3-33) indicates that the major difference is the behavior of the levels of the spectral components. The spectral components derived with nonzero pulse widths gradually diminish with frequency and follow a sin $m\pi d/m\pi d$ envelope. However, the spectral components derived from ideal impulse sampling are all of equal magnitude and do not diminish with frequency.

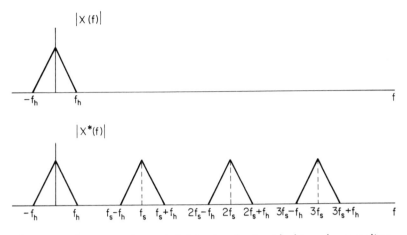

Figure 3-9 Spectrum of sampled-data signal using ideal impulse sampling.

An important deduction from this discussion is that the spectrum of an impulse sampled-data signal is a periodic function of frequency. The period in the frequency domain is equal to the sampling frequency f_s. The sampling process in the time domain leads to a periodic function in the frequency domain. This concept will continually appear in many forms throughout the text, so it is important that it be understood at this point.

As an additional relationship for use in the next chapter, assume now that the signal $x(t)$ is defined only in the positive time region $0 \leq t \leq \infty$. With this assumption, the one-sided Laplace transform may be applied to (3-28). The result is readily obtained as

$$X^*(s) = \sum_{n=0}^{\infty} x(nT)\epsilon^{-nTs} \qquad (3\text{-}34)$$

3-5 HOLDING CIRCUIT

It was mentioned in Sec. 3-3 that a continuous-time signal could be recovered from its sampled-data form by passing the sampled-data signal through a low-pass filter having a cutoff somewhere between f_h and $f_s - f_h$. This process of reconstruction can be aided by the use of a *holding circuit*, which actually performs a portion of the filtering required, thus permitting the use of a less complex filter for the final smoothing. Although a number of holding circuits of varying complexity have been devised, we will restrict the consideration here to the *zero-order* holding circuit.

The zero-order holding circuit is best explained by first assuming that we are dealing with real samples having sufficiently small widths that the variation in the peak is insignificant during the interval τ. Hence, a given pulse may be assumed as rectangular. The holding circuit simply accepts the value of the pulse at the beginning of a sampling interval and holds it to the beginning of the next interval, at which time it changes to the new value. This process is illustrated in Fig. 3-10. The resulting function is, of course, not normally the same as the original signal before sampling, but it is now in the form of a continuous-time function, and it will be easier to perform subsequent processing on it in this form.

For analytical purposes, the implementation of a zero-order holding circuit shown in Fig. 3-11 will be considered. The delay block represents an ideal analog delay line having a delay of T seconds. The delayed signal is subtracted from the direct signal, and the net difference is integrated over the sampling interval to yield the output.

The sequence of events for a sampled-data signal begins with the appearance of a very short pulse at the beginning of an interval. Since the delayed signal will not initially appear at the input of the difference circuit, the integrator reaches a value proportional to the area of the pulse in a time τ. This value is held until the delayed signal reaches

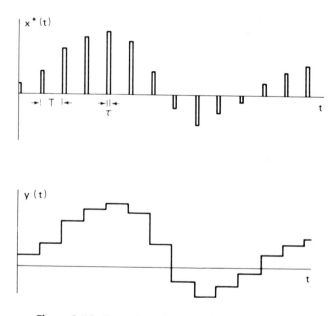

Figure 3-10 Operation of zero-order holding circuit.

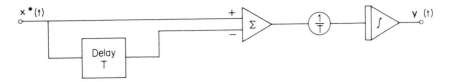

Figure 3-11 Implementation of zero-order holding circuit used in deriving frequency response.

the inverted input after T seconds. By superposition, the effect of the delayed and inverted pulse is to cancel out the output of the integrator previously established. Hence, the next output value of the integrator will be a function of the next input pulse only.

A continuous transfer function may be derived for the zero-order holding circuit. This is best achieved by assuming now that a given input pulse may be approximated by an impulse. For convenience, assume that the given impulse occurs at $t = 0$. The output $y(t)$ produced by this impulse is illustrated in Fig. 3-12. It can be expressed as

$$y(t) = \frac{1}{T}[u(t) - u(t - T)] \tag{3-35}$$

We may now take the Laplace transforms of both sides of (3-35). Furthermore, since $X(s) = 1$, then $Y(s)$ is the same as the transfer function $G(s)$, and we have

$$G(s) = \frac{1}{sT}(1 - \epsilon^{-sT}) \tag{3-36}$$

The steady-state frequency response $G(j\omega)$ is obtained by setting $s = j\omega$ in (3-36). We will leave as an exercise (Prob. 3-18) for the reader to show that the amplitude response $A(f)$ and the phase response $\beta(f)$ of this circuit may be expressed as

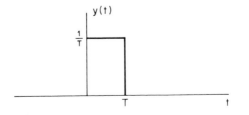

Figure 3-12 Impulse response of zero-order holding circuit.

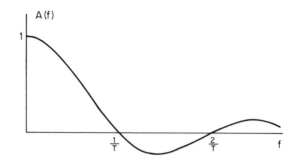

Figure 3-13 Amplitude response of zero-order holding circuit.

$$A(f) = \frac{\sin \pi fT}{\pi fT} \qquad (3\text{-}37)$$

and

$$\beta(f) = \pi fT \qquad (3\text{-}38)$$

(As in the case of some previous functions, we are permitting $A(f)$ to assume negative values here.) The amplitude response is shown in Fig. 3-13. We see that the circuit does function as a type of low-pass filter, although it is not particularly outstanding in this capacity. Normally, additional filtering of the signal will be required to effectively remove components of the sampled-data signal about the sampling frequency and its harmonics, but the presence of the holding circuit eases the requirements.

—————————————— **PROBLEMS** ——————————————

3-1 Verify Equations (3-6), (3-7), and (3-8).

3-2 Determine the frequency spectrum of the function of Fig. P3-2. Express in the form of an amplitude spectrum and a phase spectrum.

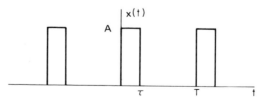

Figure P3-2

3-3 Determine the frequency spectrum of the function of Fig. P3-3. (Hint: How does this function differ from the pulse train of Ex. 3-1?)

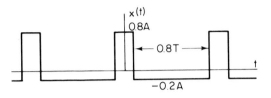

Figure P3-3

3-4 A voltage pulse train of the form given in Ex. 3-1 with A = 10 V, a repetition frequency of 1 kHz, and a duty cycle $d = 0.2$ is used to excite the first-order low-pass filter shown in Fig. P3-4. (a) Determine an expression for the output frequency spectrum c_{m2}. Express in the form of an amplitude spectrum and a phase spectrum. (b) Determine an expression for the output steady-state time signal $v_2(t)$ in terms of the spectral components.

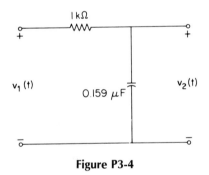

Figure P3-4

3-5 Prove the following two statements for a periodic signal $x(t)$ and its spectrum c_m:

(a) If $x(t)$ is *even*, c_m is *real*

(b) If $x(t)$ is *odd*, c_m is *imaginary*.

3-6 A pulse train of the form given in Ex. 3-1 has a fixed pulse repetition rate of 1 kHz, but the pulse width τ can be varied. Sketch the amplitude spectrum for each of the following values of τ, and label the frequencies of all spectral components in each case: (a) $\tau = 0.5$ ms, (b) $\tau = 0.2$ ms, (c) $\tau = 0.05$ ms.

3-7 A pulse train of the form given in Ex. 3-1 has a fixed pulse width of $\tau = 1$ μs, but the period T can be varied. Sketch the amplitude spectrum for each of the following values of T, and label the frequencies of all spectral components in each case:

(a) $T = 4\ \mu s$, (b) $T = 10\ \mu s$, (c) $T = 30\ \mu s$.

3-8 Consider a pulse train of the form given in Ex. 3-1 with duty cycle d. Consider the case where $1/d = T/\tau$ is an integer N. Show that the spectral components are zero at the set of frequencies $n N f_1$, where n is any integer except zero, and f_1 is the fundamental frequency.

3-9 Derive the following Fourier transform operation pairs: (a) (FO-2), (b) (FO-3), (c) (FO-4), (d) (FO-5), (e) (FO-6).

3-10 Determine the Fourier transform of the function shown in Fig. P3-10 two ways: (a) by direct application of the definition, and (b) by use of one of the operation pairs in conjunction with the results developed in the text.

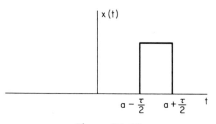

Figure P3-10

3-11 The function shown in Fig. P3-11 represents the amplitude response of an ideal frequency domain filter (which is not realizable). Assuming a phase response of zero, determine the impulse response $g(t)$ of the ideal filter by taking the inverse Fourier transform.

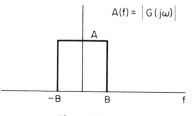

Figure P3-11

3-12 Prove the following two statements for a signal $x(t)$ and its Fourier transform $X(f)$.

(a) If $x(t)$ is *even*, $X(f)$ is *real*.

(b) If $x(t)$ is *odd*, $X(f)$ is *imaginary*.

3-13 Sketch the amplitude spectrum of a single pulse with a width $\tau = 1\ \mu s$.

3-14 A signal having a spectrum ranging from near dc to 10 kHz is to be sampled and converted to discrete form. What is the theoretical minimum number of samples per second that must be taken to ensure recovery?

3-15 A certain continuous-time signal is 2 minutes long. The spectrum of the signal ranges from near dc to 100 Hz. It is to be sampled and converted to digital form for computer processing. (a) What is the theoretical minimum number of samples that must be taken? (b) Assume that each sample is represented as a 12-bit binary number. What is the minimum core storage in bits required to handle this signal?

3-16 A certain continuous-time signal contains a dc component and the following three additional frequencies: 1 kHz, 2 kHz, 3 kHz. The signal is sampled at a rate of 10 kHz by a narrow pulse train. Draw the spectrum of the sampled signal, showing all components between dc and 45 kHz.

3-17 Assume that the signal of Prob. 3-16 is sampled at a rate of 5 kHz. By drawing a spectral diagram, show that it would be impossible to recover the original signal by simple filtering.

3-18 Show that the amplitude and phase response functions of the zero-order holding circuit are given by equations (3-37) and (3-38), respectively.

4

DISCRETE-TIME
SYSTEM ANALYSIS

4-0 INTRODUCTION

The starting point for developing the concept of a digital signal processor such as a digital filter is the theory of the discrete-time system. Much of this theory was originally developed in conjunction with sampled-data control systems but is equally applicable to digital filters. In this chapter the techniques for discrete-time system analysis will be developed and discussed. This will include both z-transform procedures and related numerical concepts. It should be understood that a *discrete-time* signal may represent either a purely *digital* signal, as would be employed in a computer, or a *sampled-data* signal, which occurs in certain hybrid systems. However, the underlying theory is essentially the same, so we will emphasize the broader discrete-time concepts in this chapter in order to obtain more generality. Of course, the major application considered in this book will be in digital systems designed or programmed for signal processing or simulation.

Some of the developments given in this chapter utilize the concepts of contour integration and residue theory. However, it is expected that many readers may not be familiar with these techniques. Such readers will usually be able to omit these developments without any great loss of continuity. Actually, while the analytical methods of complex integration are very powerful in developing some of the material given in this chapter, the end results are presented in simpler forms in most cases. Interested readers may refer to various textbooks on applied mathematics, which usually have treatments of complex integration and residue theory.

4-1   DISCRETE-TIME SIGNALS

In the preceding chapter, the concept of a sampled-data signal was established. This was achieved by expressing the sampled signal as the product of a reference continuous-time or analog signal and a pulse train consisting of narrow rectangular pulses. If the pulses are assumed to become very narrow, the pulse train can be conveniently represented mathematically as an impulse train.

To enhance the process of steady-state Fourier analysis, the sampled-data signals in the last chapter were permitted to extend over both the negative and positive time regions. On the other hand, the developments of this chapter are best achieved by assuming that the signal exists only for positive time. Thus, we will begin by representing any sampled-data signal of interest in the form

$$x^*(t) = \sum_{n=0}^{\infty} x(nT)\delta(t - nT) \qquad (4\text{-}1)$$

The Laplace transform of (4-1) is given by

$$X^*(s) = \sum_{n=0}^{\infty} x(nT)\epsilon^{-nTs} \qquad (4\text{-}2)$$

The interpretation of (4-1), along with its Laplace transform in (4-2), is a very important one, and we will return to it frequently in developing various discrete-time system results. In fact, this result serves somewhat as a link in relating some of the purely continuous-time system results to those of discrete-time systems.

Consider now the case of a general discrete-time signal that is defined only at integer multiples of a basic interval T. This signal differs from the sampled-data signal $x^*(t)$ only in the sense that it may not necessarily have arisen from sampling a continuous-time signal. Instead, it may have arisen from some purely discrete or digital process. Nevertheless, we can still interpret the signal in the form of (4-1) whenever desirable.

Except where it is desirable to use the sampled-data interpretation, the most straightforward notation for a discrete-time signal is simply $x(n)$, where n is an integer defined over some range

$n_1 \leq n \leq n_2$. The integer n defines the particular location in the sequence corresponding to a given sample. If the discrete-time signal is derived from sampling a continuous-time signal $x_1(t)$, the signals are related by

$$x(n) = x_1(nT) \text{ for } n \text{ an integer}$$

$$= 0 \text{ otherwise} \qquad (4\text{-}3)$$

In effect, (4-3) states that the discrete-time signal is equal to the continuous-time signal at sample points and is zero elsewhere.

4-2 Z-TRANSFORM

The z-transform is an operational function that may be applied to discrete-time systems in the same manner as the Laplace transform is applied to continuous-time systems. We will develop this concept through the use of the *one-sided* z-transform, which is most conveniently related to the concepts of continuous-time systems as discussed earlier in the book. The z-transform of a discrete-time signal $x(n)$ is denoted by $X(z)$. The symbolic forms for the z-transform and inverse z-transform are given by

$$X(z) = \mathfrak{Z} \, [x(n)] \qquad (4\text{-}4)$$

and

$$x(n) = \mathfrak{Z}^{-1} [X(z)] \qquad (4\text{-}5)$$

The actual definition of the one-sided z-transform is

$$X(z) = \sum_{n=0}^{\infty} x(n) z^{-n} \qquad (4\text{-}6)$$

The function $X(z)$ is a series which converges outside the circle $|z| > R$, where R is called the radius of absolute convergence.

A comparison of (4-2) and (4-6), with recognition of the fact that T does not appear in (4-6), yields some useful relationships between the s-plane and the z-plane. We note that

$$X(z) = [X^*(s)]_{z = \epsilon^{sT}} \qquad (4\text{-}7)$$

The s and z variables are related by

$$z = \epsilon^{sT} \qquad (4\text{-}8)$$

and

$$s = \frac{1}{T} \, ln \, z \tag{4-9}$$

It is of interest to note the effect of the transformation of (4-8) and (4-9) as shown in Fig. 4-1. The left-hand half of the s-plane maps to the interior of the unit circle in the z-plane, and the right-hand half of the s-plane maps to the exterior of the unit circle in the z-plane. The $j\omega$ axis in the s-plane maps to the boundary of the unit circle in the z-plane. The transformation from z to s is a multivalued transformation, as can be seen from (4-9), with recognition of the properties of the complex logarithm. In fact, there are an infinite number of values in the s-plane

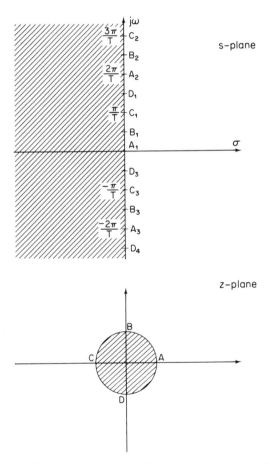

Figure 4-1 Complex mapping relationship between s-plane and z-plane.

corresponding to a given point in the z-plane. This property is closely related to the concept of the spectrum of a sampled signal developed in the previous chapter.

The boundaries of major interest in this transformation are the $j\omega$ axis in the s-plane and the unit circle in the z-plane. This situation results from letting $s = j\omega$, which is equivalent to

$$z = \epsilon^{j\omega T} \qquad\qquad (4\text{-}10)$$

As the cyclic frequency f varies over the range $-1/2T \leqslant f \leqslant 1/2T$, the argument of (4-10) varies from $-\pi$ to π. This is equivalent to a complete rotation around the unit circle in the z-plane. As the frequency increases beyond $1/2T$, the locus in the z-plane continues to rotate around the same path again, with a complete rotation for each increase of $\omega T = 2\pi$. Once again, the concept of the sampling theorem is evident. In later work, we will be particularly interested in the sinusoidal steady-state behavior of discrete-time systems, and the expression of (4-10) will serve as a major step in observing this behavior. This is essentially the same procedure as letting $s = j\omega$ in a continuous-time system.

We will now consider the process of actually calculating the z-transform of a given discrete signal. In general, this may be accomplished by either (a) use of the definition as given by (4-6), or (b) application of a contour integral to the Laplace transform of a corresponding continuous-time signal (if such can be found).

Application of the basic definition of (4-6) results in a series in which the value of a particular sample in the sequence is readily observed by the weight of the corresponding z coefficient. For a finite-length signal, the basic power series may be the most ideal form in which to express the transform, particularly if the series is fairly short in duration. On the other hand, for either long or infinite series, it is often desirable, if possible, to represent the transform as a closed-form expression. This is rarely possible with a "real-life" random signal. However, in the same spirit that continuous-time systems are continually analyzed with simple inputs such as the impulse, step, sinusoid, etc., so it is with discrete-time systems. The response of a discrete-time system to such standard waveforms serves to define clear impressions and boundaries of what the response due to any waveform would be like, and thus it is very useful to give these signals great attention.

To apply the contour integral method, we have to refer the discrete-time signal $x(n)$ back to a particular continuous-time signal $x(t)$ from which the sampled signal $x^*(t)$ could be derived. Let $X^*(s)$ represent the Laplace transform of $x^*(t)$. It can be shown that $X^*(s)$ can be derived from the Laplace transform of the unsampled signal $x(t)$ by means of the contour integral

$$X^*(s) = \frac{1}{2\pi j} \int_C \frac{X(p)\,dp}{1 - \epsilon^{-sT}\,\epsilon^{pT}} \qquad (4\text{-}11)$$

where C is a contour enclosing all singularities of $X(s)$ in the s-plane and p is a dummy variable.

The z-transform of $x(n)$ is then obtained by application of (4-7) to (4-11). This results in

$$X(z) = \frac{1}{2\pi j} \int_C \frac{X(p)\,dp}{1 - z^{-1}\,\epsilon^{pT}} \qquad (4\text{-}12)$$

By means of Cauchy's Residue Theorem, (4-12) can be expressed as

$$X(z) = \sum_m \text{Res}\left[\frac{X(p)}{1 - z^{-1}\,\epsilon^{pT}}\right]_{p\,=\,p_m} \qquad (4\text{-}13)$$

where p_m represents the set of poles of $X(p)$ and Res [ ] represents the residue of the argument at a particular pole. The residues are summed over all the poles of $X(p)$. This result allows one to determine the z-transform of a discrete-time signal from the Laplace transform of the continuous-time signal that can be thought of as the "generator" for the signal.

A summary of some of the most common function pairs is given in Table 4-1, and a summary of certain operations is given in Table 4-2. As a point of convenience, the corresponding Laplace transforms of the unsampled functions are given in the last column of Table 4-1. These are not intended as comprehensive tables, but they provide adequate information to deal with most of the standard waveforms of interest in digital signal processing. The examples that follow and the problems at the end of the chapter illustrate the derivation of some of these entries.

Example 4-1

Derive the z-transform of the discrete unit step function $u(n)$ in two ways: (a) application of the definition, and (b) use of the contour integral method.

Table 4-1
Z-transform function pairs.

x(n)	X(z)	X(s)	
$\delta(n)$	1	1	(ZT–1)
1 or u(n)	$\dfrac{z}{z-1}$	$\dfrac{1}{s}$	(ZT–2)
nT	$\dfrac{Tz}{(z-1)^2}$	$\dfrac{1}{s^2}$	(ZT–3)
ϵ^{-naT}	$\dfrac{z}{z-\epsilon^{-aT}}$	$\dfrac{1}{s+a}$	(ZT–4)
a^n	$\dfrac{z}{z-a}$	$\dfrac{1}{s-\frac{\underline{Lna}}{T}}$	(ZT–5)
sin naT	$\dfrac{z\sin aT}{z^2-2z\cos aT+1}$	$\dfrac{a}{s^2+a^2}$	(ZT–6)
cos naT	$\dfrac{z^2-z\cos aT}{z^2-2z\cos aT+1}$	$\dfrac{s}{s^2+a^2}$	(ZT–7)

Solution

(a) The discrete unit step function $u(n)$ is defined by

$$u(n) = 1 \text{ for } n \geqslant 0$$
$$= 0 \text{ for } n < 0 \tag{4-14}$$

Utilization of the definition of the z-transform yields

$$X(z) = \sum_0^\infty x(n)z^{-n} = \sum_0^\infty (1)z^{-n} \tag{4-15}$$

The infinite summation given by (4-15) can be expressed in closed form for $|z| > 1$ as

$$X(z) = \frac{1}{1-z^{-1}} = \frac{z}{z-1} \tag{4-16}$$

(b) We may consider that the discrete-time signal has been derived from the reference continuous-time signal $x(t) = u(t)$, whose Laplace transform is $X(s) = 1/s$. Thus, there is only one pole of $X(s)$, located at $s = 0$. By use of (4-13), $X(z)$ can be expressed as

$$X(z) = \text{Res} \left[\frac{1}{p(1 - z^{-1} \epsilon^{pT})} \right]_{p=0}$$

$$= \frac{1}{1 - z^{-1}} = \frac{z}{z - 1}$$

(4-17)

Example 4-2

Derive operation pair (ZO-2).

Table 4-2
Z-transform operation pairs.

$x(n)$	$X(z) = 3\left[x(n)\right]$	
$ax_1(n) + bx_2(n)$	$aX_1(z) + bX_2(z)$	(ZO-1)
$^1x(n-m)$	$z^{-m}X(z)$	(ZO-2)
$\epsilon^{-naT}x(n)$	$X(\epsilon^{aT}z)$	(ZO-3)
$a^{-n}x(n)$	$X(az)$	(ZO-4)
$n^{\ell}x(n)$	$(-z\frac{d}{dz})^{\ell}X(z)$	(ZO-5)
$x(0)$	$\lim\limits_{z \to \infty} X(z)$	(ZO-6)
$x(\infty)$	$^2\lim\limits_{z \to 1} \frac{z-1}{z} X(z)$	(ZO-7)
$x(n)h(n)$	$\frac{1}{2\pi j} \cdot \int_c \frac{X(\bar{z})H(z/\bar{z})d\bar{z}}{\bar{z}}$	(ZO-8)
$\sum\limits_{m=0}^{n} x(m)h(n-m)$	$X(z)H(z)$	(ZO-9)

^{1}It is assumed that $x(n-m) = 0$ for $n < m$. Otherwise, initial condition terms are required.

^{2}This theorem is valid only if all the poles of $\frac{z-1}{z} X(z)$ lie inside the unit circle.

Solution

Considering that $x(n - m) = 0$ for $n < m$, application of the definition of the z-transform yields

$$\mathfrak{Z}\,[x(n - m)] = \sum_{n=m}^{\infty} x(n - m)z^{-n} \qquad (4\text{-}18)$$

Let $n - m = k$. Substitution of this quantity yields

$$\mathfrak{Z}\,[x(n - m)] = \sum_{k=0}^{\infty} x(k)z^{-k}z^{-m}$$

$$= z^{-m} \sum_{k=0}^{\infty} x(k)z^{-k} = z^{-m}\,X(z) \qquad (4\text{-}19)$$

4-3   TRANSFER FUNCTION

Let us now consider a discrete-time, linear, time-invariant (DTLTI) system consisting of a single input $x(n)$ and a single output $y(n)$. Such a system can be described by a linear difference equation with constant coefficients of the form

$$y(n) + b_1 y(n - 1) + b_2 y(n - 2) + \cdots + b_k y(n - k) =$$
$$a_0 x(n) + a_1 x(n - 1) + a_2 x(n - 2) + \cdots + a_k x(n - k) \qquad (4\text{-}20)$$

This equation describes an ordinary difference equation of order k with constant coefficients. For convenience in notation, the difference order k has been chosen to be the same on both sides of (4-20). In the event they are different, one need only specify that certain coefficients are zero. It should be observed that this equation has certain features similar to the differential equation input-output relationship of a continuous-time system, as described in Chapt. 2.

If (4-20) is solved for $y(n)$, the result is

$$y(n) = \sum_{i=0}^{k} a_i x(n - i) - \sum_{i=1}^{k} b_i y(n - i) \qquad (4\text{-}21)$$

A very interesting feature of (4-21) is that it can be completely solved by the basic arithmetic operations of multiplication, addition, and subtraction. All that is required to start a solution is to specify the input function $x(n)$ and the first k values of the output $y(n)$. The algorithm of (4-21) is then applied step by step. As each successive value of $y(n)$ is calculated, the integer n is advanced one step, and a computation of the next value is made. The solution of a difference equation is seen to be considerably simpler in concept than that of the corresponding differential equation.

Let us now consider a *relaxed* system, i.e., one with no initial values stored in the system. If we take the z-transforms of both sides of (4-20) and employ operation (ZO-2) of Table 4-2, we obtain, after factoring,

$$(1 + b_1 z^{-1} + b_2 z^{-2} + \cdots + b_k z^{-k})\, \mathrm{Y}(z) =$$

$$(a_0 + a_1 z^{-1} + a_2 z^{-2} + \cdots + a_k z^{-k})\, \mathrm{X}(z) \qquad (4\text{-}22)$$

Solving for $\mathrm{Y}(z)$, we obtain

$$\mathrm{Y}(z) = \frac{(a_0 + a_1 z^{-1} + a_2 z^{-2} + \cdots + a_k z^{-k})}{(1 + b_1 z^{-1} + b_2 z^{-2} + \cdots + b_k z^{-k})}\, \mathrm{X}(z) \qquad (4\text{-}23)$$

We now may define the *transfer function* $\mathrm{H}(z)$ of the discrete-time system as

$$\mathrm{H}(z) = \frac{\mathrm{N}(z)}{\mathrm{D}(z)} = \frac{a_0 + a_1 z^{-1} + a_2 z^{-2} + \cdots + a_k z^{-k}}{1 + b_1 z^{-1} + b_2 z^{-2} + \cdots + b_k z^{-k}} \qquad (4\text{-}24)$$

where $\mathrm{N}(z)$ is the numerator polynomial and $\mathrm{D}(z)$ is denominator polynomial.

The expression of (4-24) is arranged in *negative* powers of z, which is usually the most natural form in which the function occurs. On the other hand, it is frequently desirable to express $\mathrm{H}(z)$ in *positive* powers of z, particularly when we wish to factor the polynomials or to perform a partial fraction expansion. This is done by multiplying numerator and denominator by z^k, and the result is

$$\mathrm{H}(z) = \frac{a_0 z^k + a_1 z^{k-1} + a_2 z^{k-2} + \cdots + a_k}{z^k + b_1 z^{k-1} + b_2 z^{k-2} + \cdots + b_k} \qquad (4\text{-}25)$$

Using the transfer function concept, the input-output relationship becomes

$$\mathrm{Y}(z) = \mathrm{H}(z)\, \mathrm{X}(z) \qquad (4\text{-}26)$$

Thus, a discrete-time system can be represented by the same type of transfer function relationship as for a continuous-time system. In this case, however, the transfer function and the transformed variables are functions of the discrete variable z. To distinguish this transfer function from that of a continuous-time system, we will refer to H(z) simply as a *discrete transfer function*.

In the same fashion as for a continuous transfer function, we may determine poles and zeros for the discrete transfer function and represent them, for this case, in the z-plane. Various geometrical techniques have been developed for analyzing system performance in terms of relative pole and zero locations. Let $z_1, z_2, \cdots, z_k$ represent the k zeros, and let $p_1, p_2, \cdots, p_k$ represent the k poles. The transfer function may then be expressed in positive powers of z as

$$H(z) = \frac{a_0(z - z_1)(z - z_2) \cdots (z - z_k)}{(z - p_1)(z - p_2) \cdots (z - p_k)} \qquad (4\text{-}27)$$

If desired, this result may also be expressed in negative powers of z as

$$H(z) = \frac{a_0(1 - z_1 z^{-1})(1 - z_2 z^{-1}) \cdots (1 - z_k z^{-1})}{(1 - p_1 z^{-1})(1 - p_2 z^{-1}) \cdots (1 - p_k z^{-1})} \qquad (4\text{-}28)$$

As in the case of a continuous-time system, we may define the *impulse response* by assuming that the input is simply $x(n) = \delta(n)$. In the case of a continuous-time system, the impulse response is often somewhat difficult to implement physically. However, for a discrete-time system, the "impulse function" is simply a number (usually unity) applied at a single sampling instant, which is readily implemented in an actual system. Since $\mathcal{3}\,[\delta(n)] = 1$, the impulse response $h(n)$ is seen to be

$$h(n) = \mathcal{3}^{-1}\,[H(z)] \qquad (4\text{-}29)$$

In general, when a discrete-time system is excited by an arbitrary input $x(n)$, the transform $X(z)$ is found and multiplied by $H(z)$ to obtain the output transform $Y(z)$. The discrete-time output signal is then determined by inverting $Y(z)$ to give $y(n)$. Of course, it may actually be faster to program the original difference equation directly on a digital computer or programmable calculator and obtain a solution point by point. However, the major advantage of the z-transform approach is the powerful conceptual and operational basis that it provides in studying discrete-time system behavior. For that reason, the next section will be devoted to various procedures for inverting z-transforms.

4-4 INVERSE Z-TRANSFORM

The next problem to be considered is that of finding the discrete-time signal $y(n)$ corresponding to a given transform $Y(z)$, which is the process of inverse transformation. In general, the inverse z-transform may be determined by at least three separate procedures: (a) partial fraction expansion and use of transform pair tables, (b) inversion integral method, and (c) power series expansion.

Partial Fraction Expansion. The method most widely used in routine problems is probably the partial fraction expansion technique. This approach is very similar to the one employed with Laplace transforms in continuous-time system analysis. One must be careful to make sure that all the terms in the expansion fit forms that may be easily recognized from a combination of the table of pairs and the table of operations. As in the case of all partial fraction expansion methods, there are "tricks" that one acquires with experience. In the end, the expansion can always be recombined as a check on its validity if there is any doubt.

Assume that we are given a z-transform $Y(z)$ for which we wish to determine the inverse $y(n)$. Any transform of interest in most digital signal processing systems can usually be described by a rational function of z. Since the transfer function $H(z)$ is also a rational function, as can be deduced from (4-24) and (4-25), the resultant $Y(z)$ is also a rational function of z and will have the same general form as the transfer function, except that it will normally have more poles and zeros due to the excitation $X(z)$. We will assume that $Y(z)$ can be represented in positive powers of z as

$$Y(z) = \frac{c_0 z^\ell + c_1 z^{\ell-1} + \cdots + c_\ell}{z^\ell + d_1 z^{\ell-1} + \cdots + d_\ell} \tag{4-30}$$

Assume now that the poles of $Y(z)$ are known. The function may then be expressed in the form

$$Y(z) = \frac{c_0 z^\ell + c_1 z^{\ell-1} + \cdots + c_\ell}{\displaystyle\prod_{m=1}^{\ell} (z - p_m)} \tag{4-31}$$

The form of the partial fraction expansion and the subsequent inverse transform will depend on the nature of the given poles. The simplest, and by far the most common, case is where all the poles are of simple order, i.e., there are no repeated roots in the denominator polynomial. The partial fraction expansion method may be adapted to multiple-order poles, but due to the additional labor involved, we will defer this case to one of the later methods. In general, poles may be either real or complex. In the case of complex poles, a pole will always be accompanied by its complex conjugate in the case where all the polynomial coefficients are real.

Probably the most straightforward procedure for the case where all the poles are of simple order is to first divide both sides of (4-31) by z and then expand $Y(z)/z$ in a partial fraction expansion. Such an expansion will usually be of the form

$$\frac{Y(z)}{z} = \frac{A_1}{z - p_1} + \frac{A_2}{z - p_2} + \cdots + \frac{A_\ell}{z - p_\ell} \qquad (4\text{-}32)$$

A given coefficient A_m may be determined by multiplying both sides of (4-32) by $z - p_m$ and setting $z = p_m$. This results in zero for all the resulting terms on the right except the A_m term, in which the multiplicative factor has been cancelled by the denominator. The result is then

$$A_m = (z - p_m) \frac{Y(z)}{z} \Bigg]_{z = p_m} \qquad (4\text{-}33)$$

This expression is valid only for poles of simple order.

If the coefficients of both the numerator and denominator polynomials of $Y(z)$ are real, then it can be shown that complex poles of $Y(z)$ always occur in conjugate pairs. Furthermore, in this case the corresponding coefficients are also complex conjugates. (See Prob. 4-15.) This means that such a pair can be manipulated into the product of an exponential function and a sinusoidal function. To illustrate this process, assume that a given first-order complex pole $p_r = |p_r| \angle \theta_r$ and its conjugate $\tilde{p}_r = |p_r| \angle -\theta_r$ are present. Assume that the corresponding coefficients are $A_r = |A_r| \angle \phi_r$ and $\tilde{A}_r = |A_r| \angle -\phi_r$. The reader is invited to show (Prob. 4-16) that this combination can be expressed as

$$A_r(p_r)^n + \tilde{A}_r(\tilde{p}_r)^n = 2|A_r|(|p_r|)^n \cos(n\theta_r + \phi_r) \qquad (4\text{-}34)$$

Example 4-3

By partial fraction expansion, obtain the inverse z-transform of

$$Y(z) = \frac{1}{(1 - z^{-1})(1 - 0.5z^{-1})} \qquad (4\text{-}35)$$

Solution

As a first step, we eliminate the negative powers of z by multiplying numerator and denominator by z^2.

$$Y(z) = \frac{z^2}{(z-1)(z-0.5)} \qquad (4\text{-}36)$$

We now form $Y(z)/z$ and express it in partial fraction form as

$$\frac{Y(z)}{z} = \frac{z}{(z-1)(z-0.5)} = \frac{A_1}{z-1} + \frac{A_2}{z-0.5} \qquad (4\text{-}37)$$

Application of (4-33) yields $A_1 = 2$ and $A_2 = -1$. Multiplication of both sides of (4-37) by z and inversion yields

$$y(n) = 2 - (0.5)^n \qquad (4\text{-}38)$$

Several values are tabulated as follows:

n	0	1	2	3	4	5	6	∞
$y(n)$	1	1.5	1.75	1.875	1.9375	1.96875	1.984375	2

Example 4-4

The difference equation describing the input-output relationship of a certain initially relaxed DTLTI system is given by

$$y(n) - y(n-1) + 0.5\,y(n-2) = x(n) + x(n-1) \qquad (4\text{-}39)$$

Find (a) the transfer function $H(z)$, (b) the impulse response $h(n)$, and (c) the output response when a unit step function is applied at $n = 0$.

Solution

(a) Taking the z-transform of both sides of (4-39) and arranging in the form of (4-24) yields

$$H(z) = \frac{1 + z^{-1}}{1 - z^{-1} + 0.5z^{-2}} \qquad (4\text{-}40)$$

The transfer function can be arranged in positive powers of z by multiplying numerator and denominator by z^2. This yields

$$H(z) = \frac{z(z+1)}{z^2 - z + 0.5} \qquad (4\text{-}41)$$

The zeros are $z_1 = 0$ and $z_2 = -1$, and the poles are $p_1, p_2 = 0.5 \pm j0.5$ $= 0.707107 \, \underline{/\pm 45°}$. The factored form of $H(z)$ is then

$$H(z) = \frac{z(z+1)}{(z - 0.5 - j0.5)(z - 0.5 + j0.5)} \qquad (4\text{-}42)$$

(b) To obtain the impulse response, we expand $H(z)$ in a partial fraction expansion according to the procedure previously discussed. The result is

$$H(z) = \frac{Az}{z - 0.5 - j0.5} + \frac{\widetilde{A}z}{z - 0.5 + j0.5} \qquad (4\text{-}43)$$

where $A = 1.581139 \, \underline{/-71.5651°}$ and $\widetilde{A} = 1.581139 \, \underline{/71.5651°}$. Inversion and use of (4-34) yield

$$h(n) = 3.162278\,(0.707107)^n \cos(45n° - 71.5651°) \qquad (4\text{-}44)$$

where the argument of the cosine function is expressed in degrees for convenience. An alternate approach would be to force the given transform into the approximate forms of pairs (ZT-6) and (ZT-7) with modification by use of operation (ZO-4). However, this approach is probably more cumbersome.

(c) In order to solve for the response due to a step excitation, we multiply the transfer function by the transform of the step function in accordance with (4-26). The result is

$$Y(z) = \frac{z^2(z+1)}{(z-1)(z^2 - z + 0.5)} \qquad (4\text{-}45)$$

Expansion yields

$$Y(z) = \frac{A_1 z}{z - 1} + \frac{A_2 z}{z - 0.5 - j0.5} + \frac{\widetilde{A}_2 z}{z - 0.5 + j0.5} \qquad (4\text{-}46)$$

where $A_1 = 4$, $A_2 = 1.581139 \, \underline{/-161.5651°}$, and $\widetilde{A}_2 = 1.581139$ $\underline{/161.5651°}$. Inversion and subsequent simplification result in

$$y(n) = 4 + 3.162278\,(0.707107)^n \cos(45n° - 161.5651°) \qquad (4\text{-}47)$$

Inversion Integral. A powerful analytical method for determining the inverse z-transform is the inversion integral method. The function $Y(z)$ can be considered as a Laurent series in the complex z-plane. A given coefficient in such a series may be determined by an integral relationship. It can be shown that application of this concept to $Y(z)$ yields, for the inverse transform,

$$y(n) = \frac{1}{2\pi j} \int_C Y(z) z^{n-1} dz \qquad (4\text{-}48)$$

where C is a contour chosen to include all singularities of the integrand. By Cauchy's Residue Theorem, this integral can be reduced to

$$y(n) = \sum_m \text{Res}[Y(z) z^{n-1}]_{z = p_m} \qquad (4\text{-}49)$$

where p_m represents a pole of $Y(z)z^{n-1}$ and Res [ ] represents the residue at $z = p_m$.

So far, we have restricted the consideration in this text to the one-sided z-transform as defined by (4-6). This implies that $y(n) = 0$ for $n < 0$; thus, we are not normally interested in (4-49) for negative n. Assume that $Y(z)$ has a zero of order r at the origin, i.e., a numerator factor z^r, where $r > 0$. In this case, the product of z^r times z^{n-1} in (4-49) results in a net factor z^{r+n-1}. If $r \geq 1$, then $r + n - 1 \geq 0$ for $n \geq 0$, and there is no pole at $z = 0$ in the total integrand. On the other hand, if $r \leq 0$, there will be a pole at $z = 0$ for one or more nonnegative values of n. A separate inversion of (4-49) will be required at one or more values of n for this case. This concept will be illustrated in Ex. 4-6.

Example 4-5

Invert the transform of Ex. 4-3 by means of the inversion integral and residue procedure.

Solution

The function is

$$Y(z) = \frac{z^2}{(z-1)(z-0.5)} \qquad (4\text{-}50)$$

From (4-49), this can be expressed as

$$y(n) = \sum_m \text{Res} \left[\frac{z^{n+1}}{(z-1)(z-0.5)} \right]_{z=p_m} \tag{4-51}$$

The degree of z in the numerator of (4-51) is positive for $n \geq 0$, so there is no pole at $z = 0$ for this range of n. The poles are at $z = 1$ and $z = 0.5$. The residues are calculated as follows:

$$\text{Res} \left[\frac{z^{n+1}}{(z-1)(z-0.5)} \right]_{z=1} = \left[\frac{z^{n+1}}{z-0.5} \right]_{z=1} = 2 \tag{4-52}$$

$$\text{Res} \left[\frac{z^{n+1}}{(z-1)(z-0.5)} \right]_{z=0.5} = \left[\frac{z^{n+1}}{z-1} \right]_{z=0.5} = -(0.5)^n \tag{4-53}$$

Addition of (4-52) and (4-53) yields the solution previously obtained, which was given by (4-38).

Example 4-6

Determine the inverse transform of

$$Y(z) = \frac{1 + 2z^{-1} + z^{-3}}{(1 - z^{-1})(1 - 0.5z^{-1})} \tag{4-54}$$

Solution

Note that the maximum negative power of z in the numerator is larger than for the denominator. Multiplication of numerator and denominator by z^3 results in

$$Y(z) = \frac{z^3 + 2z^2 + 1}{z(z-1)(z-0.5)} \tag{4-55}$$

According to (4-49), we may determine the inverse transform from

$$y(n) = \sum_m \text{Res} \left[\frac{(z^3 + 2z^2 + 1)z^{n-2}}{(z-1)(z-0.5)} \right]_{z=p_m} \tag{4-56}$$

We must examine z^{n-2} to see if there are any values of n for which there is a pole at the origin. Indeed, for $n = 0$ there is a second-order pole at $z = 0$, and for $n = 1$ there is a simple pole at $z = 0$. However for $n \geq 2$, the only poles are $z = 1$ and $z = 0.5$. Let us first determine the inverse transform pertinent to this latter range. We have

$$y(n) = \text{Res} [\ ]_{z=1} + \text{Res} [\ ]_{z=0.5}$$

$$= 8 - 13(0.5)^n \text{ for } n \geq 2 \qquad (4\text{-}57)$$

The values of $y(0)$ and $y(1)$ can be determined from the expressions

$$y(0) = \sum_m \text{Res} \left[\frac{z^3 + 2z^2 + 1}{z^2(z-1)(z-0.5)} \right]_{z=p_m}$$

$$= \text{Res} [\ ]_{z=0} + \text{Res} [\ ]_{z=1} + \text{Res} [\ ]_{z=0.5} \qquad (4\text{-}58)$$

$$y(1) = \sum_m \text{Res} \left[\frac{z^3 + 2z^2 + 1}{z(z-1)(z-0.5)} \right]_{z=p_m}$$

$$= \text{Res} [\ ]_{z=0} + \text{Res} [\ ]_{z=1} + \text{Res} [\ ]_{z=0.5} \qquad (4\text{-}59)$$

The reader is invited to demonstrate that the sum of the last two residues in each of (4-58) and (4-59) is the same as would be obtained by taking (4-57) and evaluating it for $n = 0$ and $n = 1$, respectively. Thus, instead of performing a complete evaluation of all the residues for $n = 0$ and $n = 1$, it is necessary only to determine the additional residues at $z = 0$ in each case. For (4-58), we have

$$\text{Res} \left[\frac{z^3 + 2z^2 + 1}{z^2(z-1)(z-0.5)} \right]_{z=0} = 6 \qquad (4\text{-}60)$$

For (4-59), we have

$$\text{Res} \left[\frac{z^3 + 2z^2 + 1}{z(z-1)(z-0.5)} \right]_{z=0} = 2 \qquad (4\text{-}61)$$

This gives

$$y(0) = 6 + 8 - 13 = 1 \qquad (4\text{-}62)$$

$$y(1) = 2 + 8 - 13(0.5) = 3.5 \qquad (4\text{-}63)$$

For $n \geq 2$, the expression of (4-57) is applicable. An alternative way to write $y(n)$ for $n \geq 0$ in one expression is the equation

$$y(n) = 6\delta(n) + 2\delta(n-1) + 8 - 13(0.5)^n \qquad (4\text{-}64)$$

A few values are tabulated in the following table:

n	0	1	2	3	4	5	6	∞
$y(n)$	1	3.5	4.75	6.375	7.1875	7.59375	7.796875	8

Power-Series Expansion. The last method that we will consider for inverting z-transforms is the power-series method. This method is particularly useful when the inverse transform has no simple closed-form solution or when it is desired to represent the signal as a sequence of numbers defined at sample points. The key to this approach is the basic definition of the z-transform as given by (4-6). A given transform is manipulated to yield a power series of the appropriate form. The values of the signal at sample points are then read directly from the coefficients of the terms in the power series. The pertinent power series may be obtained by dividing the numerator polynomial by the denominator polynomial, both arranged in descending powers of z.

Example 4-7

Determine several points in the inverse z-transform of the function given in Ex. 4-6 by the power series method.

Solution

We first arrange as a ratio of polynomials.

$$Y(z) = \frac{z^3 + 2z^2 + 1}{z^3 - 1.5z^2 + 0.5z} \qquad (4\text{-}65)$$

The power series is obtained by a division process as follows:

$$
\begin{array}{r}
1 + 3.5z^{-1} + 4.75z^{-2} + 6.375z^{-3} + \cdots \\
z^3 - 1.5z^2 + 0.5z \overline{\smash{\big)}\ z^3 + \quad 2z^2 \qquad\qquad + 1} \\
\underline{z^3 - 1.5z^2 + 0.5z} \\
3.5z^2 - 0.5z \ + 1 \\
\underline{3.5z^2 - 5.25z + 1.75} \\
4.75z - 0.75 \\
\underline{4.75z - 7.125 + 2.375z^{-1}} \\
6.375 - 2.375z^{-1}
\end{array}
$$

The first few terms of the series may then be written as

$$Y(z) = 1 + 3.5z^{-1} + 4.75z^{-2} + 6.375z^{-3} + \cdots \qquad (4\text{-}66)$$

By inspection, we see that $y(0) = 1, y(1) = 3.5, y(2) = 4.75$, and $y(3) = 6.375$. These results are in agreement with Ex. 4-6.

Example 4-8

Determine the inverse transform of

$$Y(z) = 1 + 5z^{-1} - 3z^{-2} + 2z^{-4} \qquad (4\text{-}67)$$

Solution

This transform is already in the form of a power series. Note that this corresponds to a signal of finite length having only a few specified points. By inspection, we note that $y(0) = 1$, $y(1) = 5$, $y(2) = -3$, $y(3) = 0$, and $y(4) = 2$. All other values of $y(n)$ are zero.

4-5 RESPONSE FORMS AND STABILITY _____

We will not investigate the different forms associated with the response terms of DTLTI systems. It will be seen that this development closely parallels the corresponding situation for a CTLTI system as given in Chapt. 2.

It has previously been shown that the transfer function of a DTLTI system can be expressed in the form

$$H(z) = \frac{a_0(z - z_1)(z - z_2) \cdots (z - z_k)}{(z - p_1)(z - p_2) \cdots (z - p_k)} \qquad (4\text{-}68)$$

When the system is excited by an arbitrary signal $x(n)$, the transform of the output signal $y(n)$ is obtained by multiplying $H(z)$ by $X(z)$. The poles contained in $Y(z)$ may result from two sources: poles due to the transfer function $H(z)$, and poles due to the input $X(z)$.

The *natural response* is defined as that portion of the response due to the poles of $H(z)$. The *forced response* is defined as that portion of the response due to the poles of $X(z)$. If the natural response vanishes after a sufficiently long time, it is called a *transient response*. In this case only the forced response remains, and it is called a steady-state response. In order for this latter condition to exist, the system must be *stable*.

As in the case of a continuous-time system, a discrete-time system is said to be stable if every finite input produces a finite output. The stability concept may be readily expressed by conditions relating to the impulse response $h(n)$. These conditions are:

(a) *Stable system.* A DTLTI system is stable if $h(n)$ vanishes after a sufficiently long time.

(b) *Unstable system.* A DTLTI system is unstable if $h(n)$ grows without bound after a sufficiently long time.

(c) *Marginally stable system.* A DTLTI system is marginally stable if $h(n)$ approaches a constant nonzero value or a bounded oscillation after a sufficiently long time.

Stability may be determined directly from the transfer function if the poles are given. A complex pole of the form $p_m = |p_m| \angle \phi_m$ can be thought of as producing one or more time response terms of the form

$$y_m(n) = A n^r p_m{}^n \qquad (4\text{-}69)$$

It can be shown that the only condition required for $y_m(n)$ to eventually vanish is that $|p_m| < 1$. Likewise, if $|p_m| > 1$, then $y_m(n)$ will grow without bound. If $|p_m| = 1$ and $r = 0$ (corresponding to a first-order pole), $y_m(n)$ will be either a constant ($p_m = 1$) or a constant amplitude oscillation. However, if $|p_m| = 1$ and $r > 0$ (corresponding to a multiple-order pole), $y_m(n)$ will grow without bound.

A summary of the preceding points and a few other inferences follow:

(a) Poles of a discrete transfer function inside the unit circle represent stable terms regardless of their order.

(b) Poles of a discrete transfer function outside the unit circle represent unstable terms regardless of their order.

(c) First-order poles on the unit circle represent marginally stable terms, but multiple-order poles on the unit circle represent unstable terms.

(d) A discrete system is only as stable as its least stable part. Thus, all poles of a perfectly stable system must lie *inside* the unit circle.

(e) In general, zeros are permitted to lie anywhere in the z-plane.

Example 4-9

A system is described by the difference equation

$$y(n) + 0.1y(n-1) - 0.2y(n-2) = x(n) + x(n-1) \qquad (4\text{-}70)$$

(a) Determine the transfer function H(z) and discuss its stability.

(b) Determine the impulse response $h(n)$.

(c) Determine the response due to a unit step function excitation if the system is initially relaxed.

Solution

(a) Taking the z-transforms of both sides of (4-70) and solving for H(z), we obtain

$$H(z) = \frac{Y(z)}{X(z)} = \frac{1 + z^{-1}}{1 + 0.1z^{-1} - 0.2z^{-2}} \qquad (4\text{-}71)$$

The poles and zeros are best obtained by momentarily arranging numerator and denominator polynomials in positive powers of z.

$$H(z) = \frac{z^2 + z}{z^2 + 0.1z - 0.2} = \frac{z(z+1)}{(z-0.4)(z+0.5)} \qquad (4\text{-}72)$$

The poles are located at $+0.4$ and -0.5, which are inside the unit circle. Thus, the system is stable.

(b) The impulse response may be obtained by expanding H(z) in a partial fraction expansion according to the procedure of the preceding section. This yields

$$H(z) = \frac{1.555556z}{z - 0.4} - \frac{0.555556z}{z + 0.5} \qquad (4\text{-}73)$$

Inversion of (4-73) yields

$$h(n) = 1.555556(0.4)^n - 0.555556(-0.5)^n \qquad (4\text{-}74)$$

It can be readily seen that the impulse response $h(n)$ vanishes after a sufficiently long time, as expected, since this is a stable transfer function.

(c) To obtain the response due to $x(n) = 1$, we multiply X(z) by H(z) and obtain

$$Y(z) = \frac{z^2(z+1)}{(z-1)(z-0.4)(z+0.5)} \qquad (4\text{-}75)$$

Partial fraction expansion yields

$$Y(z) = \frac{2.222222z}{z-1} - \frac{1.037037z}{z-0.4} - \frac{0.185185z}{z+0.5} \qquad (4\text{-}76)$$

The inverse transform is

$$y(n) = 2.222222 - 1.037037(0.4)^n - 0.185185(-0.5)^n \qquad (4\text{-}77)$$

4-6 DISCRETE-TIME CONVOLUTION

An alternate approach for relating the input and output of a discrete-time system is through the convolution concept. We will choose to develop this concept through a rather intuitive approach, which provides some insight into the process itself. Assume that a given DTLTI system has an impulse response $h(n)$. This means that an impulse (unit sample) occurring at $n = 0$ will produce a response $h(n)$. A delayed impulse $\delta(n - m)$ occurring at $n = m$ will produce a delayed response $h(n-m)$. The discrete-time input signal can be thought of as an impulse train in which each successive impulse has a weight equal to that particular sample value. The forms for the various impulses and the responses they produce can be outlined as follows:

$$
\begin{aligned}
x(0)\delta(n) &\longrightarrow x(0)h(n) \\
x(1)\delta(n-1) &\longrightarrow x(1)h(n-1) \\
x(2)\delta(n-2) &\longrightarrow x(2)h(n-2)
\end{aligned}
$$

$$\qquad (4\text{-}78)$$

$$
\begin{aligned}
\cdot\\
\cdot\\
\cdot\\
x(m)\delta(n-m) &\longrightarrow x(m)h(n-m)
\end{aligned}
$$

In general, the response at any arbitrary value of n is obtained by summing all the components that have occurred up to that point, i.e.,

$$y(n) = \sum_{m=0}^{n} x(m)h(n-m) \qquad (4\text{-}79)$$

The convolution operation can be shown to be commutative, which means that (4-79) can be expressed as

$$y(n) = \sum_{m=0}^{n} h(m) x(n - m) \qquad (4\text{-}80)$$

From earlier work in this chapter, it is known that

$$Y(z) = H(z) X(z) \qquad (4\text{-}81)$$

Performing the z-transformation on both sides of (4-79) and comparing with (4-81), operation (ZO-9) of Table 4-2 is readily obtained. In some discrete-time system developments, it is desirable to replace the upper limit on the summations of (4-79) and (4-80) with ∞. This change in notation does not affect the value of the summation for a causal system since $h(n - m) = 0$ for $n < m$.

The convolution approach represents an alternative technique for analyzing a discrete system or for signal processing as compared with the direct difference equation approach. With the convolution approach, the values of $h(n)$ may be stored in the system memory. As the samples of the input signal enter the system, the operation of (4-79) or (4-80) is performed to yield successive output samples.

The direct convolution approach to signal processing, as discussed in this section, is used primarily when the impulse response is relatively short in duration. Otherwise, the number of operations required to compute each new value of $y(n)$ will become excessive. On the other hand, fast Fourier transfer methods can be used to achieve high-speed convolution for relatively long impulse responses. This approach will be discussed in Chaps. 9 and 10.

PROBLEMS

4-1 Derive transform pair ZT-4 two ways: (a) by application of the basic z-transform definition, and (b) by use of the contour integral method.

4-2 Derive transform pair ZT-3 three ways: (a) by application of the basic z-transform definition, (b) by use of the contour integral method, and (c) from transform pair ZT-2 and the use of an appropriate operation pair.

4-3 Derive transform pairs ZT-6 and ZT-7 from ZT-4 with the help of Euler's equation.

4-4 Derive operation pairs ZO-3 and ZO-4.

4-5 Derive $x(n)$ from $X(z)$ for transform pairs ZT-4 and ZT-5 two ways: (a) by use of the inversion integral, and (b) from a power series expansion.

4-6 Determine the inverse transform of

$$X(z) = z^{-1} + 6z^{-4} - 2z^{-7}$$

4-7 By the simplest procedure, determine the first three values of the inverse transform of

$$X(z) = \frac{3z^3 + 2z^2 + 2z + 5}{z^3 + 4z^2 + 3z + 2}$$

4-8 Determine the inverse transform of the function listed below two ways: (a) by partial fraction expansion, and (b) by use of the inversion integral.

$$X(z) = \frac{10}{(1 - 0.5z^{-1})(1 - 0.25z^{-1})}$$

4-9 Determine the inverse transform of the function listed below two ways: (a) by partial fraction expansion, and (b) by use of the inversion integral.

$$X(z) = \frac{10z^2}{(z - 1)(z + 1)}$$

4-10 Determine the inverse transform of

$$X(z) = \frac{1 + z^{-3}}{(1 - 0.5z^{-1})(1 - 0.25z^{-1})}$$

4-11 Determine if each of the following transfer functions is stable, unstable, or marginally stable. In each case, write the difference equation algorithm relating $x(n)$ and $y(n)$.

(a) $\dfrac{z + 2}{8z^2 - 2z - 3}$
(b) $\dfrac{8(1 - z^{-1} + z^{-2})}{2 + 5z^{-1} + 2z^{-2}}$

(c) $\dfrac{2z^2 + 4}{2z^2 + z - 1}$
(d) $\dfrac{1 + z^{-1}}{1 - z^{-1} + z^{-2}}$

4-12 A system is described by the difference equation

$$y(n) + y(n - 1) = x(n) \qquad\qquad y(n) = 0 \text{ for } n < 0$$

(a) Determine the transfer function and discuss the stability of the system.

(b) Determine the impulse response $h(n)$ and show that it behaves according to the conclusion of (a).

(c) Determine the response when $x(n) = 10$ for $n \geq 0$. Assume that the system is initially relaxed.

4-13 (a) Determine the transfer function of the zero-order integrator described by the algorithm

$$y(n) = y(n-1) + Tx(n-1)$$

(b) Assuming that the system is initially relaxed, determine the response due to the exponential input

$$x(n) = \epsilon^{-n\alpha T}$$

and compare with the exact integral of the continuous-time exponential

$$x(t) = \epsilon^{-\alpha t}$$

4-14 (a) Determine the transfer function of the first-order trapezoidal integrator

$$y(n) = \frac{T}{2}[x(n) + x(n-1)] + y(n-1)$$

(b) Assuming that the system is initially relaxed, determine the response due to the exponential input of Prob. 4-13, and compare with the exact integral of the continuous-time exponential.

4-15 Assume that all the polynomial coefficients in a rational function $H(z)$ are restricted to be real. Show then that the numerator coefficients at conjugate poles in a partial fraction expansion are also conjugates of each other.

4-16 Show that the result of equation (4-34) is correct.

4-17 Because of the emphasis on the transfer function concept in this chapter, we have assumed initially relaxed systems for most of our work. The form of (ZO-2) as given in Table 4-2 was appropriate in this case. Assume now that $x(n-m) \neq 0$ for $n < m$. continuing to use the one-sided z-transform, show that

$$\mathbf{3}\,[x(n-m)] = z^{-m}\,X(z) + \sum_{i=1}^{m} x(-i)z^{i-m}$$

4-18 Using the result of Prob. 4-17, solve the difference equation below subject to the initial conditions given.

$$y(n) + 0.1y(n-1) - 0.02y(n-2) = 10$$

$$y(-1) = 4, y(-2) = 6$$

5

REALIZATION AND
FREQUENCY RESPONSE OF
DISCRETE-TIME SYSTEMS

5-0 INTRODUCTION

The basic concepts of discrete-time systems were introduced in the last chapter. Emphasis was directed toward the use of z-transform methods for analyzing difference equations that arise in discrete-time systems, and the transfer function concept was developed in some detail.

In this chapter, continued emphasis will be made on the development and application of transfer function concepts. The first aspect that will be considered is that of system realization from the transfer function or difference equation. The realization of a discrete-time system consists of determining the physical layout of a combination of arithmetic and storage operations that would produce the given transfer function or difference equation. The end result might eventually be a software realization such as a computer program, or it might be a hardware realization involving digital circuitry.

The second primary area of emphasis in this chapter is that of the steady-state frequency response of discrete-time systems. As in the case of continuous-time systems, the concept of the frequency response serves a very important role in both the analysis and design of discrete-time systems. Various properties of the steady-state frequency response will be developed in detail.

5-1   DISCRETE-TIME SYSTEM OPERATIONS ⸻⸻⸻⸻⸻

The first problem considered in this chapter is the realization of a discrete-time system from a knowledge of the transfer function (or from the difference equation). For the moment, we will not be concerned with where the transfer function is obtained, but rather we wish to investigate the manner in which the system can be designed. In later chapters, such transfer functions will be obtained through the process of digital filter design.

   The realization problem will be considered first because its treatment relates very nicely to the basic theory of the discrete-time system as considered in the previous chapter. On the other hand, the approximation problem will require more development through the next several chapters before a complete solution can be discussed.

   The realization of a discrete-time system may involve either *hardware* or *software* (or both in some cases). In the hardware approach, it is desirable to actually design and construct a discrete-time system using digital circuitry. The ultimate goal in this case might be a special-purpose processor (e.g., for radar or sonar signals) that would more or less be committed to a specific purpose.

   In the software approach, the end product might be a computer program for a general-purpose computer or minicomputer. In some cases, a special-purpose processor with programmable characteristics might be used. When the design represents software, the computer might be programmed to process some real-life signal, or the program might represent the simulation of another physical system whose characteristics are to be studied.

   Regardless of the ultimate goal, the form achieved will be that of a *realization diagram* providing the layout of the signal processing functions required. The realization diagram can then be used for either a hardware or a software design.

   In this text, we will consider the basic operations outlined in Fig. 5-1 for developing realizations. The operations will now be discussed individually.

   The *unit delay* operation shown in (a) represents the process of delaying or storing a particular sample by T seconds, at which time it appears at the output. Since all operations in a uniformly sampled system occur at integer multiples of the basic sample time T, we refer to a delay of T as a "unit delay." The output of the unit delay block can be expressed as

$$y(n) = x(n-1) \qquad (5\text{-}1)$$

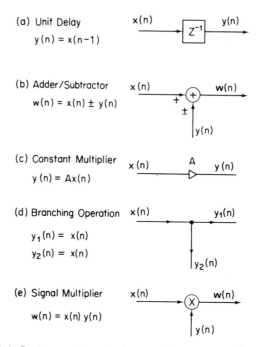

(a) Unit Delay

$y(n) = x(n-1)$

(b) Adder/Subtractor

$w(n) = x(n) \pm y(n)$

(c) Constant Multiplier

$y(n) = Ax(n)$

(d) Branching Operation

$y_1(n) = x(n)$
$y_2(n) = x(n)$

(e) Signal Multiplier

$w(n) = x(n)\,y(n)$

Figure 5-1 Basic operations in discrete-time system realizations.

The *adder/subtractor* operation shown in (b) represents the arithmetic process of combining the two signals $x(n)$ and $y(n)$ by either addition or subtraction in the form

$$w(n) = x(n) \pm y(n) \qquad (5\text{-}2)$$

In many realization diagrams, more than two signals will be combined in the same unit. In such cases, the signs adjacent to the various input branches may be used to identify whether a given value is added or subtracted. If the signs are omitted, it will be understood that all of the signals are *added* algebraically in the adder itself.

The *constant multiplier* shown in (c) represents the arithmetic process of multiplying the signal $x(n)$ by a constant according to the equation

$$y(n) = Ax(n) \qquad (5\text{-}3)$$

The constant A may be rigidly fixed in the system, or it may be programmable. However, if the system is considered to be time invariant, it will usually be constant for definite intervals of time.

The *branching operation* shown in (d) simply refers to the process of simultaneously connecting a signal to two or more points in the system. If $y_1(n)$ and $y_2(n)$ represent the two points for which $x(n)$ is to appear, we have

$$y_1(n) = x(n)$$
$$(5\text{-}4)$$
$$y_2(n) = x(n)$$

The primary limitation on branching in hardware design is the fact that for each additional branch, more power must be supplied by the previous stage. Consequently, there will be some maximum number of branches that could be driven by a specific digital circuit, depending on the type of circuitry and the nature of the input circuitry that follows.

The *signal multiplier* shown in (e) refers to the process of multiplication of two dynamic signals $x(n)$ and $y(n)$. The output is

$$w(n) = x(n)y(n) \qquad (5\text{-}5)$$

The signal multiplier differs from the constant multiplier in the sense that the signal unit multiplies samples of two separate discrete-time signals whose values may both continually vary with time.

5-2   DIRECT REALIZATION FORMS

We will now consider several forms for the actual realization diagrams of discrete-time systems. In the theory of continuous-time systems, the complexity of the realization problem has necessitated the development of a large body of synthesis procedures. It appears that such a massive effort is not necessary in the case of discrete-time systems. In fact, a few basic forms seem to be adequate as a starting point for most realization problems. We will consider the transfer function form of interest to be

$$H(z) = \frac{N(z)}{D(z)} = \frac{\displaystyle\sum_{i=0}^{k} a_i z^{-i}}{1 + \displaystyle\sum_{i=1}^{k} b_i z^{-i}} \qquad (5\text{-}6)$$

The first approach will be designated as the *direct form 1* method. The difference equation corresponding to (5-6) is given by

$$y(n) = \sum_{i=0}^{k} a_i x(n-i) - \sum_{i=1}^{k} b_i y(n-i) \qquad (5\text{-}7)$$

The realization diagram of Fig. 5-2 represents a direct implementation of this equation. Notice that the delay operations on the left provide successively shifted values of $x(n)$, while those on the right provide the comparable values of $y(n)$. One disadvantage of the *direct form 1* method is that it may require up to $2k$ delay elements or operations for a kth order system.

The second approach will be designated as the *direct form 2* method. This method is best understood by manipulating H(z) in a different form. We start with

$$Y(z) = H(z)X(z) = \frac{N(z)X(z)}{D(z)} \qquad (5\text{-}8)$$

We will define a new variable W(z) by the equation

$$W(z) = \frac{X(z)}{D(z)} \qquad (5\text{-}9)$$

It follows from (5-8) and (5-9) that

$$Y(z) = N(z)W(z) \qquad (5\text{-}10)$$

The inverse transforms of (5-9) and (5-10) can be expressed as

$$w(n) = x(n) - \sum_{i=1}^{k} b_i w(n-i) \qquad (5\text{-}11)$$

and

$$y(n) = \sum_{i=0}^{k} a_i w(n-i) \qquad (5\text{-}12)$$

The layout of the direct form 2 realization is shown in Fig. 5-3. The variable $w(n)$ represents the output of the first adder on the left. Moving to the right, the output of the first delay element represents $w(n-1)$; the output of the second element represents $w(n-2)$, etc. The relationships of (5-9) and (5-11) are best seen by momentarily disconnecting all the forward a_i paths. The various values of $w(n-i)$ are then multiplied by the b_i coefficients and added to form $w(n)$ according to (5-11). Connection of the forward paths does not change this relationship since these paths merely sense the values at the output of the

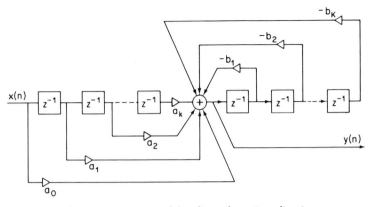

Figure 5-2 Layout of the direct form 1 realization.

successive delay elements, multiply these values by the appropriate constants, and sum them at the output to yield $y(n)$. The sum of all the forward paths can be seen to satisfy the conditions of (5-10) and 5-12). Notice that the *direct form 2* method requires only k delay elements or operations for a kth-order system.

In some of the literature the direct form 1 realization is called simply the *direct form*, and the direct form 2 realization is called the *canonic form*. However, both of these forms (and some others) are generally considered to be canonic forms, so we will use the terms previously discussed.

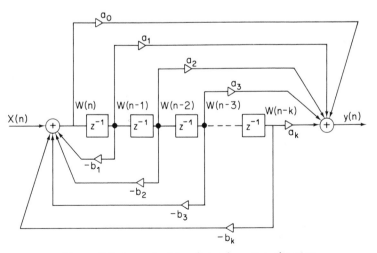

Figure 5-3 Layout of the direct form 2 realization.

Example 5-1

Develop realization diagrams for the system described by the transfer function below in two forms: (a) direct form 1, and (b) direct form 2.

$$H(z) = \frac{3 + 3.6z^{-1} + 0.6z^{-2}}{1 + 0.1z^{-1} - 0.2z^{-2}} \qquad (5\text{-}13)$$

Solution

(a) For the direct form 1, we will convert (5-13) to the difference equation form and solve for $y(n)$.

$$y(n) = 3x(n) + 3.6x(n-1) + 0.6x(n-2) - 0.1y(n-1) + 0.2y(n-2) \qquad (5\text{-}14)$$

The realization is readily implemented by the procedure of the last section and is shown in Fig. 5-4a.

(b) For the direct form 2, we can solve for $W(z)$ and $Y(z)$ as indicated by (5-9) and 5-10) and invert them as indicated by (5-11) and (5-12). The quantities $w(n)$ and $y(n)$ are then given by

$$w(n) = x(n) - 0.1w(n-1) + 0.2w(n-2) \qquad (5\text{-}15)$$

and

$$y(n) = 3w(n) + 3.6w(n-1) + 0.6w(n-2) \qquad (5\text{-}16)$$

This realization is shown in Fig. 5-4b. If desired, one can always go directly to the standard form in a "mechanical" fashion, but the preceding development provides some insight into the process.

5-3   PARAMETER QUANTIZATION EFFECTS _____

Before proceeding with the development of realization schemes, we will pause for a brief look at the effects of parameter quantization in discrete-time system design. The problem arises because of the practical necessity to limit the number of bits representing various signal samples and coefficients. This subject has been introduced at this point because the realization procedures to be discussed in the next section are used to minimize certain of these effects.

In general, there are three major sources of parameter quantization error: (a) quantization of the input signal into a finite number of

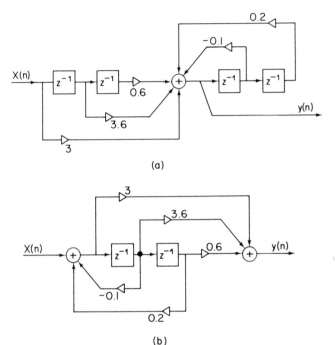

(a)

(b)

Figure 5-4 Realizations for system of Ex. 5-1.

discrete levels, (b) accumulation of roundoff errors in the arithmetic operations in the system, and (c) quantization of the transfer function coefficients a_i and b_i when represented by a finite number of bits. A complete analysis of these various effects requires the use of statistical methods, and it is not within the intended scope of this book. In this section, we will present some of the qualitative aspects of these problems as they relate to the practical realization of discrete transfer functions.

The first source of error is due to the quantization of the input signal into a finite number of discrete levels. This problem was briefly discussed in Chapt. 1, and it was explained there that the resulting uncertainty in the amplitude can be considered as an additive source of noise, which is called *quantization noise*. Let q represent the interval between successive levels in the quantizer. Assume that a given analog sample is rounded to the nearest level in each case. The quantization noise is usually considered as white noise, with a uniform probability density function over the range from $-q/2$ to $q/2$. In this case, it can be shown that the variance of the noise is $\sigma^2 = q^2/12$.

The second source of error is due to the accumulation of roundoff errors in the arithmetic processes of a discrete-time system. Roundoff errors occur when the sum or product of two numbers for a particular arithmetic operation exceeds the number of bits available, and it is necessary to represent the result with fewer bits. There are some unusual effects caused by roundoff that may appear. One is a *deadband* effect in which the steady-state output due to a constant input or initial condition may reach a single output value, which is fixed for a certain limited range of the input. Another related effect is the possible presence of small oscillations about the correct output signal.

The third source of error is due to the representation of the coefficients a_i and b_i of the transfer function by a finite number of bits. It has been shown that this problem becomes more severe for either of the following two conditions: (a) The sampling rate increases relative to the frequency range of the transfer function being realized. (b) The order of the difference equation increases.

In many cases, the first condition is inherently fixed as a portion of the design process and cannot be changed. For the second condition, it has been shown that if a higher order difference equation is represented in terms of two or more lower order equations rather than as a single higher order equation, the effects can be reduced drastically. This leads to the conclusion that the direct forms of realization discussed in the last section should be carefully examined for coefficient accuracies when they are used for higher order systems.

5-4 CASCADE AND PARALLEL REALIZATION FORMS

The direct forms of realization discussed earlier in the chapter are more sensitive to coefficient quantization errors as the order of the transfer function increases, as was mentioned in the last section. This may not necessarily present a problem for software realizations of moderate orders on general-purpose computers where high precision is available. In addition, realizations having no feedback, i.e., all values of $b_i = 0$, may not be particularly sensitive even for relatively large orders. However, the problem can become serious in many realizations, particularly those involving special-purpose hardware designs with limited coefficient accuracies.

The two methods discussed in this section are actually decomposition procedures that permit complex transfer functions to be realized in terms of several simpler functions. In this manner, a system may be made to be less sensitive to coefficient inaccuracies.

The *cascade canonic form* (or *series form*) is obtained by decomposing H(z) into the *product* of several simpler transfer functions as given by

$$H(z) = a_0 H_1(z) H_2(z) \cdots H_\ell(z)$$

$$= a_0 \prod_{i=1}^{\ell} H_i(z) \tag{5-17}$$

In most cases, the individual transfer functions are chosen to be either *first-order* or *second-order* sections. A first-order section will have the form

$$H_i(z) = \frac{1 + a_{i1} z^{-1}}{1 + b_{i1} z^{-1}} \tag{5-18}$$

A second-order section will have the form

$$H_i(z) = \frac{1 + a_{i1} z^{-1} + a_{i2} z^{-2}}{1 + b_{i1} z^{-1} + b_{i2} z^{-2}} \tag{5-19}$$

Note that if it is desired to place any a_{i0} coefficients in any of the individual sections, the overall gain constant in (5-17) would not be a_0. The general layout of a cascade realization is shown in Fig. 5-5. The individual sections may be realized by either of the direct methods. The typical forms for these sections are illustrated in Fig. 5-6 using the direct form 2 realization in each case.

The *parallel canonic form* is obtained by decomposing H(z) into the sum of several simpler transfer functions (first or second order) and a constant as expressed by

$$H(z) = A + H_1(z) + H_2(z) + \cdots + H_r(z)$$

$$= A + \sum_{i=1}^{r} H_i(z) \tag{5-20}$$

Because of the presence of the constant term in (5-20), a first-order section can be chosen in the simple form

$$H_i(z) = \frac{a_{i0}}{1 + b_{i1} z^{-1}} \tag{5-21}$$

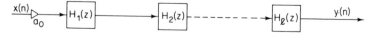

Figure 5-5 Form of a cascade or series realization.

A second-order section can be chosen in the form

$$H_i(z) = \frac{a_{i0} + a_{i1}z^{-1}}{1 + b_{i1}z^{-1} + b_{i2}z^{-2}} \qquad (5\text{-}22)$$

The general layout of a parallel realization is shown in Fig. 5-7. Once again, the individual sections may be realized by either of the direct methods. The typical forms for these sections are illustrated in Fig. 5-8 using the direct form 2 realization in each case.

Both the cascade and the parallel forms require that the transfer function be mathematically decomposed for realization. If the poles and zeros of the overall transfer function are known, the sections of a cascade realization can be obtained by grouping complex conjugate pairs of poles and complex conjugate pairs of zeros to produce second-order sections, and by grouping real poles and real zeros to produce either first- or second-order sections. Of course, a pair of real zeros may be grouped with a pair of complex conjugate poles, or vice versa.

The same procedure discussed for the cascade realization applies to the parallel realization as far as the *poles* are concerned. The various

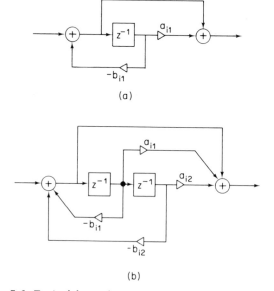

Figure 5-6 Typical forms for sections used in cascade realization.

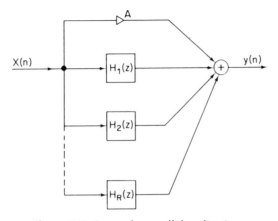

Figure 5-7 Form of a parallel realization.

denominator polynomials may be determined by grouping pairs of complex conjugate poles, grouping pairs of real poles, or by use of a single real pole. However, the numerator polynomials cannot be determined directly from the zeros. Instead, it is necessary to first carry out a partial fraction expansion in terms of individual poles or in terms of a combination of first-order and second-order denominator polynomials. These procedures are best illustrated by the examples that follow this section.

In general, there are no simple guidelines that can be given re-

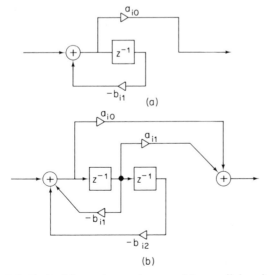

Figure 5-8 Typical forms for sections used in parallel realization.

garding the groupings for the decomposition. This may be quite arbitrary in many cases, and a comprehensive design effort might warrant the investigation of several possible designs. Various tradeoffs such as the number of arithmetic operations, the range of coefficients, and the availability of components could be studied for each alternative.

Example 5-2

For the sake of illustration, develop both (a) cascade and (b) parallel realization schemes for the system of Ex. 5-1.

Solution

(a) It should be pointed out that decomposition is done here only for the sake of illustration, as the system is a second-order function, and it would not normally require a cascade or a parallel type of realization. In fact, it would not be possible to decompose it into functions with real coefficients if either the poles or the zeros were complex. However, the poles and zeros are all real in this case, as we shall see shortly.

As a first step in decomposition, we shall express (5-13) in positive powers of z as

$$H(z) = \frac{3z^2 + 3.6z + 0.6}{z^2 + 0.1z - 0.2} \tag{5-23}$$

Factorization of the numerator and denominator polynomials yields zeros at -1 and -0.2 and poles at -0.5 and 0.4. (Note that the system is stable.) The function may then be expressed as

$$H(z) = \frac{3(z + 1)(z + 0.2)}{(z + 0.5)(z - 0.4)} \tag{5-24}$$

As an arbitrary grouping, the first polynomial factor in the numerator will be grouped with the first factor in the denominator, and a similar grouping will be used for the second factors. The gain constant will be maintained as a separate constant factor, as suggested in (5-17). After conversion back to negative powers of z, the separate functions may be expressed as

$$H_1(z) = \frac{1 + z^{-1}}{1 + 0.5z^{-1}} \tag{5-25}$$

$$H_2(z) = \frac{1 + 0.2z^{-1}}{1 - 0.4z^{-1}} \tag{5-26}$$

The realization is shown in Fig. 5-9a.

(b) The parallel development is best achieved by first expanding $H(z)/z$ in a partial fraction expansion. We have

$$\frac{H(z)}{z} = \frac{3(z+1)(z+0.2)}{z(z+0.5)(z-0.4)} = \frac{A_1}{z} + \frac{A_2}{z+0.5} + \frac{A_3}{z-0.4} \qquad (5\text{-}27)$$

The coefficients are determined to be $A_1 = -3$, $A_2 = -1$, and $A_3 = 7$. After multiplication by z and conversion back to negative powers of z, the various quantities may be expressed as

$$A = -3 \qquad (5\text{-}28)$$

$$H_1(z) = \frac{-1}{1+0.5z^{-1}} \qquad (5\text{-}29)$$

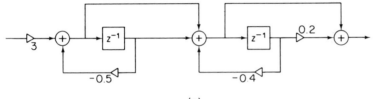

(a)

Figure 5-9a Realizations for system of Ex. 5-2.

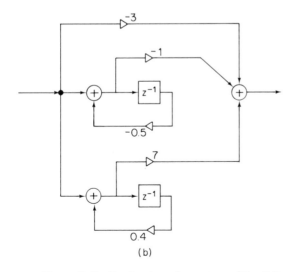

(b)

Figure 5-9b Realizations for system of Ex. 5-2.

$$H_2(z) = \frac{7}{1 - 0.4z^{-1}} \qquad (5\text{-}30)$$

The realization is shown in Fig. 5-9b.

Example 5-3

The partially factored form of a certain transfer function is given by

$$H(z) = \frac{2(z - 1)(z^2 + 1.4142136z + 1)}{(z + 0.5)(z^2 - 0.9z + 0.81)} \qquad (5\text{-}31)$$

Develop a cascade realization of the function using a first-order section and a second-order section.

Solution

As a check to determine various possible grouping combinations, the roots of the two quadratics will be determined. Factorization of the numerator quadratic reveals that two zeros are located at $z = 1$ $\underline{/\pm135°}$. A similar procedure applied to the denominator quadratic indicates that two poles are located at $z = 0.9$ $\underline{/\pm60°}$.

As long as we are restricted to real coefficients, this means that the decomposition must contain a second-order section representing the two second-order polynomials and a first-order section representing the two first-order polynomials. Arranging in negative powers of z and allowing for $a_0 = 2$, we have

$$H_1(z) = \frac{1 - z^{-1}}{1 + 0.5z^{-1}} \qquad (5\text{-}32)$$

and

$$H_2(z) = \frac{1 + 1.4142136z^{-1} + z^{-2}}{1 - 0.9z^{-1} + 0.81z^{-2}} \qquad (5\text{-}33)$$

The realization is shown in Fig. 5-10.

Example 5-4

Develop a parallel realization for the system of Ex. 5-3.

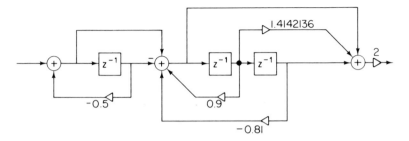

Figure 5-10 Realization for system of Ex. 5-3.

Solution

The development is best achieved by expanding $H(z)/z$ in a partial fraction expansion. In some cases, it appears that less labor is involved by expanding $H(z)/z$ in a complete partial fraction breakdown involving all poles separately and then recombining certain of the pole pairs (especially complex conjugate pairs) into second-order functions. In other cases, it may be simpler to retain portions of the expansion having complex conjugate poles in their second-order polynomial forms. No general guidelines may be given on this point since it depends, to some extent, on individual preferences.

We will follow the approach here of maintaining the two complex poles in the form of a second-degree polynomial in the expansion, which reads

$$\frac{H(z)}{z} = \frac{2(z-1)(z^2 + 1.4142136z + 1)}{z(z+0.5)(z^2 - 0.9z + 0.81)}$$

$$= \frac{A_1}{z} + \frac{A_2}{z+0.5} + \frac{A_3 z + A_4}{z^2 - 0.9z + 0.81}$$

(5-34)

The constants A_1 and A_2 can be determined by the usual partial fraction procedure for first-order poles, but A_3 and A_4 must be determined in a different fashion. One way this can be achieved is to simply choose some nonsingular values of z and substitute on both sides of (5-34) to yield a series of simultaneous linear equations.

Following the preceding steps, we first determine that $A_1 = -4.9382716$ and $A_2 = 2.1571915$. Placing these two values in (5-34), we next seek some simple values of z to substitute in the equation. The values $z = 1$ and $z = -1$ seem suitable. After some simplification, substitution of these values results in the following simultaneous equations:

$$A_3 + A_4 = 3.1851310$$

$$-A_3 + A_4 = -6.3770293 \qquad (5\text{-}35)$$

Solution of (5-35) yields $A_3 = 4.7810802$ and $A_4 = -1.5959492$. After substituting these values in (5-34), the proper form of the expansion is obtained by multiplying both sides by z and rearranging in negative powers. Note that A in (5-20) corresponds to A_1 in (5-34). The parallel functions are

$$A = -4.9382716 \qquad (5\text{-}36)$$

$$H_1(z) = \frac{2.1571915}{1 + 0.5z^{-1}} \qquad (5\text{-}37)$$

$$H_2(z) = \frac{4.7810802 - 1.5959492z^{-1}}{1 - 0.9z^{-1} + 0.81z^{-2}} \qquad (5\text{-}38)$$

The system realization is shown in Fig. 5-11.

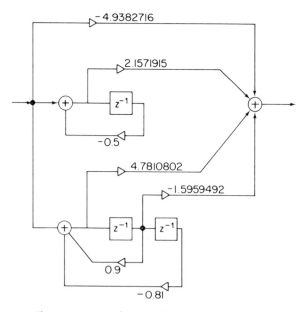

Figure 5-11 Realization for system of Ex. 5-4.

5-5 STEADY-STATE FREQUENCY RESPONSE CONCEPTS

As in the case of continuous-time systems, the most important special case of interest for discrete-time systems is probably the steady-state response due to a sinusoidal input. In this case, the input sinusoid is a sequence of samples representing points on the sinusoidal curve.

In order for the steady-state response to have meaning, it is necessary that the system be perfectly stable; i.e., all poles must lie inside the unit circle. In this case, the steady-state output will be a sampled sinusoid of the same frequency as the input sinusoid. Thus, it is necessary to determine only the magnitude and phase of the output.

Assume that the input is of the form

$$x(n) \;=\; X \epsilon^{j(n\,\omega T + \phi_x)} \tag{5-39}$$

where ω is the radian frequency, f is the cyclic frequency, and $\omega = 2\pi f$. We may specify either the real or the imaginary part depending on whether we desire a cosine or a sine input. Letting $y(n)$ represent the *steady-state* response in this case, it will be of the form

$$y(n) \;=\; Y \epsilon^{j(n\,\omega T + \phi_y)} \tag{5-40}$$

We need only determine Y and ϕ_y to complete the solution.

Taking the z-transform of (5-39) and multiplying by the discrete transfer function $H(z)$, the output transform is given by

$$Y(z) \;=\; \frac{z\,X \epsilon^{j\,\phi_x}}{z - \epsilon^{j\,\omega T}}\, H(z) \tag{5-41}$$

Inversion of the steady-state portion only of (5-41) yields

$$y(n) \;=\; H(\epsilon^{j\,\omega T})\, X \epsilon^{j(n\,\omega T + \phi_x)} \tag{5-42}$$

Substitution of (5-40) in (5-42) and cancellation of the exponential factors yield

$$Y \epsilon^{j\,\phi_y} = H(\epsilon^{j\,\omega T})\, X \epsilon^{j\,\phi_x} \tag{5-43}$$

The input and output variables may now be expressed as phasors.

$$\overline{X} = X \epsilon^{j\,\phi_x} \stackrel{\Delta}{=} X \underline{/\phi_x} \tag{5-44}$$

$$\overline{Y} = Y \, \epsilon^{j \, \phi_y} \overset{\Delta}{=} Y \underline{/\phi_y} \qquad (5\text{-}45)$$

We then have

$$\overline{Y} = H(\epsilon^{j \, \omega T}) \, \overline{X} \qquad (5\text{-}46)$$

or

$$\frac{\overline{Y}}{\overline{X}} = H(\epsilon^{j \, \omega T}) \qquad (5\text{-}47)$$

The quantity $H(\epsilon^{j \, \omega T})$ represents the *steady-state* or *Fourier transfer function* for a discrete-time system. While a single frequency has been assumed in the preceding development, the result can now be generalized by considering ω as a variable. The function obtained describes the *frequency response* of the system, and this can be expressed in complex form as

$$H(\epsilon^{j \, \omega T}) = A_0(f) \, \epsilon^{j \, \beta_0 (f)} = A_0(f) \underline{/\beta_0(f)} \qquad (5\text{-}48)$$

The function $A_0(f)$ is called the *amplitude* or *magnitude response,* and $\beta_0(f)$ is called the *phase response.* (The subscripts are used at this point because the forms of these functions will be modified later in the section.) Normally, $A_0(f)$ is simply the magnitude of the complex function $H(\epsilon^{j \, \omega T})$, but there are a few situations in which the amplitude response is permitted to assume negative values. Both the amplitude and phase are real functions of frequency.

The steady-state transfer function for the discrete-time system is simply the z-domain transfer function evaluated for $z = \epsilon^{j \, \omega T}$. Moreover, since $\epsilon^{j \, \omega T}$ is a periodic function with period $\omega T = 2\pi$, then $H(\epsilon^{j \, \omega T})$ is also periodic. The conventional forms for complex number representations lead to the conditions that $A_0(f)$ is an *even* function of frequency, and $\beta_0(f)$ is an *odd* function of frequency. These properties result in the constraint that the behavior of $H(\epsilon^{j \, \omega T})$ in the range of $\pi < \omega T < 2\pi$ is uniquely related to the behavior in the range $0 < \omega T < \pi$. Thus, the maximum unambiguous positive value for ωT is π. This corresponds to the *folding* frequency f_0 since $2\pi f_0 T = \pi$, or

$$f_0 = \frac{1}{2T} = \frac{f_s}{2} \qquad (5\text{-}49)$$

Because of the importance of the folding frequency f_0 in establishing the frequency limits in a discrete-time system, this author has found it extremely convenient to normalize all frequencies with respect to the folding frequency in practical problem solutions. We will define a *normalized frequency variable v* as

$$v = \frac{f}{f_0} = 2Tf \qquad (5\text{-}50)$$

where f is any particular frequency of interest.

The quantity ωT can be expressed in terms of the normalized frequency as

$$\omega T = \pi \frac{f}{f_0} = \pi v \qquad (5\text{-}51)$$

Similarly, the quantity $H(\epsilon^{j\,\omega T})$ can be expressed in either of the forms

$$H(\epsilon^{j\,\omega T}) = H(\epsilon^{j\,\pi(f/f_0)}) = H(\epsilon^{j\,\pi v}) \qquad (5\text{-}52)$$

The notation expressed in (5-51) and (5-52) will be used freely in subsequent work, and these different forms will be interchanged when desirable.

As ωT varies over the range $0 \le \omega T \le 2\pi$, the normalized frequency varies over the range $0 \le v \le 2$, so the period on the normalized scale is 2 units. As previously explained, the frequency response is unique over only half this range. Thus, the highest normalized frequency at which the response is unambiguous is $v = 1$, and this value corresponds to the folding frequency.

The amplitude and phase functions can now be expressed in terms of v. The functions will be denoted as $A(v)$ and $\beta(v)$ and are defined as

$$A(v) = A_0(f)$$
$$\qquad\qquad\qquad\qquad (5\text{-}53)$$
$$\beta(v) = \beta_0(f)$$

Thus, the form of the steady-state transfer function that will be used in most subsequent work is

$$H(\epsilon^{j\,\omega v}) = A(v) \;\underline{/\beta(v)} \qquad (5\text{-}54)$$

The general form of a representative amplitude response expressed in terms of v is shown in Fig. 5-12. (Most of the negative frequency range is not shown.) In many of the problems in the text, we will display the frequency response only in the range $0 \le v \le 1$, since this is the range of practical interest.

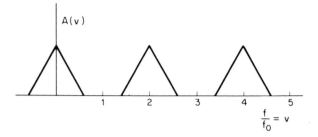

Figure 5-12 General form for amplitude response of discrete-time system.

A discrete-time sinusoidal signal may also be expressed in terms of its normalized frequency. Consider a function of the form

$$x(n) = A \sin(n\omega_1 T + \theta) \qquad (5\text{-}55)$$

Let $f_1 = \omega_1/2\pi$ represent the cyclic frequency of the sinusoid, and let $v_1 = f_1/f_0$. We will leave as an exercise (Prob. 5-6) for the reader to show that $x(n)$ can be expressed as

$$x(n) = A \sin(n\pi v_1 + \theta) \qquad (5\text{-}56)$$

As in continuous-time systems, it is often desirable to express the amplitude response in terms of a *decibel* (dB) level relative to some reference value. Let A_r represent any arbitrary reference level. The decibel amplitude response $A_{db}(v)$ can be defined as

$$A_{db}(v) = 20 \text{ Log}_{10} \frac{A(v)}{A_r} \qquad (5\text{-}57)$$

In most of our work, the reference level used will be $A_r = 1$. Thus, relative to a reference level of unity, the decibel response is

$$A_{db}(v) = 20 \text{ Log}_{10} A(v) = 10 \text{ Log}_{10} A^2(v) \qquad (5\text{-}58)$$

The form of the decibel response in (5-58) is expressed in the sense of a *gain*. This means that if $A(v) > 1$, the decibel level is positive, but if $A(v) < 1$, the decibel level is negative. In some cases, particularly for filter functions having $A(v) \ll 1$ over a wide range of frequencies, it may be more convenient to express the amplitude response as a positive *attenuation* or *loss*. Using a reference value of unity again, the decibel attenuation or loss function $\alpha_{db}(v)$ can be defined as

$$\alpha_{db}(v) = 20 \text{ Log}_{10} \frac{1}{A(v)} = -20 \text{ Log}_{10} A(v) = -A_{db}(v) \qquad (5\text{-}59)$$

In the case of the attenuation function, a positive decibel value indicates that the output is lower than the input, i.e., some attenuation has taken place.

Some additional definitions pertaining to the steady-state frequency response of discrete-time systems are the *phase delay* and *group delay*. Momentarily returning to the phase function $\beta_0(f)$ given in (5-48), the definitions of phase delay $T_p(f)$ and group delay $T_g(f)$ are

$$T_p(f) = \frac{-\beta_0(f)}{\omega} = \frac{-\beta_0(f)}{2\pi f} \qquad (5\text{-}60)$$

$$T_g(f) = \frac{-d\beta_0(f)}{d\omega} = \frac{-1}{2\pi} \frac{d\beta_0(f)}{df} \qquad (5\text{-}61)$$

We may now define the *normalized phase delay* $\gamma_p(v)$ and the *normalized group delay* $\gamma_g(v)$ as

$$\gamma_p(v) = \frac{-\beta(v)}{v} \qquad (5\text{-}62)$$

$$\gamma_g(f) = \frac{-d\beta(v)}{dv} \qquad (5\text{-}63)$$

(Different types of symbols are used here because these functions are dimensionless.) The definitions given by (5-62) and (5-63) are those that would be used directly in dealing with a frequency response function expressed in terms of the normalized frequency v. However, while the actual levels of the amplitude and phase functions are not affected by the scaling change involved with using the normalized frequency, the phase and group delay functions are affected. We will leave as an exercise (Prob. 5-7) for the reader to show that the actual phase and group delay functions are related to the normalized functions by

$$T_p(f) = \frac{\gamma_p(v)}{2\pi f_0} = \frac{T}{\pi} \gamma_p(v) \qquad (5\text{-}64)$$

and

$$T_g(f) = \frac{\gamma_g(f)}{2\pi f_0} = \frac{T}{\pi} \gamma_g(v) \qquad (5\text{-}65)$$

where f_0 is the folding frequency, T is the sampling interval, and $v = f/f_0$.

Definitions for the phase and group delay functions for continuous-time systems were given in Chapt. 2, and a discussion of the practical significance of these quantities will be given in Chapt. 6. The discussion there applies equally well to the corresponding functions for a discrete-time system, so we will postpone further consideration of these concepts until then.

Example 5-5

(a) Determine the frequency response (amplitude and phase) for the system described by the difference equation

$$y(n) = 0.5y(n-1) + x(n) + x(n-1) \qquad (5\text{-}66)$$

(b) For a sampling frequency of 1 kHz, determine the *steady-state* output for an input sine wave with an amplitude of 10 and a frequency of 100 Hz.

Solution

(a) The transfer function is readily determined from (5-66) as

$$H(z) = \frac{Y(z)}{X(z)} = \frac{1+z^{-1}}{1-0.5z^{-1}} \qquad (5\text{-}67)$$

The folding frequency is $f_0 = 1000/2 = 500$ Hz. For convenience, the normalized frequency variable will be used. For any actual frequency f, the normalized frequency v is

$$v = \frac{f}{500} \qquad (5\text{-}68)$$

The steady-state transfer function is obtained by substitution of $\epsilon^{j\pi v}$ into (5-67). This yields

$$H(\epsilon^{j\pi v}) = \frac{1+\epsilon^{-j\pi v}}{1-0.5\epsilon^{-j\pi v}} \qquad (5\text{-}69)$$

This expression must be converted into the form of a magnitude and a phase. This could always be done by expanding the numerator and denominator into their real and imaginary parts and applying the basic rules of complex number manipulations. In some cases, a clever rearrangement of numerator and denominator polynomials may lead to groupings in which trigonometric functions may be identified. However, this latter approach seems to develop with experience, so we will postpone it until some later examples. Expressing numerator and denominator polynomials of (5-69) in real and imaginary parts, we have

$$H(\epsilon^{j\pi v}) = \frac{1 + \cos \pi v - j \sin \pi v}{1 - 0.5 \cos \pi v + j 0.5 \sin \pi v} \qquad (5\text{-}70)$$

For convenience, the amplitude response will be expressed in squared form. From (5-70), we have

$$A^2(v) = \frac{(1 + \cos \pi v)^2 + (-\sin \pi v)^2}{(1 - 0.5 \cos \pi v)^2 + (0.5 \sin \pi v)^2} \qquad (5\text{-}71)$$

and

$$\beta(v) = \tan^{-1}\left[\frac{-\sin \pi v}{1 + \cos \pi v}\right] - \tan^{-1}\left[\frac{0.5 \sin \pi v}{1 - 0.5 \cos \pi v}\right] \qquad (5\text{-}72)$$

If desired, these results can be simplified by the use of standard trigonometric identities. We leave as exercise (Prob. 5-8) for the interested reader to show that (5-71) and (5-72) can be expressed as

$$A^2(v) = \frac{2 + 2 \cos \pi v}{1.25 - \cos \pi v} \qquad (5\text{-}73)$$

and

$$\beta(v) = -\tan^{-1}\left(3 \tan \frac{\pi v}{2}\right) \qquad (5\text{-}74)$$

(b) The normalized frequency of the input signal is $v_1 = 100/500 = 0.2$. The amplitude and phase evaluated at this frequency are obtained from (5-73) and (5-74) as

$$\begin{aligned} A(0.2) &= 2.864345 \\ \beta(0.2) &= -44.26770° \\ &= -0.77261712 \text{ rad} \end{aligned} \qquad (5\text{-}75)$$

The phase angle of the input sine wave will be assumed to be zero, so that the signal can be expressed as

$$\begin{aligned} x(n) &= 10 \sin 36n° && \text{(angle in degrees)} \\ &= 10 \sin (0.2\pi n) && \text{(angle in radians)} \end{aligned} \qquad (5\text{-}76)$$

The output *steady-state* signal is

$$\begin{aligned} y(n) &= 28.64345 \sin (36n° - 44.26770°) \\ && \text{(angle in degrees)} \\ &= 28.64345 \sin (0.2\pi n - 0.77261712) \\ && \text{(angle in radians)} \end{aligned} \qquad (5\text{-}77)$$

For the sake of illustration, the arguments of the functions in (5-76) and (5-77) have been expressed both in terms of *radians* and *degrees*. Either form can be used as long as *all* terms are expressed in the same units *and* it is understood what units are involved.

Example 5-6

Determine general expressions for the amplitude and phase of the system of Example 4-9.

Solution

The transfer function is

$$H(z) = \frac{1 + z^{-1}}{1 + 0.1z^{-1} - 0.2z^{-2}} \tag{5-78}$$

The steady-state transfer function is

$$H(\epsilon^{j\pi v}) = \frac{1 + \epsilon^{-j\pi v}}{1 + 0.1\epsilon^{-j\pi v} - 0.2\epsilon^{-2j\pi v}} \tag{5-79}$$

$$= \frac{1 + \cos \pi v - j \sin \pi v}{(1 + 0.1 \cos \pi v - 0.2 \cos 2\pi v) + j(-0.1 \sin \pi v + 0.2 \sin 2\pi v)}$$

$$= \frac{A_1 + j A_2}{B_1 + j B_2}$$

where A_1 and A_2 are the real and imaginary parts of the numerator and B_1 and B_2 are the real and imaginary parts of the denominator. In terms of these quantities, the amplitude and phase are

$$A(v) = \sqrt{\frac{A_1{}^2 + A_2{}^2}{B_1{}^2 + B_2{}^2}} \tag{5-80}$$

and

$$\beta(v) = \tan^{-1} \frac{A_2}{A_1} - \tan^{-1} \frac{B_2}{B_1} \tag{5-81}$$

If the appropriate quantities are substituted in (5-80) and (5-81), the resulting expressions could eventually be reduced to simpler forms by the use of various trigonometric identities. However, since we are not interested in any final numerical results, we shall leave the answer in the form developed.

The results of this problem illustrate that as the order of a transfer function increases, the form of the complex steady-state function $H(\epsilon^{j\pi v})$ becomes increasingly more difficult to express quickly and simply in the form of amplitude and phase functions. Furthermore, it is quite difficult to obtain much insight regarding the nature of the frequency response from the forms of these functions. On the other hand, a computer program may be readily written to evaluate the amplitude and phase functions for discrete transfer functions on a point-by-point basis. Since the only significant frequency range of interest is $0 \le v \le 1$, the frequency may be stepped through this range in as many points as desired in a loop, and the amplitude and phase can be calculated at each point.

Example 5-7

A programmable calculator is used to perform a smoothing or averaging process on a set of random measurements $x(n)$. As each measured value is received, the calculator computes a simple average of the four values consisting of the present measurement and the preceding three measurements. Calculate the frequency response corresponding to this operation.

Solution

Letting $y(n)$ represent the output of the calculator, the averaging algorithm can be expressed as

$$y(n) = \tfrac{1}{4}[x(n) + x(n-1) + x(n-2) + x(n-3)] \qquad (5\text{-}82)$$

The transfer function corresponding to (5-82) is

$$H(z) = \frac{1 + z^{-1} + z^{-2} + z^{-3}}{4} \qquad (5\text{-}83)$$

The steady-state transfer function is

$$H(\epsilon^{j\pi v}) = \frac{1 + \epsilon^{-j\pi v} + \epsilon^{-j2\pi v} + \epsilon^{-j3\pi v}}{4} \qquad (5\text{-}84)$$

The series in (5-84) is a finite geometric series and can be expressed as

$$H(\epsilon^{j\pi v}) = \frac{1 - \epsilon^{-j4\pi v}}{4(1 - \epsilon^{-j\pi v})} \qquad (5\text{-}85)$$

After several manipulations in (5-85), the following form results:

$$H(\epsilon^{j\pi v}) = \frac{(\epsilon^{j\,2\pi v} - \epsilon^{-j\,2\pi v})}{4(\epsilon^{j\,(\pi/2)v} - \epsilon^{-j\,(\pi/2)v})}\,\epsilon^{-j\,(3\pi/2)v} \qquad (5\text{-}86)$$

This result can finally be expressed as

$$H(\epsilon^{j\pi v}) = \frac{\sin 2\pi v}{4\sin(\pi/2)v} \diagdown \frac{3\pi v}{2} \qquad (5\text{-}87)$$

The amplitude and phase functions are

$$A(v) = \frac{\sin 2\pi v}{4\sin(\pi v/2)} \qquad (5\text{-}88)$$

$$\beta(v) = \frac{-3\pi}{2}\,v \qquad (5\text{-}89)$$

The phase response is seen to be a linear function of frequency, and the delay can be computed as $T_g = T_p = 1.5T$. The form of the amplitude response given in (5-88), which was obtained by various manipulations used to express the result in the simplest trigonometric form, actually assumes negative values over certain ranges of v (e.g., $0.5 < v < 1$).

The form of the function $|A(v)|$ over the range $0 \le v \le 1$ is shown in Fig. 5-13. Some insight into the averaging process can be deduced from this curve. Note that the overall response decreases as the frequency increases, indicating that the algorithm is functioning somewhat as a low-pass filter. This seems logical, since the averaging process is used to reduce random fluctuations that occur in the different

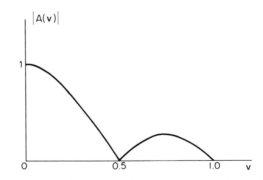

Figure 5-13 Amplitude response for averaging algorithm of Ex. 5-7.

values of measured data. Such fluctuations can be considered as "higher frequencies" so that they are suppressed by this process. On the other hand, it is assumed that the true value being sought by the measurements does not fluctuate as much over a longer period of time, and that it falls in the lower portion of the frequency range.

5-6 PROPERTIES OF THE AMPLITUDE RESPONSE

In this section, some useful properties of the amplitude response of a discrete-time system will be developed. These properties provide some insight into the general form of an amplitude response with reference to both the analysis and design of discrete-time systems.

The square of the magnitude of a complex number can be expressed as the product of the number and its complex conjugate. Using $\sim$ to represent the complex conjugate, we can write

$$A^2(v) = \left| H(\epsilon^{j\pi v}) \right|^2 = H(\epsilon^{j\pi v}) \, \widetilde{H}(\epsilon^{j\pi v}) \tag{5-90}$$

where $H(z)$ is assumed to be stable. Although there are some special transfer functions in which the numerator and denominator coefficients a_i and b_i are permitted to be complex, we will restrict the consideration here to the case where all coefficients of $H(z)$ are real. In this case, the reader may wish to verify (Prob. 5-9) that

$$\widetilde{H}(\epsilon^{j\pi v}) = H(\epsilon^{-j\pi v}) \tag{5-91}$$

Substituting (5-91) in (5-90) yields

$$A^2(v) = H(\epsilon^{j\pi v}) \, H(\epsilon^{-j\pi v}) \tag{5-92}$$

Since $H(\epsilon^{j\pi v})$ can be considered as $H(z)$ evaluated for $z = \epsilon^{j\pi v}$, (5-92) can be expressed in the form

$$A^2(v) = H(z) \, H(z^{-1})]_{z = \epsilon^{j\pi v}} \tag{5-93}$$

The function $H(z) H(z^{-1})$ has an interesting pole-zero pattern in the z-plane. For a given pole or zero of $H(z)$ at $z = z_i$, there will be a pole or zero of $H(z^{-1})$ at $z = 1/z_i$. Thus, the poles and zeros of $H(z) H(z^{-1})$ occur in pairs having an inverse relationship with respect to the unit circle. Since $H(z)$ is presently assumed to have only real coefficients, all complex poles and zeros of $H(z)$ occur in conjugate pairs. Thus, complex poles and zeros of $H(z)\, H(z^{-1})$ will occur in symmetrical groups of four, and real poles and zeros will occur in groups of two. It can be shown (Prob. 5-10) that zeros on the unit circle occur in even multiplicity. We will assume that there are no poles of $H(z)$ on the unit circle since we are considering a stable system. Hence, there can be no poles of $H(z)$ $H(z^{-1})$ on the unit circle.

The nature of this symmetry is illustrated for a typical case in Fig. 5-14. The integer 2 above the two unit-circle zeros identifies them as second-order zeros.

The numerator and denominator polynomials resulting from the multiplication of $H(z)$ by $H(-z)$ display an interesting type of symmetry. Let $p(z)$ represent either a numerator or denominator polynomial. Expressed in positive powers of z, the degree of $p(z)$ will always be even, and the polynomial can be expressed as

$$p(z) = c_k z^{2k} + c_{k-1} z^{2k-1} + \cdots + c_1 z^{k+1} + c_0 z^k$$

$$+ c_1 z^{k-1} + c_2 z^{k-2} + \cdots + c_{k-1} z + c_k$$

$$(5\text{-}94)$$

where k is the degree of the original polynomial from which $p(z)$ is derived. Although the degree of $p(z)$ is $2k$, there are only $k + 1$ unique coefficients. The coefficients at the same distance on either side of c_0 are equal, and a symmetrical pattern thus exists about c_0. This type of polynomial is called a *mirror-image polynomial*.

The next step that we will perform is to multiply both sides of

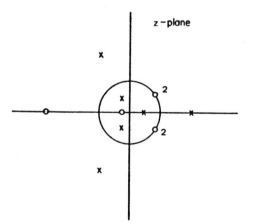

Figure 5-14 Typical pole-zero pattern for $H(z)H(z^{-1})$ illustrating symmetry involved.

(5-94) by z^{-k} and rearrange the terms in symmetrical groups. This operation yields

$$z^{-k}\, p(z) = c_0 + c_1(z + z^{-1}) + c_2(z^2 + z^{-2}) \\ + \cdots + c_k(z^k + z^{-k}) \tag{5-95}$$

Letting $z = \epsilon^{j\pi v}$, we have

$$\epsilon^{-jk\pi v}\, p(\epsilon^{j\pi v}) = c_0 + c_1(\epsilon^{j\pi v} + \epsilon^{-j\pi v}) + c_2(\epsilon^{j2\pi v} + \epsilon^{-j2\pi v}) \\ + \cdots + c_k(\epsilon^{jk\pi v} + \epsilon^{-jk\pi v}) \tag{5-96}$$

$$= c_0 + 2c_1 \cos \pi v + 2c_2 \cos 2\pi v + \cdots + 2c_k \cos k\pi v$$

We will assume that the degrees of the numerator and denominator polynomials of $H(z)$ are the same. Multiplication of $H(z)$ by $H(z^{-1})$ yields the following form for $A^2(v)$:

$$A^2(v) = \frac{c_0 + c_1 \cos \pi v + \cdots + c_k \cos k\pi v}{d_0 + d_1 \cos \pi v + \cdots + d_k \cos k\pi v}$$

$$= \frac{\displaystyle\sum_{i=0}^{k} c_i \cos i\pi v}{\displaystyle\sum_{i=0}^{k} d_i \cos i\pi v} \tag{5-97}$$

The result of (5-97) provides some interesting insights into the amplitude response of a DTLTI system. From an analysis viewpoint, the amplitude response can always be expressed in this form if desired. Of course, trigonometric functions occur in a variety of different forms, so (5-97) is not the *only* way, or even necessarily the best way, in which to express a given amplitude response, but it is always a form that could be used when needed. From a synthesis viewpoint, this form could be used to produce a required amplitude response by determining the coefficients c_i and d_i in (5-97) properly. More will be said about this problem in later chapters.

Example 5-8

Using the procedure of this section, calculate the amplitude-squared response corresponding to the discrete transfer function

$$H(z) = \frac{z^2 + 1}{z^2 - 0.9z + 0.81} \tag{5-98}$$

Solution

As a first step, we form the product

$$H(z)\,H(z^{-1}) = \left[\frac{z^2 + 1}{z^2 - 0.9z + 0.81}\right]\left[\frac{z^{-2} + 1}{z^2 - 0.9z^{-1} + 0.81}\right]$$

$$= \frac{(z^2 + 1)(z^2 + 1)}{(z^2 - 0.9z + 0.81)(0.81z^2 - 0.9z + 1)} \qquad (5\text{-}99)$$

$$= \frac{z^4 + 2z^2 + 1}{0.81z^4 - 1.629z^3 + 2.4661z^2 - 1.629z + 0.81}$$

It can be observed at this point that both the numerator and denominator polynomials of $H(z)\,H(z^{-1})$ are mirror-image polynomials, as expected. If desired, the poles and zeros may be determined. The poles and zeros are

$$\begin{aligned}
p_1 &= 0.45 + j0.779423 = 0.9\ \underline{/60^\circ}\\
p_2 &= 0.45 - j0.779423 = 0.9\ \underline{/-60^\circ}\\
p_3 &= 0.555556 + j0.962250 = 1.111111\ \underline{/60^\circ}\\
p_4 &= 0.555556 - j0.962250 = 1.111111\ \underline{/-60^\circ}
\end{aligned} \qquad (5\text{-}100)$$

$$\begin{aligned}
z_1, z_2 &= j = 1\ \underline{/90^\circ}\ \text{(2nd order)}\\
z_3, z_4 &= -j = 1\ \underline{/-90^\circ}\ \text{(2nd order)}
\end{aligned} \qquad (5\text{-}101)$$

Note that p_4 is the reciprocal of p_1, p_3 is the reciprocal of p_2, and z_3 and z_4 are the reciprocals of z_1 and z_2. Observe that the zeros on the unit circle occur in even multiplicity, as expected.

The amplitude response is determined by multiplying numerator and denominator of (5-99) by z^{-2} and letting $z = \epsilon^{j\pi v}$. This yields

$$A^2(v) = \frac{2 + \epsilon^{j2\pi v} + \epsilon^{-j2\pi v}}{2.4661 - 1.629(\epsilon^{j\pi v} + \epsilon^{-j\pi v}) + 0.81(\epsilon^{j2\pi v} + \epsilon^{-j2\pi v})}$$

$$= \frac{2 + 2\cos 2\pi v}{2.4661 - 3.258\cos \pi v + 1.62\cos 2\pi v} \qquad (5\text{-}102)$$

―――――――――――― **PROBLEMS** ――――――――――――

5-1 Draw a realization diagram for the system of Ex. 5-3 as a single direct form 1 section.

5-2 Draw a realization diagram for the system of Ex. 5-3 as a single direct form 2 section.

5-3 The partially factored form of a certain transfer function is given by

$$H(z) = \frac{4(1 - z^{-1})(1 - z^{-1} + z^{-2})}{(1 - 0.5z^{-1})(1 - 1.272792z^{-1} + 0.81z^{-2})}$$

Develop a cascade realization of the function using a first-order section and a second-order section.

5-4 Develop a parallel realization for the system of Prob. 5-3.

5-5 (a) Write a pair of difference equations relating $g(n)$ to $x(n)$ and $y(n)$ to $g(n)$ for the system of Fig. P5-5. (b) Obtain the transfer function $H(z) = Y(z)/X(z)$.

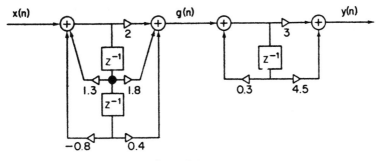

Figure P5-5

5-6 Show that equation (5-55) can be expressed in the form of equation (5-56).

5-7 Verify equations (5-64) and (5-65).

5-8 Show that the functions given in (5-71) and (5-72) can be expressed in the forms of (5-73) and (5-74).

5-9 Verify equation (5-91).

5-10 Show that the zeros of $H(z)\,H(z^{-1})$ on the unit circle occur in even multiplicity.

5-11 Determine the frequency response (amplitude and phase) for the system of Prob. 4-12.

5-12 Determine the frequency response (amplitude and phase) of the zero-order integrator of Prob. 4-13.

5-13 Determine the frequency response (amplitude and phase) of the first-order trapezoidal integrator of Prob. 4-14.

5-14 Determine the frequency response (amplitude and phase) of the simple averaging algorithm given by

$$y(n) = \frac{1}{2}[x(n) + x(n-1)]$$

5-15 Obtain the amplitude response of the function in Ex. 5-5 by the procedure of Sec. 5-6.

5-16 Obtain the amplitude response of the function in Ex. 5-6 by the procedure of Sec. 5-6.

5-17 Assume that the averaging algorithm in Ex. 5-7 is to be generalized to take the average of N measurements, which are to be the present and past N-1 values.

(a) Show that the amplitude and phase functions are

$$A(v) = \frac{sin\ (N\pi v/2)}{N\ sin\ (\pi v/2)}$$

$$\beta(v) = -(N-1)\pi v/2$$

(b) Sketch the general shape of A(v) for some reasonably large value of N and compare with the case of N = 4 as given in Fig. 5-13.

6

PROPERTIES OF
ANALOG FILTERS

6-0 INTRODUCTION

The purpose of this chapter is to present some of the more important general properties of continuous-time, linear, time-invariant filter characteristics. Because of widespread usage, the term *analog* will be freely used in reference to these characteristics. Although our ultimate goal is that of digital processing, analog filter functions are used extensively as prototype models for developing digital filters. Consequently, it is necessary to consider some of the more basic analog filter properties.

   Primary emphasis in the chapter is directed toward functions that approximate the behavior of an ideal frequency-domain filter in terms of amplitude and/or phase. Several filter approximations will be discussed, and filter functions of the low-pass, band-pass, band-rejection, and high-pass varieties will be considered. Some useful design data, including tables of transfer function coefficients and curves for predicting the amplitude response of certain filters, will be presented.

6-1 IDEAL FREQUENCY-DOMAIN FILTER MODELS

Before considering any realistic filter characteristics, the properties of the ideal frequency-domain filter will be discussed. While such a filter is not realizable, the concept serves as a very useful reference model for comparing actual filter designs.

Consider the block diagram of a filter as illustrated in Fig. 6-1. Assume that the input can be expressed as $x(t) + u(t)$, where $x(t)$ represents a desired signal at the input and $u(t)$ represents an undesired signal (or composite of signals). The purpose of the filter is to eliminate $u(t)$ while preserving $x(t)$ as close to its original form as possible. The process of filtering requires a certain amount of delay and possible changes in the signal level, so the best we can hope for is that the output signal will be a delayed version of the original desired signal with a possible difference in amplitude, but with the correct shape preserved. Thus, the output of a distortionless filter can be expressed as

$$y(t) = Kx(t - \tau) \tag{6-1}$$

where K represents a level change and τ is the delay. This concept is illustrated in Fig. 6-2.

The frequency-domain interpretation of the ideal filter can be seen by taking the Fourier transforms of both sides of (6-1). This operation yields

$$Y(f) = K\epsilon^{-j\omega\tau} X(f) \tag{6-2}$$

Solving for the steady-state transfer function $G(j\omega)$, we obtain

$$G(j\omega) = K\epsilon^{-j\omega\tau} = K \underline{/-\omega\tau} \tag{6-3}$$

The amplitude response $A(f)$ and the phase response $\beta(f)$ are determined as

$$A(f) = K \tag{6-4}$$

$$\beta(f) = -\omega\tau \tag{6-5}$$

From these results, it can be seen that the amplitude response of the ideal filter should be constant and the phase response should be a linear function of frequency. However, these conditions apply only with

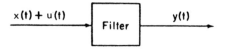

Figure 6-1 Block diagram of filter.

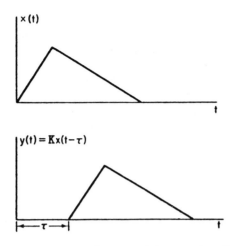

Figure 6-2 Input and output of distortionless filter.

respect to the frequency range of the desired signal $x(t)$. If the amplitude response were constant everywhere, the undesired signal would not be removed at all! To utilize the most basic form of frequency-domain filtering, it must be assumed that the spectrum of the undesired signal occupies a different frequency range from that of the desired signal, and the amplitude response must approximate zero in the frequency range of the undesired signal. The conclusion is that a distortionless frequency-domain filter should have constant amplitude response and linear phase response over the frequency band representing the spectrum of the desired signal. Outside this band, the amplitude response should drop toward zero as rapidly as possible, and the phase response in this range is usually unimportant. The frequency range in which a signal is transmitted through the filter is called the *passband*, and the frequency range in which a signal is rejected is called the *stopband*.

It can be shown that the attainment of both ideal constant amplitude and ideal linear phase is physically impossible in a practical filter. Furthermore, as the amplitude approximation is improved, the phase response often becomes poorer, and vice versa. However, it is possible to provide approximations that approach the ideal conditions sufficiently close to satisfy most applications, particularly if a relatively complex filter is permitted.

Practical filters are characterized by a *transition band* between the passband and the stopband. The exact locations of the boundaries of these different bands are somewhat arbitrary. The forms of the amplitude and phase characteristics of a filter having nearly ideal characteristics in the passband, but with a nonzero transition band, are illustrated in Fig. 6-3. The phase shift is often best represented as a negative quantity, so $-\beta(f)$ is shown for convenience.

In certain applications, the time delay of a signal passing through a filter is more significance than the phase shift. It can be recalled that two definitions of delay functions were given in Chapt. 2. These were the *phase delay* T_p and the *group* (or *envelope*) *delay* T_g; the definitions are repeated here for convenience.

$$T_p(f) = \frac{-\beta(f)}{\omega} \tag{6-6}$$

$$T_g(f) = \frac{-d\beta(f)}{d\omega} \tag{6-7}$$

The graphical significance of these definitions is illustrated in Fig. 6-4. It can be seen that the phase delay at a given frequency represents the slope of the secant line from dc to the particular frequency and is a sort of overall average delay parameter. The group delay at a given frequency represents the slope of the tangent line at the particular frequency and represents a local or narrow-range delay parameter.

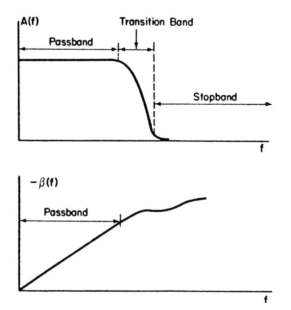

Figure 6-3 Amplitude and phase characteristics of a filter with ideal passband response.

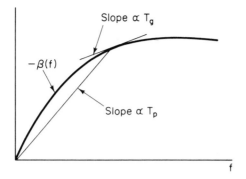

Figure 6-4 Graphical significance of phase delay and group delay.

Consider now the case of a filter with a constant-amplitude response and a linear-phase response as described by (6-4) and (6-5). It is readily seen that

$$T_p(f) = T_g(f) = \tau \qquad (6-8)$$

For the ideal filter, the phase and group delays are identical and represent the exact delay of the signal, which has not been distorted in this case. In the general case, where the amplitude response is not constant in the passband and the phase response is not linear, it is more difficult to precisely define the exact delay since a signal will undergo some distortion in passing through the filter. In fact, any attempt to define the exact delay will result in some variation of delay as different types of signals are applied to the filter. Nevertheless, the preceding definitions are quite useful in describing the approximate delay characteristics of a filter.

The phase delay parameter is often used to estimate the delay of a low-pass type signal, such as a basic pulse waveform, when it is passed through a low-pass filter. The phase delay is computed over the frequency range representing the major portion of the input signal spectrum. If the phase response does not deviate too far from linearity over the range involved, this value may represent a reasonable approximation to the actual delay of the waveform involved.

A case of significance involving both phase delay and group delay is that of a narrow-band modulated signal. It can be shown (Prob. 6-16) that when a narrow-band modulated signal is passed through a filter, the carrier is delayed by a time equal to the phase delay, while the envelope (or intelligence) is delayed by a time approximately equal to the group delay. Since the intelligence represents the desired information contained in such signals, strong emphasis on good group delay characteristics is often made in filters designed for processing modulated waveforms.

Returning to the ideal frequency-domain filter concept, it is convenient to consider several models representing the amplitude responses for various classes of filters as illustrated in Fig. 6-5. The four models shown are the *low-pass, high-pass, band-pass,* and *band-rejection* ideal frequency-domain amplitude functions. The corresponding ideal phase functions should be linear over the passband in each case. It should be emphasized again that these *exact* ideal functions are not physically realizable, but they may be approximated sufficiently close to meet engineering requirements.

So far, we have studied the ideal filter concept only from the frequency-domain point of view. An alternative, and often equally important, point of view is the time-domain, or transient, behavior of the filter. From that standpoint, the ideal filter considered here exhibits significant ringing and overshoot. This property is caused by the finite discontinuity in the assumed ideal block amplitude characteristic. The form of the step-response of the ideal low-pass filter (with some assumed delay) is illustrated in Fig. 6-6. (See Prob. 6-18.) The actual transient response of a real filter results from a combination of both the amplitude and phase characteristics. As long as the phase response does not deviate too far from linearity, the transient response of a real filter will be superior to that of the ideal filter. Thus, while the ideal frequency-domain filter represents a goal that we constantly seek, it is not necessarily the best result we could achieve, particularly from the transient point of view.

6-2 GENERAL APPROACHES

The treatment in this chapter will be devoted to a discussion of filters designed from CTLTI lumped system functions. The basic time-domain and frequency-domain properties of such systems were developed in Chapt. 2. The desired filter functions are obtained by determining an appropriate transfer function $G(s)$ whose frequency or time response meets the desired specifications. In actual analog filter design applications, it is necessary to realize the filter function in the form of a physical network. However, the principal purpose here is to consider only the approximation problem for analog filters, so we will devote primary attention to the problem of relating the prescribed amplitude and/or phase characteristics to the transfer function. Certain of the digital filter design procedures that will be developed in later chapters center around the concept of forcing the digital filter frequency re-

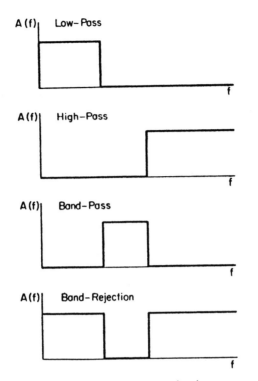

Figure 6-5 Ideal frequency-domain amplitude response models.

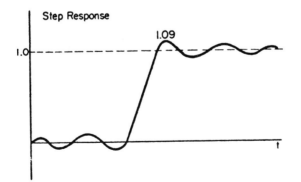

Figure 6-6 Step response of ideal frequency-domain low-pass filter.

sponse to closely approximate a reference analog response over a reasonable frequency range.

In general, it is necessary to convert a given set of design specifications into the form of a realizable transfer function. Fortunately, a number of very useful approximating functions and their associated realizations have been derived and tabulated. This permits the designer to use tables for many standard filter requirements.

The most common approach for representing a filter function, and the one on which we shall concentrate primary emphasis, is to specify the amplitude response $A(f)$. It was shown in Chapt. 2 that the amplitude-squared function $A^2(f)$ can be expressed in the form

$$A^2(f) = G(s)\ G(-s)]_{s=j\omega} \tag{6-9}$$

Since $G(s)$ is a rational function and (6-9) is equivalent to multiplying a complex function by its conjugate, $A^2(f)$ can be expressed as a nonnegative rational function of ω^2 having the general form

$$A^2(f) = \frac{K(c_k\omega^{2k} + c_{k-1}\omega^{2k-2} + \cdots + c_0)}{(d_k\omega^{2k} + d_{k-1}\omega^{2k-2} + \cdots + d_0)} \tag{6-10}$$

Assume now that (6-10) is specified in a given application. How do we determine the $G(s)$ that corresponds to the given $A^2(f)$? In effect, this means that we have to go "backwards" to find a function $G(s)$ that, when multiplied by $G(-s)$ and evaluated for $s = j\omega$, yields the given function. The key to this question is related to the s-plane interpretation of (6-9). Assume that a given critical frequency (either pole or zero) of $G(s)$ is located at $s = s_0$. The corresponding critical frequency of $G(-s)$ is located at $s = -s_0$. In the case of a critical frequency of $G(s)$ on the negative real axis, the corresponding critical frequency of $G(-s)$ is located on the positive real axis. In the case of a complex pair of critical frequencies of $G(s)$ located at $-a \pm jb$, the corresponding critical frequencies of $G(-s)$ are located at $a \mp jb$. Note that purely imaginary critical frequencies result in *double-order* roots. The behavior of these critical frequencies in the s-plane is displayed in Fig. 6-7. The resulting symmetrical pattern is said to have *quadrantal symmetry*. The exponent above the $j\omega$-axis zeros identifies them as second-order roots.

From the s-plane plot, it is possible to associate the various critical frequencies with $G(s)$ and $G(-s)$. Any practical filter of interest will be stable. Consequently, its poles must lie in the left-hand half-plane. The poles in the left-hand half-plane may then be associated with $G(s)$, and those in the right-hand half-plane may be associated with $G(-s)$.

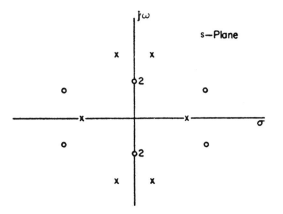

Figure 6-7 Pole-zero plot of $G(s)G(-s)$ illustrating quadrantal symmetry.

The association of the zeros is not unique unless the transfer function is a *minimum-phase* type. For the minimum-phase type, all left-hand half-plane zeros are associated with $G(s)$ in the same manner as poles. For nonminimum phase systems, various other combinations involving both left- and right-hand half-plane zeros of $G(s)$ and $G(-s)$ are possible. In any event, the amplitude response is unaffected, but the phase will depend on the choice of zeros. Since nonminimum phase functions are used primarily in special filter applications involving phase or delay control, one is usually aware of those applications in which right-hand half-plane zeros are to be used.

The procedure for determining $G(s)$ from $A^2(f)$ may now be stated. From (6-9) it follows that

$$G(s)\,G(-s) = A^2(f)\,]_{\omega^2 = -s^2} \qquad (6\text{-}11)$$

By substituting $\omega^2 = -s^2$, we obtain an s-plane function that has been shown to have quadrantal symmetry. The various poles and zeros are then determined by factoring the numerator and denominator polynomials of (6-11). Assuming that the transfer function is to be a minimum-phase form, the poles and zeros in the left-hand half-plane are assigned to $G(s)$. Any $j\omega$-axis zeros and poles must occur in even multiplicity, so that half of each conjugate set is assigned to $G(s)$. The gain constant is determined by comparing either the low-frequency or the high-frequency behavior of $A(f)$ with $G(s)$, depending on which pair is easier to use. The transfer function is determined by forming the numerator and denominator polynomials from the various zeros and poles and multiplying by the gain constant.

The heart of the approximation problem consists of determining the various constants in (6-10) so that the resulting amplitude function meets the desired specifications. In general, this is a difficult task, and there is usually no single unique solution. Because of simplicity, it is often convenient to use the *low-pass* filter as a basis for developing approximating functions. There are transformations available that permit one to "map" a low-pass form into either a band-pass, band-rejection, or high-pass form, and some of these transformations will be explored later in the chapter.

The simplest type of low-pass amplitude-squared function is one in which all zeros of G*(s)* are located at $s = \infty$. In this case, (6-10) reduces to the form

$$A^2(f) = \frac{d_0}{d_0 + d_1\omega^2 + d_2\omega^4 + \cdots + d_k\omega^{2k}} \qquad (6\text{-}12)$$

where the dc gain has been adjusted to unity. The low-pass functions that will be considered in more depth in this chapter are of this form.

At high frequencies, (6-12) reduces to

$$A^2(f) \approx \frac{d_0/d_k}{\omega^{2k}} \qquad (6\text{-}13)$$

It can be readily shown that this corresponds to a $6k$ dB/octave (or a $20k$ dB/decade) attenuation rate. Of course, the response in the passband may have a variety of forms, and the actual level of the response in the stopband will depend on d_0 and d_k. Nevertheless, it is interesting to note that the high-frequency attenuation rate of any low-pass filter of order k, having all transmission zeros at infinity, will eventually become asymptotic to a curve with a slope of $-6k$ dB/*octave* (or $-20k$ dB/decade).

An additional point of significance before considering specific approximations is the concept of frequency normalization or scaling. The development of specific approximating functions or models is often enhanced by choosing a simple value such as $\omega = 1$ rad/s as a reference cutoff or center frequency. The final results may then be scaled to any particular desired frequency range. Most available design tables and charts have been developed using this normalized approach, and we will use it extensively in later sections.

Example 6-1

Determine the transfer function corresponding to the amplitude-squared function

$$A^2(f) = \frac{25(4 - \omega^2)^2}{(9 + \omega^2)(16 + \omega^2)} \qquad (6\text{-}14)$$

Solution

The function satisfies the requirements for an amplitude-squared function since it is a rational, nonnegative function of ω^2, and the zeros on the $j\omega$-axis are of even multiplicity. We first replace ω^2 by $-s^2$ according to (6-11) and obtain

$$G(s)\,G(-s) = \frac{25(4 + s^2)^2}{(9 - s^2)(16 - s^2)} \qquad (6\text{-}15)$$

The zeros of (6-15) are located at $s = \pm j2$ (second order). The poles are located at $s = \pm 3$ and ± 4. Selecting the left-hand half-plane poles, one pair of the imaginary-axis zeros, and a gain constant such as to make $G(0) = A(0)$, the required transfer function is

$$G(s) = \frac{5(s^2 + 4)}{(s + 3)(s + 4)} = \frac{5s^2 + 20}{s^2 + 7s + 12} \qquad (6\text{-}16)$$

6-3 BUTTERWORTH APPROXIMATION _____

The first function that will be considered is the *Butterworth* or *maximally flat* amplitude approximation. The Butterworth low-pass amplitude-squared function is defined by

$$A^2(f) = \frac{1}{1 + (\omega/\omega_c)^{2k}} = \frac{1}{1 + (f/f_c)^{2k}} \qquad (6\text{-}17)$$

where k represents the order of the corresponding transfer function. The cyclic frequency f_c (or radian frequency $\omega_c = 2\pi f_c$) is defined as the "cutoff" frequency in (6-17). At this frequency, the amplitude response is $1/\sqrt{2}$ times the dc gain, corresponding to an attenuation of 3.01 dB. In most applications, this value is rounded off to 3 dB, and this assumption will be made in subsequent filter calculations. In many developments, it is convenient to normalize the frequency scale by selecting $\omega_c = 1$ rad/s in (6-17). The general form of a typical Butterworth amplitude response on a linear scale is illustrated in Fig. 6-8.

The Butterworth amplitude response can be shown to be optimum at dc in the maximally flat sense. This means that the difference between the ideal amplitude response and the approximation and as many lower order derivatives as possible are equated to zero at $\omega = 0$.

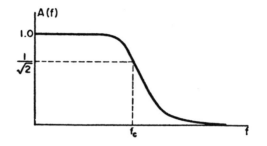

Figure 6-8 Form of the amplitude response of a Butterworth filter.

(See Probs. 6-19 and 6-21.) The Butterworth response is a monotonically decreasing function of frequency in the positive frequency range. As the order k increases, the response becomes "flatter" in the pass-band, and the attenuation is greater in the stopband. Above cutoff, the Butterworth amplitude response of order k approaches a high-frequency asymptote having a slope of $-6k$ dB/octave.

Example 6-2

Derive the transfer function for the third-order Butterworth low-pass filter with $\omega_c = 1$ rad/s.

Solution

The amplitude-squared function is

$$A^2(f) = \frac{1}{1 + \omega^6} \qquad\qquad (6\text{-}18)$$

Setting $\omega^2 = -s^2$, we have

$$G(s)\,G(-s) = \frac{1}{1 - s^6} \qquad\qquad (6\text{-}19)$$

The poles of (6-19) are determined as follows:

$$s_1 = 1 \,\underline{/0^\circ} \qquad = 1$$

$$s_2 = 1 \,\underline{/60^\circ} \qquad = \frac{1}{2} + j\,\frac{\sqrt{3}}{2}$$

$$s_3 = 1 \underline{/120°} \quad = -\frac{1}{2} + j\frac{\sqrt{3}}{2} \tag{6-20}$$

$$s_4 = 1 \underline{/180°} \quad = -1$$

$$s_5 = 1 \underline{/-120°} = -\frac{1}{2} - j\frac{\sqrt{3}}{2}$$

$$s_6 = 1 \underline{/-60°} \quad = \frac{1}{2} - j\frac{\sqrt{3}}{2}$$

Notice that all of the poles lie on a circle. This is one of the characteristics of the Butterworth function. The transfer function is formed from the left-hand half-plane poles (s_3, s_4, and s_5) and is

$$G(s) = \frac{1}{s^3 + 2s^2 + 2s + 1} \tag{6-21}$$

6-4   CHEBYSHEV APPROXIMATION

The next function that will be considered is the *Chebyshev* or *equiripple* amplitude approximation. This approximation is derived from the Chebyshev polynomials $C_k(x)$, which are a set of orthogonal functions possessing certain interesting properties. Some of the basic properties are: (a) The polynomials have equiripple amplitude characteristics over the range $-1 \leqslant x \leqslant 1$, with ripple oscillating between -1 and $+1$. (b) $C_k(x)$ increases more rapidly for $x > 1$ than any other polynomial of order k bounded by the limits stated in (a).

   There are numerous other properties and variations of the Chebyshev polynomials, but our purposes can be met by considering only a few. These polynomials can be derived from either of the equations

$$C_k(x) = \cos(k \cos^{-1} x) \tag{6-22}$$

and

$$C_k(x) = \cosh(k \cosh^{-1} x) \tag{6-23}$$

The form of (6-22) is most useful in the range $|x| < 1$, and (6-23) is most useful in the range $|x| > 1$. While neither (6-22) nor (6-23) appears to be a polynomial, it can be shown that these expressions can be expanded in polynomial form. The Chebyshev polynomials of orders one through six are listed in Table 6-1. The forms for the polynomials of orders two through five are illustrated in Fig. 6-9. The behavior for negative x is readily obtained by noting that $C_k(x)$ is even for k even, and odd for k odd.

The basic Chebyshev amplitude response is defined by

$$A^2(f) = \frac{\alpha}{1 + \epsilon^2 C_k{}^2(\omega/\omega_c)} = \frac{\alpha}{1 + \epsilon^2 C_k{}^2(f/f_c)} \tag{6-24}$$

where k represents both the order of the Chebyshev polynomial and the order of the corresponding transfer function. The quantity ϵ^2 is a parameter chosen to provide the proper passband ripple, and α is a constant chosen to determine the proper dc gain level. The cyclic frequency f_c (or radian frequency ω_c) is defined as the "cutoff frequency," and its significance will be discussed shortly. The form of the Chebyshev amplitude response for k odd ($k = 3$ and 2 dB ripple) is illustrated in Fig. 6-10, and the form for k even ($k = 4$ and 2 dB ripple) is illustrated in Fig. 6-11.

Several properties of the Chebyshev amplitude response should be carefully noted. The passband is defined as the range over which the ripple is constrained to oscillate between constant bounds, i.e., the range from dc to f_c. The frequency f_c is the "cutoff frequency," and it is the highest frequency at which the response is governed by the passband ripple bound. Above f_c, the response moves into the transition band. The passband dB ripple r is defined by

$$r = 10 \, \text{Log}_{10} \frac{A_{max}^2}{A_{min}^2} = 20 \, \text{Log}_{10} \frac{A_{max}}{A_{min}} \tag{6-25}$$

Table 6-1
Several of the Chebyshev polynomials.

k	$C_k(x)$
1	x
2	$2x^2 - 1$
3	$4x^3 - 3x$
4	$8x^4 - 8x^2 + 1$
5	$16x^5 - 20x^3 + 5x$
6	$32x^6 - 48x^4 + 18x^2 - 1$

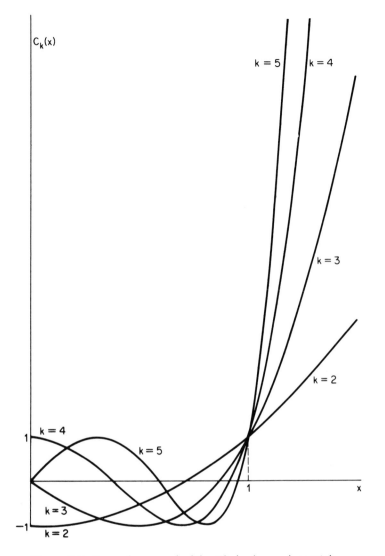

Figure 6-9 Forms for several of the Chebyshev polynomials.

where A_{max} is the maximum value of $A(f)$, and A_{min} is the minimum value of $A(f)$, within the passband.

The quantity ϵ^2 may be related to the passband ripple by utilizing (6-24) and (6-25). The maximum and minimum values of $A^2(f)$ are $A_{max}^2 = \alpha$ and $A_{min}^2 = \alpha/(1 + \epsilon^2)$. The dB ripple is then given by

$$r = 10 \, \text{Log}_{10} \, (1 + \epsilon^2) \qquad (6\text{-}26)$$

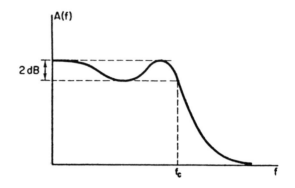

Figure 6-10 Chebyshev amplitude response for $k = 3$ and 2 dB passband ripple.

or

$$\epsilon^2 = 10^{(r/10)} - 1 \tag{6-27}$$

The stopband attenuation at a given frequency will increase as the passband ripple is allowed to increase for a given number of poles. Thus, a Chebyshev design always represents a tradeoff between the allowable passband ripple and the desired attenuation in the stopband.

The total number of maxima and minima in the passband is equal to the order k. For k odd, there is a maximum at $f = 0$, and if it is desired that the dc gain be unity, the numerator constant in (6-24) should be selected as $\alpha = 1$ in this case. On the other hand, for k even, there is a

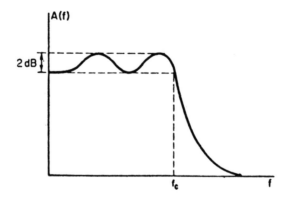

Figure 6-11 Chebyshev amplitude response for $k = 4$ and 2 dB passband ripple.

minimum at $f = 0$, and the choice of α depends on additional considerations. It is left as an exercise (Prob. 6-7) for the reader to show that if it is still desired that the dc gain be unity, the gain constant should be selected to be $\alpha = 1 + \epsilon^2$. In this case, the gain at the maxima will be greater than unity. In some passive synthesis procedures, this condition poses certain constraints on the realization forms, but this fact is of no major consequence for our purposes.

In some cases, it is desirable that the maximum gain be adjusted to unity. This is accomplished by setting $\alpha = 1$ in (6-24). The gain at dc will now be less than unity for k even. This approach was used in determining the relative response curves given in Sec. 6-10, so it is important to recognize this fact when comparing the Chebyshev response curves in that section.

The manner in which the cutoff frequency is defined for a Chebyshev filter is compatible with the Butterworth filter only for a 3 dB passband ripple. The Chebyshev definition is convenient because many filter specifications are stated in terms of a maximum allowable passband ripple over a particular frequency range, so the highest frequency satisfying this constraint is usually of primary interest. As in the case of the Butterworth function, the Chebyshev amplitude response of order k approaches a high-frequency asymptote having a slope of $-6k$ dB/octave. Also, the radian cutoff frequency ω_c is often normalized to unity in developing Chebyshev designs.

Example 6-3

Derive the transfer function for the second-order Chebyshev transfer function with 1 dB passband ripple, a normalized cutoff frequency $\omega_c = 1$ rad/s, and unity dc gain.

Solution

The required value of ϵ^2 is determined from (6-27) as

$$\epsilon^2 = 10^{0.1} - 1 = 0.25892541 \tag{6-28}$$

$C_2(x)$ is then obtained from Table 6-1 and substituted in (6-24) to yield

$$A^2(f) = \frac{1.2589254}{1.0357016\omega^4 - 1.0357016\omega^2 + 1.2589254} \tag{6-29}$$

where the numerator constant has been chosen to make the dc gain unity. Setting $\omega^2 = -s^2$, we have

$$G(s)\,G(-s) = \frac{1.2589254}{1.0357016s^4 + 1.0357016s^2 + 1.2589254} \quad (6\text{-}30)$$

The poles are determined from the roots of the denominator polynomial to be

$$s_1 = 1.0500049 \,\underline{/58.484569^\circ}$$
$$s_2 = 1.0500049 \,\underline{/121.51543^\circ}$$
$$s_3 = 1.0500049 \,\underline{/-121.51543^\circ} \quad (6\text{-}31)$$
$$s_4 = 1.0500049 \,\underline{/-58.484569^\circ}$$

It can be shown that the poles of a Chebyshev polynomial lie on an ellipse. The transfer function is formed from the left-hand half-plane roots (s_2 and s_3), and the gain constant is again set to give unity gain at dc. The result is

$$G(s) = \frac{1.1025103}{s^2 + 1.0977343s + 1.1025103} \quad (6\text{-}32)$$

6-5   SURVEY OF OTHER APPROXIMATIONS

In this section, a general survey of several other important analog filter frequency response approximations will be made. The actual details of these and other approximations are developed in various texts on network synthesis.

The Butterworth and Chebyshev functions were both obtained from approximations involving only the amplitude response, and no attention was paid to the phase response in either case. We will now consider the *maximally flat time-delay* (MFTD) approximation. The major characteristic of this function is that the group delay is made to be maximally flat in the vicinity of dc.

The amplitude characteristic that results from the MFTD approximation has a low-pass shape with a monotonically decreasing behavior as the frequency is increased. However, the passband response is not as flat as for the Butterworth function, and the stophand attenuation is not as great at a given frequency as for either the Butterworth or the Chebyshev function of the same order. As the order k increases, the amplitude response of the MFTD approximation approaches the form of a Gaussian probability density function.

Variations of this filter are referred to by each of the names Bessel filter, Gaussian filter, Thomson filter, Storch filter. The first name results from the fact that Bessel polynomials are used in the development of the approximation, and the second name refers to the property mentioned in the last paragraph. The last two names are those of investigators who made contributions to the development of the approximation.

The MFTD filter is used where excellent phase shift (or time delay) characteristics are required, but where the amplitude response need not display a rapid attenuation increase just above cutoff. As in the case of both the Butterworth and Chebyshev functions, the high-frequency attenuation rate of the MFTD filter will eventually approach $6k$ dB/octave, but the total attenuation will not be as great. The general form of the amplitude response is illustrated in Fig. 6-12.

The three filter functions considered thus far have all the zeros of transmission at infinity. Of these three types, the Chebyshev is normally considered to have the "best" amplitude response (more attenuation in the stopband for a given passband ripple bound) and the "poorest" phase response (most nonlinear). At the opposite extreme, the MFTD filter has the "best" phase response and the "poorest" amplitude response. The Butterworth filter represents a reasonable compromise between amplitude and phase. No doubt this is one of the reasons for its widespread popularity.

Filter functions having all of the zeros of transmission at infinity have the limitation that infinite attenuation cannot be achieved at any finite frequency. In some cases, it may be desirable to provide a very large attenuation in the lower portion of the stopband. This can be accomplished by permitting the transfer function to contain one or

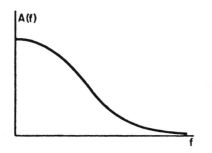

Figure 6-12 Form of the amplitude response for the maximally flat time-delay filter.

more pairs of purely imaginary zeros. The attenuation in the neighborhood of such a zero can be made to increase very rapidly, thus providing the possibility of extremely sharp cutoff characteristics if the zeros are located properly.

The first function of this type that will be considered is the *inverted Chebyshev approximation*. (This function is sometimes called a Chebyshev type II response in contrast to the standard form, which could be called a Chebyshev type I response.) The amplitude-squared response for this approximation can be expressed in the form

$$A^2(f) = \frac{\epsilon^2 C_k{}^2(\omega_s/\omega)}{1 + \epsilon^2 C_k{}^2(\omega_s/\omega)} \qquad (6\text{-}33)$$

The development of some of the properties of this function will be left as exercises for the reader (Probs. 6-22 through 6-26). It can be shown that this amplitude response has a maximally flat characteristic at low frequencies (Prob. 6-22), but an equiripple nature in the stopband.

The form of the Chebyshev inverted amplitude response for k odd ($k = 5$ in this case) is illustrated in Fig. 6-13, and the form for k even ($k = 4$ in this case) is illustrated in Fig. 6-14. The cyclic frequency f_s (or radian frequency ω_s) defines the *beginning of the stopband* in this case. For $f > f_s$, the amplitude response oscillates between 0 and $\epsilon^2/(1 + \epsilon^2)$, meaning that the decibel attenuation oscillates between infinity and some finite large value, depending on the value of ϵ^2. For frequencies well above the highest infinite attenuation frequency, the amplitude response eventually becomes asymptotic to a curve with slope -6 dB/octave for k odd and to a constant finite level of attenuation for k even. (See Probs. 6-24 and 6-25.)

The last filter type that we will mention is the *Cauer* or *elliptic function* filter, which is characterized by equiripple response in both the passband and in the stopband. The general form of the low-pass amplitude-squared function is given by

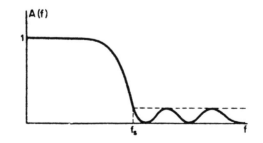

Figure 6-13 Form of the inverted Chebyshev amplitude response with $k = 5$.

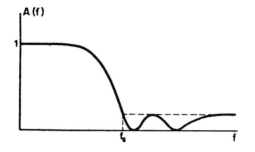

Figure 6-14 Form of the inverted Chebyshev amplitude response with $k = 4$.

$$A^2(f) = \frac{1}{1 + R_k{}^2(f)} \qquad (6\text{-}34)$$

The functions $R_k{}^2(f)$ are called *Chebyshev rational functions*. The form of an elliptic function response for k odd ($k = 5$ in this case) is illustrated in Fig. 6-15, and the form for k even ($k = 4$ in this case) is illustrated in Fig. 6-16. With elliptic function filters, it is possible to specify both the maximum ripple level in the passband and the minimum attenuation level in the stopband.

Filter functions with zeros on the $j\omega$-axis have been shown to offer the advantages of sharper transition bands and greater control over the minimum attenuation level in the lower portion of the stopband. These advantages must be weighted against certain disadvantages, which are: (a) The resulting transfer functions are more complex, with a possible increase in the sensitivity of the response to parameter value inaccuracies. (b) For a given number of poles, the eventual high-frequency attenuation rate will be less than that of filters having all zeros at infinity.

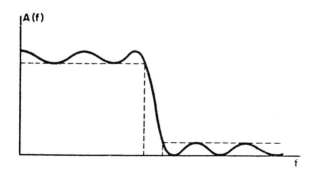

Figure 6-15 Form of the elliptic function amplitude response with $k = 5$.

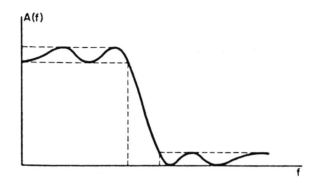

Figure 6-16 Form of the elliptic function amplitude response with $k = 4$.

6-6   FILTER DESIGN DATA

The pole locations of various Butterworth and Chebyshev filters and the coefficients of the corresponding polynomials have been derived and tabulated by Weinberg (see reference accompanying Table 6-2). An abbreviated set of the polynomial coefficients for the Butterworth and Chebyshev functions are presented here. In addition, and for convenience in developing certain types of digital filter designs later in the book, partially factored forms of these polynomials have been calculated and tabulated.

The polynomials are given in the basic form required for constructing the low-pass transfer function. The radian cutoff frequencies in both (6-17) and (6-24) are normalized to $\omega_c = 1$ rad/s. The general form for the low-pass transfer functions in the table is

$$G(s) = \frac{A_0}{B_0 + B_1 s + B_2 s^2 + \cdots + B_k s^k} \qquad (6\text{-}35)$$

The denominator coefficients of (6-35) are tabulated in Table 6-2 for the Butterworth function and Chebyshev functions for four possible values of passband ripple (0.5 dB, 1 dB, 2 dB, and 3 dB). The orders of the filters used are from $k = 1$ through $k = 5$. If unity gain at dc is desired, the numerator constant is selected as $A_0 = B_0$.

Partially factored forms of the denominator polynomials of (6-35) are tabulated in Table 6-3. Letting $D(s)$ represent any one of the polynomials, the form of the transfer function is given by

$$G(s) = \frac{A_0}{D(s)} \qquad (6\text{-}36)$$

Table 6-2

Coefficients of low-pass filter denominator polynomials. (Note: Coefficients are defined in accordance with equation 6-35.)

Order	B_0	B_1	B_2	B_3	B_4	B_5
			BUTTERWORTH			
1	1					
2	1	1.4142136	1			
3	1	2	2	1		
4	1	2.6131259	3.4142136	2.6131259	1	
5	1	3.2360680	5.2360680	5.2360680	3.2360680	1
		CHEBYSHEV 0.5 DB RIPPLE $(\epsilon^2 = 0.1220184)$				
1	2.8627752	1				
2	1.5162026	1.4256245	1			
3	0.7156938	1.5348954	1.2529130	1		
4	0.3790506	1.0254553	1.7168662	1.1973856	1	
5	0.1789234	0.7525181	1.3095747	1.9373675	1.1724909	1
		CHEBYSHEV 1 DB RIPPLE $(\epsilon^2 = 0.2589254)$				
1	1.9652267	1				
2	1.1025103	1.0977343	1			
3	0.4913067	1.2384092	0.9883412	1		
4	0.2756276	0.7426194	1.4539248	0.9528114	1	
5	0.1228267	0.5805342	0.9743961	1.6888160	0.9368201	1
		CHEBYSHEV 2 DB RIPPLE $(\epsilon^2 = 0.5848932)$				
1	1.3075603	1				
2	0.8230604	0.8038164	1			
3	0.3268901	1.0221903	0.7378216	1		
4	0.2057651	0.5167981	1.2564819	0.7162150	1	
5	0.0817225	0.4593491	0.6934770	1.4995433	0.7064606	1
		CHEBYSHEV 3 DB RIPPLE $(\epsilon^2 = 0.9952623)$				
1	1.0023773	1				
2	0.7079478	0.6448996	1			
3	0.2505943	0.9283480	0.5972404	1		
4	0.1769869	0.4047679	1.1691176	0.5815799	1	
5	0.0626391	0.4079421	0.5488626	1.4149847	0.5744296	1

(These results were obtained from L. A. Weinberg, *Network Analysis and Synthesis*, McGraw–Hill, 1962, with permission of the author.)

The choice for A_0 follows the same logic discussed in the preceding paragraph.

In using the tables, it is important to remember that these functions are normalized with respect to a *radian frequency* of $\omega_c = 1$ rad/s, whereas most specifications are given in terms of *cyclic frequency*. As obvious as this may seem, a very common source of error in using such

Table 6-3

Partially factored forms for low-pass filter denominator polynomials. (Refer to equation 6-36.)

Order		BUTTERWORTH
1	$(1 + s)$	
2		$(1 + 1.4142136s + s^2)$
3	$(1 + s)$	$(1 + s + s^2)$
4		$(1 + 0.7653668s + s^2)$ $(1 + 1.8477590s + s^2)$
5	$(1 + s)$	$(1 + 0.6180340s + s^2)$ $(1 + 1.6180340s + s^2)$

CHEBYSHEV 0.5 DB RIPPLE

1	$(2.8627752 + s)$	
2		$(1.5162026 + 1.4256244s + s^2)$
3	$(0.6264565 + s)$	$(1.1424477 + 0.6264564s + s^2)$
4		$(1.0635187 + 0.3507062s + s^2)$ $(0.3564119 + 0.8466796s + s^2)$
5	$(0.3623196 + s)$	$(1.0357841 + 0.2239258s + s^2)$ $(0.4767669 + 0.5862454s + s^2)$

CHEBYSHEV 1.0 DB RIPPLE

1	$(1.9652267 + s)$	
2		$(1.1025104 + 1.0977344s + s^2)$
3	$(0.4941706 + s)$	$(0.9942046 + 0.4941706s + s^2)$
4		$(0.9865049 + 0.2790720s + s^2)$ $(0.2793981 + 0.6737394s + s^2)$
5	$(0.2894933 + s)$	$(0.9883149 + 0.1789168s + s^2)$ $(0.4292978 + 0.4684100s + s^2)$

CHEBYSHEV 2.0 DB RIPPLE

1	$(1.3075603 + s)$	
2		$(0.8230604 + 0.8038164s + s^2)$
3	$(0.3689108 + s)$	$(0.8860951 + 0.3689108s + s^2)$
4		$(0.9286753 + 0.2097744s + s^2)$ $(0.2215684 + 0.5064404s + s^2)$
5	$(0.218308\ \ + s)$	$(0.9521670 + 0.1349220s + s^2)$ $(0.3931500 + 0.3532302s + s^2)$

CHEBYSHEV 3.0 DB RIPPLE

1	$(1.0023773 + s)$	
2		$(0.7079478 + 0.6448996s + s^2)$
3	$(0.2986202 + s)$	$(0.8391740 + 0.2986202s + s^2)$
4		$(0.9030867 + 0.1703408s + s^2)$ $(0.1959800 + 0.4112390s + s^2)$
5	$(0.1775085 + s)$	$(0.9360176 + 0.1097062s + s^2)$ $(0.3770008 + 0.2872148s + s^2)$

(These results are based on data obtained from L. A. Weinberg, *Network Analysis and Synthesis*, McGraw–Hill, 1962, with permission of author.)

tables is the failure to convert properly between radian and cyclic frequencies in scaling to the required frequency range.

The process of scaling the filter functions obtained from the table to the required frequency range consists of a linear scale change on the frequency axis. All frequencies are scaled in direct proportion. For example, if the scale change is such that the normalized cutoff of 1 rad/s is scaled to a cyclic frequency of 10 kHz, the original normalized response at 3 rad/s corresponds to the final scaled response at 30 kHz.

Let ω_{rn} represent some reference radian frequency in the normalized response, and assume that the desired corresponding reference radian frequency in the scaled response is to be ω_r. Note that ω_r may or may not be the cutoff frequency of the normalized response, as the scaling can center around any particular frequency desired. Let $G(s)$ represent the normalized transfer function, and let $G_1(s)$ represent the final transfer function after scaling. The scaled transfer function is obtained by replacing s by $\omega_{rn}s/\omega_r$ in all terms of the original transfer function. Hence,

$$G_1(s) = G\left(\frac{\omega_{rn}s}{\omega_r}\right) \tag{6-37}$$

If desired, the subscript in $G_1(s)$ could now be dropped as long as it is understood that this function has been scaled to the correct frequency range.

Example 6-4

Determine the transfer function for a third-order low-pass Butterworth filter with a cutoff frequency of 1 kHz.

Solution

The normalized transfer function $G(s)$ is obtained from Table 6-2 and is

$$G(s) = \frac{1}{s^3 + 2s^2 + 2s + 1} \tag{6-38}$$

In this case, the reference frequency of the scaled function is the cutoff frequency and is $\omega_r = 2\pi f_r = 2\pi \times 10^3 \text{ rad/s}$. The normalized reference frequency is, of course, $\omega_{rn} = 1 \text{ rad/s}$. The final transfer function $G_1(s)$ is

$$G_1(s) = G\left(\frac{s}{2\pi \times 10^3}\right) \tag{6-39}$$

Application of (6-39) to (6-38) yields, after some manipulation,

$$G_1(s) = \frac{2.4805021 \times 10^{11}}{s^3 + 1.2566371 \times 10^4 s^2 + 7.8956835 \times 10^7 s + 2.4805021 \times 10^{11}} \tag{6-40}$$

6-7 LOW-PASS TO BAND-PASS TRANSFORMATION

A very popular procedure for designing band-pass filters involves the use of a low-pass to band-pass geometric transformation. Using this approach, a low-pass prototype transfer function is first derived, and by means of the transformation is converted to a band-pass function.

In developing the transformation and others that follow in this chapter, it will be necessary to use more than one Laplace complex variable, which has previously been denoted by s. We will reserve s and ω (or f) for the *final* Laplace and steady-state frequency variables of the desired function, whether they be low-pass, band-pass, band-rejection, or anything else. This means that when we start with a low-pass function and wish to convert it to another form, we will introduce one or more dummy variables in the process. This could be confusing to the reader in cases where we start with data tabulated in the last section in terms of s and use a different variable than s in the initial formulation. Likewise, some reference frequency that was previously expressed in terms of ω will be expressed in terms of a new reference frequency variable.

The following notation will be employed in this section:

p = *low-pass* prototype Laplace variable

s = *band-pass* final Laplace variable

λ = steady-state radian frequency corresponding to p ($p = j\lambda$)

ω = steady-state radian frequency corresponding to s ($s = j\omega$)

$G_{lp}(p)$ = low-pass prototype transfer function

$G_{bp}(s)$ = band-pass final transfer function

λ_r = a particular low-pass prototype reference radian frequency (often the cutoff frequency λ_c)

f_r = $\lambda_r/2\pi$ = cyclic frequency corresponding to λ_r

ω_1 = lower radian frequency in band-pass function corresponding to $-\lambda_r$ in prototype

ω_3 = upper radian frequency in band-pass function corresponding to $+\lambda_r$ in prototype

ω_2 = geometric center radian frequency in band-pass function

f_1, f_2, f_3 = cyclic frequencies in band-pass function corresponding to ω_1, ω_2, and ω_3

The low-pass to band-pass transformation reads

$$p = \frac{s^2 + \omega_2{}^2}{s} \qquad (6\text{-}41)$$

The steady-state nature of this transformation can be seen by letting $s = j\omega$ in (6-41). The resulting function for λ is everywhere purely imaginary, meaning that the imaginary axis of the s-plane maps to the imaginary axis of the p-plane. Setting $p = j\lambda$ and cancelling j's, a relationship is obtained between the two frequency variables.

$$\lambda = \frac{\omega^2 - \omega_2^2}{\omega} \qquad (6\text{-}42)$$

In terms of cyclic frequencies, (6-42) becomes

$$\frac{\lambda}{2\pi} = \frac{f^2 - f_2^2}{f} \qquad (6\text{-}43)$$

The relationship of (6-42) is shown in Fig. 6-17 for positive ω. The low-pass frequency $\lambda = 0$ (dc) is mapped to $\omega = \omega_2$, $\lambda = +\lambda_r$ is mapped

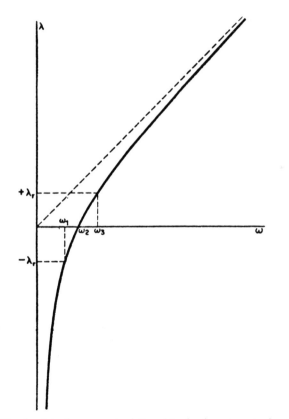

Figure 6-17 Steady-state frequency relationship for low-pass to band-pass transformation.

to $\omega = \omega_3$, and $\lambda = -\lambda_r$ is mapped to $\omega = \omega_1$. (The reader should not be disturbed by the apparent negative frequency, since this is primarily a "quirk" of the mathematical development. Actually, the amplitude response is usually considered as an even function of frequency extending over both positive and negative frequencies.)

The effect of this transformation is that the original low-pass prototype amplitude response from dc to any reference frequency f_r is shifted to the range from f_2 to f_3. Since the amplitude response is even, this same response (from dc to $-f_r$) is also translated to the range from f_2 to f_1 in a reverse sense. If the translation were perfectly linear over the range from f_1 to f_3, the resulting band-pass response would display arithmetic symmetry, and the amplitude segments on either side of f_2 would be mirror images of each other. However, this is not the case, since the transformation curve is not linear. In fact, the frequency interval from f_2 to f_3 is greater than the interval from f_1 to f_2. An illustration of the general form of the resulting band-pass function compared with the prototype low-pass function is shown in Fig. 6-18.

Some interesting quantitative relationships governing transformation parameters can be deduced by relating f_r to f_3 and $-f_r$ to f_1. From (6-43), we have

$$f_r = \frac{f_3^2 - f_2^2}{f_3} \tag{6-44}$$

and

$$-f_r = \frac{f_1^2 - f_2^2}{f_1} \tag{6-45}$$

Alternate addition and subtraction of (6-44) and (6-45) and some simplification result in two important relationships,

$$f_2 = \sqrt{f_1 f_3} \tag{6-46}$$

and

$$B = f_3 - f_1 = f_r \tag{6-47}$$

where the quantity B is defined as the *bandwidth* of interest in the band-pass filter. The first relationship implies that the band-pass response derived by this procedure will have *geometric symmetry* about the center frequency. Since f_1 and f_3 represent any arbitrary frequencies corresponding to a given reference low-pass frequency, this property of geometric symmetry holds with respect to any corresponding matched pair of frequencies on either side of the center frequency. The second relationship implies that any particular bandwidth of interest

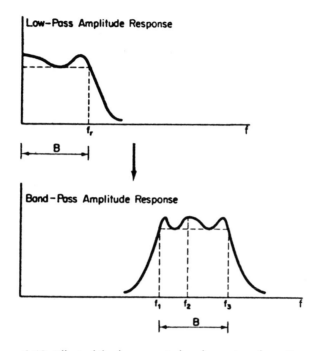

Figure 6-18 Effect of the low-pass to band-pass transformation.

in the band-pass filter will be identical to the corresponding bandwidth of the low-pass filter, as long as this bandwidth is measured between the frequencies f_3 and f_1 at which the amplitude response corresponds to the low-pass response at f_r.

Practical utilization of the low-pass to band-pass transformation for determining a band-pass transfer function $G_{bp}(s)$ can be achieved as follows:

(a) Determine a low-pass transfer function $G_{lp}(p)$ in which the reference bandwidth f_r is equal to the desired band-pass bandwidth $B = f_3 - f_1$. This will usually require frequency scaling of the low-pass function if normalized design tables are used.

(b) Obtain the band-pass transfer function $G_{bp}(s)$ by substitution of the transformation of (6-41).

$$G_{bp}(s) = G_{lp}(p)]_{p = (s^2 + \omega_2{}^2)/s} \qquad (6\text{-}48)$$

In general, if the low-pass prototype transfer function is of order k, the band-pass transfer function will be of order $2k$ and will contain $2k$ finite poles. If all the k transmission zeros of the low-pass function are located at infinity, the band-pass function will also have k zeros at infinity, and in addition, will have k zeros at the origin. At very low frequencies the response is asymptotic to a curve with slope $+6k$ dB/octave, and at very high frequencies the response is asymptotic to a curve with slope $-6k$ dB/octave.

Example 6-5

Determine the transfer function of a band-pass filter having the following characteristics: (a) 4 poles, (b) Butterworth response, (c) geometric center frequency = 1 kHz, (d) 3 dB bandwidth = 200 Hz.

Solution

Since the band-pass function is to have 4 poles, the low-pass prototype function should have 2 poles. The low-pass normalized Butterworth function of order 2 is given by

$$G_{lp}(p) = \frac{1}{p^2 + 1.4142136p + 1} \tag{6-49}$$

The first step required is to change the frequency scale of (6-49) so that the cutoff frequency is equal to the desired bandwidth of the band-pass function, namely 200 Hz. This is achieved by replacing p in (6-49) by $p/(2\pi \times 200)$. The resulting function $G_{1lp}(p)$ is

$$G_{1lp}(p) = \frac{1.5791367 \times 10^6}{p^2 + 1.7771532 \times 10^3 p + 1.5791367 \times 10^6} \tag{6-50}$$

The radian center frequency is $\omega_2 = 2\pi \times 10^3$, and the transformation is

$$p = \frac{s^2 + 3.9478418 \times 10^7}{s} \tag{6-51}$$

Substitution of (6-51) in (6-50) yields the band-pass transfer function $G_{bp}(s)$.

$$G_{bp}(s) = \frac{1.5791367 \times 10^6 s^2}{s^4 + 1.7771532 \times 10^3 s^3 + 8.0535973 \times 10^7 s^2 + 7.0159197 \times 10^{10} s + 1.5585455 \times 10^{15}} \tag{6-52}$$

6-8 LOW-PASS TO BAND-REJECTION TRANSFORMATION _____

By simple inversion and a slight modification of a constant in the transformation of the last section, a new form can be obtained that permits the transformation from a low-pass function to a band-rejection function. The notation of the last section will be used again except for the following modifications:

(a) The Laplace variable s now represents the band-rejection function variable.

(b) The frequencies ω_1, ω_2, ω_3 now represent frequencies associated with the band of rejection.

(c) The lower radian frequency ω_1 now corresponds to $+\lambda_r$ in the prototype, and the upper radian frequency ω_3 now corresponds to $-\lambda_r$ in the prototype.

(d) The quantity $B = f_2 - f_1$ now represents the width of any rejection band of interest.

The actual transformation reads

$$p = \frac{\omega_2{}^2 s}{s^2 + \omega_2{}^2} \qquad (6\text{-}53)$$

Letting $s = j\omega$ and $p = j\lambda$, it can be readily seen that the imaginary axis of the s-plane maps to the imaginary axis of the p-plane. Cancelling j's, we obtain the relationship between the frequency variables.

$$\lambda = \frac{\omega_2{}^2 \omega}{\omega_2{}^2 - \omega^2} \qquad (6\text{-}54)$$

In terms of cyclic frequencies, (6-54) becomes

$$\frac{\lambda}{2\pi} = \frac{f_2{}^2 f}{f_2{}^2 - f^2} \qquad (6\text{-}55)$$

The relationship of (6-54) is shown in Fig. 6-19 for positive ω. The low-pass frequency $\lambda = 0$ is mapped to $\omega = 0$ and $\omega = \infty$, and $\lambda = \pm\infty$ is mapped to $\omega = \omega_2$. The response at $\lambda = +\lambda_r$ maps to $\omega = \omega_1$, and the response at $\lambda = -\lambda_r$ maps to $\omega = \omega_3$.

The effect of the transformation is that the original low-pass prototype amplitude response from dc to any reference frequency f_r becomes the new response *outside* of the interval from f_1 to f_3. However,

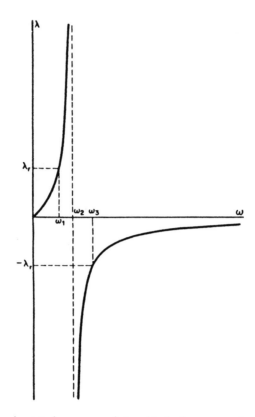

Figure 6-19 Steady-state frequency relationship for low-pass to band-rejection transformation.

the response of the low-pass function above f_r (usually the low-pass stopband) becomes the new response in the interval from f_1 to f_3. An illustration of the general form of the resulting band-rejection function compared with the prototype low-pass function is shown in Fig. 6-20.

The reader is invited to derive (Prob. 6-17) the following two relationships:

$$f_2 = \sqrt{f_1 f_3} \qquad (6\text{-}56)$$

$$\mathrm{B} = f_3 - f_1 = \frac{f_2^{\,2}}{f_r} = \frac{f_1 f_3}{f_r} \qquad (6\text{-}57)$$

The first relationship is identical with the corresponding relationship for the band-pass case. However, note that the second relationship

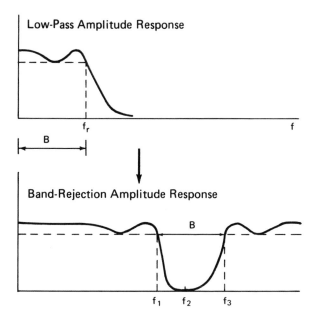

Figure 6-20 Effect of the low-pass to band-rejection transformation.

implies that the width of any rejection band of interest B is *inversely proportional* to the reference bandwidth f_r of the low-pass prototype.

Practical implementation of this transformation can be achieved as follows:

(a) Determine a low-pass transfer function $G_{lp}(p)$ in which the reference bandwidth f_r is inversely proportional to the desired width B of the rejection band according to (6-57). This will usually require frequency scaling of the low-pass function if normalized design tables are used.

(b) Obtain the band-rejection transfer function $G_{br}(s)$ by substitution of the transformation of (6-53).

$$G_{br}(s) = G_{lp}(p)]_{p = \omega_2^2 s/(s^2 + \omega_2^2)} \qquad (6\text{-}58)$$

In general, if the low-pass prototype transfer function is of order k, the band-rejection transfer function will be of order $2k$ and will contain $2k$ poles. If all the zeros of the low-pass function are located at infinity, the band-rejection function will have $2k$ zeros on the $j\omega$-axis, corresponding to k purely imaginary pairs, all located at $\pm j\omega_2$.

Example 6-6

Determine the transfer function of a band-rejection filter having the following characteristics: (a) 4 poles, (b) Butterworth response, (c) geometric center of rejection band = 1 kHz, (d) width of 3 dB rejection band = 200 Hz.

Solution

The low-pass prototype is a second-order Butterworth response, which was given in (6-49) of Ex. 6-5. The reference frequency required in the low-pass prototype can be determined from (6-57) and is

$$f_r = \frac{(10^3)^2}{200} = 5 \times 10^3 \text{ Hz} \qquad (6\text{-}59)$$

The low-pass prototype must then be scaled so that its 3 dB cutoff frequency is 5×10^3 Hz. This is achieved by replacing p by $p/(2\pi \times 5000)$, and the resulting function $G_{1lp}(p)$ is

$$G_{1lp}(p) = \frac{9.8696044 \times 10^8}{p^2 + 4.4428829 \times 10^4 p + 9.8696044 \times 10^8} \qquad (6\text{-}60)$$

The transformation is

$$p = \frac{3.9478418 \times 10^7 s}{s^2 + 3.9478418 \times 10^7} \qquad (6\text{-}61)$$

Substitution of (6-61) in (6-60) yields the band-rejection transfer function $G_{br}(s)$.

$$G_{br}(s) = \frac{(s^2 + 3.9478418 \times 10^7)^2}{\begin{array}{c} s^4 + 1.7771532 \times 10^3 s^3 + 8.0535973 \times 10^7 s^2 \\ + 7.0159196 \times 10^{10} s + 1.5585455 \times 10^{15} \end{array}} \qquad (6\text{-}62)$$

6-9 LOW-PASS TO HIGH-PASS TRANSFORMATION

In this section, a transformation for mapping a low-pass function to a high-pass function will be discussed. The following notation will be employed:

p = *low-pass* prototype Laplace variable

s = *high-pass* final Laplace variable

λ = steady-state radian frequency corresponding to p ($p = j\lambda$)

ω = steady-state radian frequency corresponding to s ($s = j\omega$)

$G_{lp}(p)$ = low-pass prototype transfer function

$G_{hp}(s)$ = high-pass transfer function

λ_r = a particular low-pass prototype reference radian frequency (often the cutoff frequency λ_c)

ω_r = radian frequency in high-pass function corresponding to λ_r in prototype.

The transformation reads

$$p = \frac{\lambda_r \omega_r}{s} \qquad (6\text{-}63)$$

Letting $s = j\omega$, it can be seen that the imaginary axis of the s-plane maps to the imaginary axis of the p-plane. Letting $p = j\lambda$ and cancelling j's, a relationship can be obtained between the two frequency variables. It turns out that the negative imaginary axis of the s-plane corresponds to the positive imaginary axis of the p-plane, and vice versa. The relationship can be expressed as

$$\frac{\lambda}{\lambda_r} = \frac{-\omega_r}{\omega} \qquad (6\text{-}64)$$

The form of (6-64) is shown in Fig. 6-21.

The low-pass frequency $\lambda = 0$ is mapped to $\omega = \infty$, and $\lambda = \infty$ is mapped to $\omega = 0$. The low-pass frequency $\lambda = -\lambda_r$ is mapped to $\omega = \omega_r$. The effect of this transformation is that the original low-pass prototype amplitude response from dc to any reference frequence λ_r is shifted to the high-pass range from ω_r to ∞ in a reverse sense. In many cases, the low-pass prototype is initially scaled in frequency so that $\lambda_r = \omega_r$. In this case, the low-pass passband width is equal to the high-pass stopband width. An illustration of the general form of the resulting high-pass function compared with the prototype low-pass function compared with the prototype low-pass function is shown in Fig. 6-22.

Practical implementation of the transformation for obtaining a high-pass transfer function can be achieved as follows:

(a) Determine a low-pass transfer function $G_{lp}(p)$, and specify the low-pass reference radian frequency λ_r at which the response is to correspond to the high-pass reference radian frequency ω_r.

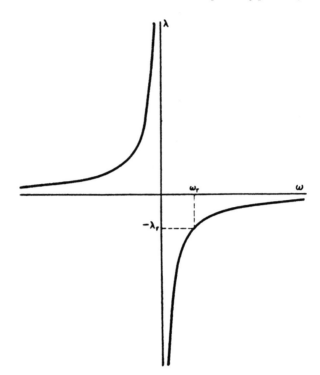

Figure 6-21 Steady-state frequency relationship for low-pass to high-pass transformation.

(b) Obtain the high-pass transfer function $G_{hp}(s)$ by substituting the transformation of (6-63).

$$G_{hp}(s) = G_{lp}(p)\,]_{p = (\lambda_r \omega_r / s)} \qquad\qquad (6\text{-}65)$$

In general, the high-pass transfer function will be of the same order as the low-pass prototype function. If all the zeros of transmission of the low-pass functions are located at $s = \infty$, then all the zeros of the high-pass function will be located at the origin. At very low frequencies, the slope of the amplitude response will then approach $6k$ dB/octave.

Example 6-7

Determine the transfer function of a high-pass transfer function having the following requirements: (a) 3 poles, (b) Butterworth response, (c) 3 dB lower cutoff frequency = 100 Hz.

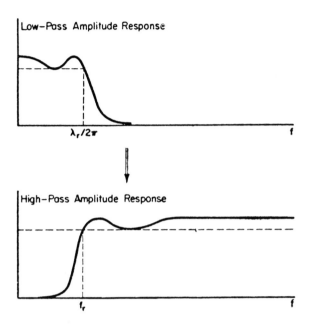

Figure 6-22 Effect of the low-pass to high-pass transformation.

Solution

The low-pass third-order Butterworth prototype response is given by

$$G_{lp}(p) = \frac{1}{p^3 + 2p^2 + 2p + 1} \tag{6-66}$$

The low-pass cutoff frequency $\lambda_r = 1$ rad/s must correspond to $\omega_r = 2\pi \times 100$ rad/s in the high-pass response. From (6-63), the transformation is

$$p = \frac{200\pi}{s} \tag{6-67}$$

Substitution of (6-67) in (6-66) yields the high-pass function

$$G_{hp}(s) = \frac{s^3}{s^3 + 1.2566371 \times 10^3 s^2 + 7.8956835 \times 10^5 s + 2.4805021 \times 10^8} \tag{6-68}$$

6-10 FILTER RESPONSE CURVES

This section will be devoted to a presentation of the stopband amplitude responses of some of the filter types previously discussed. The filter functions considered are Butterworth, 0.5 dB Chebyshev, 1 dB Chebyshev, 2 dB Chebyshev, and 3 dB Chebyshev. These functions are shown in Figures 6-23 through 6-27, respectively. For each particular characteristic, curves providing the responses ranging from two poles to seven poles are given. The number of poles (or order) is referred to either an actual low-pass filter or the low-pass prototype in the case of a filter designed through a transformation.

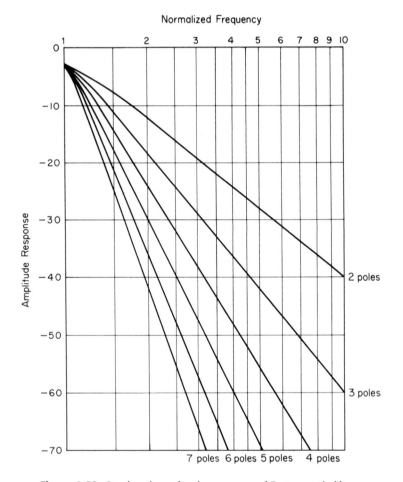

Figure 6-23 Stopband amplitude response of Butterworth filters.

Normalized Frequency

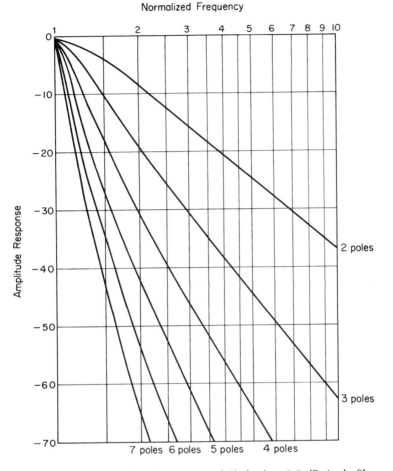

Figure 6-24 Stopband amplitude response of Chebyshev 0.5 dB ripple filters.

In each case, the reference "cutoff frequency" is the abscissa at which the curves begin (unity on the normalized scale), and the response is down at this point with reference to the maximum level according to the particular definition employed. Thus, Butterworth and 3 dB Chebyshev curves begin at a level 3 dB down from the maximum response, while the other curves begin at levels down from the maximum responses corresponding to the ripple in each case.

The abscissa "Normalized Frequency" (N.F.) has a different interpretation for different types of filters. In the discussion that follows, refer to Fig. 6-28. For each type of filter, let B represent the reference bandwidth as defined for that particular form.

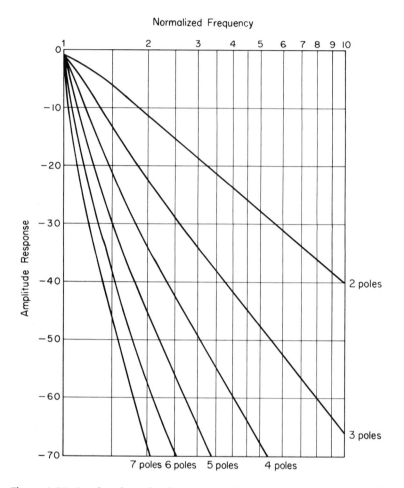

Figure 6-25 Stopband amplitude response of Chebyshev 1.0 dB ripple filters.

Let B_x represent some other bandwidth at which the response is actually desired. The normalized frequency is then defined as follows:

(a) *Low-Pass* and *Band-Pass*

$$\text{N.F.} = \frac{B_x}{B} \qquad (6\text{-}69)$$

(b) *High-Pass* and *Band-Rejection*

$$\text{N.F.} = \frac{B}{B_x} \qquad (6\text{-}70)$$

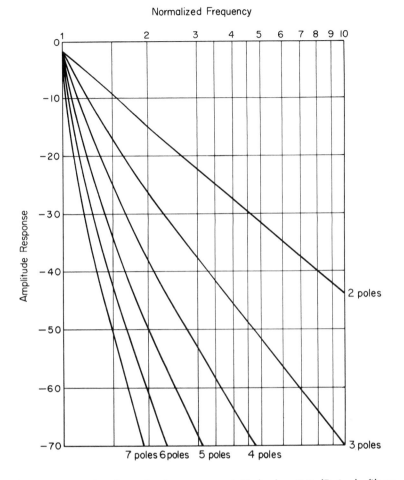

Figure 6-26 Stopband amplitude response of Chebyshev 2.0 dB ripple filters.

It should be emphasized again that the decibel responses of all the curves involved are scaled in reference to the *maximum* response in the passband. For all Butterworth functions and Chebyshev functions of odd order, this poses no unusual interpretation, since the maximum values of these functions occur at dc. On the other hand, for Chebyshev functions of even order, the maximum occurs at other than dc. This means that for these particular functions, we are comparing the response shown with the maximum response in each case rather than the dc response. If the actual response of a given filter within this group has been designed to have unity response at dc, the actual level of the

Normalized Frequency

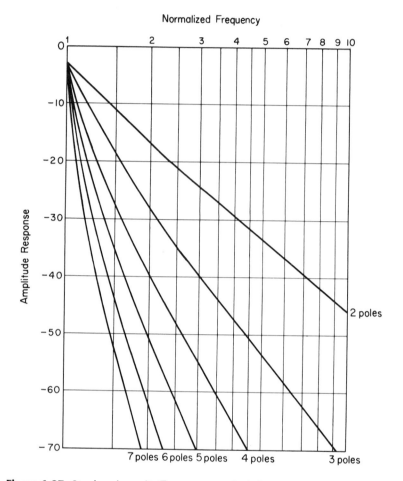

Figure 6-27 Stopband amplitude response of Chebyshev 3.0 dB ripple filters.

measured response would be greater than that shown in the curves by
the amount of passband ripple.

Example 6-8

A low-pass filter is needed to satisfy the following specifications:

(a) Amplitude response must not vary more than 3 dB from dc to 5 kHz.
(b) Attenuation ≥ 23 dB for $f \geq 10$ kHz, as referred to maximum passband
response.

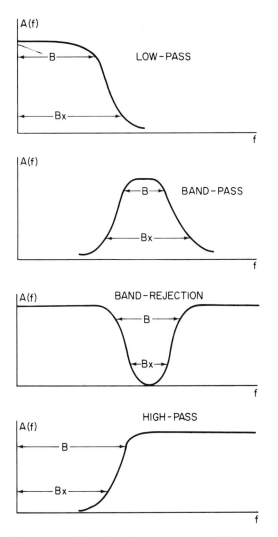

Figure 6-28 Illustration of bandwidth parameters for different types of filters.

Specify the minimum number of poles required in both a Butterworth and a Chebyshev filter that will satisfy the specifications.

Solution

While an analytical solution using the expressions for the pertinent amplitude functions could be done, the simplest procedure is to employ the curves. This approach is usually accurate enough for most applications. Since the definition of the Butterworth cutoff frequency is the 3 dB frequency, the normalized frequency at which the response must be at least 23 dB down is given by

$$\text{N.F.} = \frac{10 \text{ kHz}}{5 \text{ kHz}} = 2 \qquad (6\text{-}71)$$

Inspection of Fig. 6-23 shows that the lowest order Butterworth filter that meets the requirement is the 4-pole function. At this frequency, the attenuation is 24 dB, thus providing 1 dB more than required.

To satisfy the requirement with a Chebyshev filter, we choose the 3 dB ripple filter. Referring to Fig. 6-27, it is seen that at N.F. = 2, the attenuation of a 3-pole Chebyshev is greater than 28 dB, thus providing more than 5 dB attenuation above the requirements.

In summary, the specifications could be met with either a fourth-order Butterworth filter or a third-order Chebyshev filter with 3 dB passband ripple. In each case, the stopband attenuation would be greater than actually required if the 3 dB frequency were set to exactly 10 kHz. Because the attenuation of the Chebyshev filter at 10 kHz is well in excess of that specified, it would be possible to use a 3-pole Chebyshev filter having less passband ripple and still satisfy the stopband attenuation requirements if desired.

PROBLEMS

6-1 Determine the transfer function corresponding to the amplitude-squared function

$$A^2(f) = \frac{4}{6 + 5\omega^2 + \omega^4}$$

6-2 Determine the transfer function corresponding to the amplitude-squared function

$$A^2(f) = \frac{4(9 - \omega^2)^2}{6 + 5\omega^2 + \omega^4}$$

6-3 Determine the transfer function corresponding to the amplitude-squared function

$$A^2(f) = \frac{1}{1 - \omega^2 + \omega^4}$$

6-4 Starting with the definition of the appropriate amplitude response, derive the transfer function of a fourth-order low-pass Butterworth filter with $\omega_c = 1$ rad/s.

6-5 Starting with the definition of the appropriate amplitude response, derive the transfer function of a second-order low-pass Chebyshev filter with $\omega_c = 1$ rad/s and 3 dB passband ripple.

6-6 Determine an expression for $A^2(f)$ in final rational function form for a third-order low-pass Chebyshev function with 1.5 dB passband ripple and $\omega_c = 1$ rad/s.

6-7 Consider the Chebyshev response of equation (6-24) with k even. (a) Show that for unity dc gain, the gain constant required is $\alpha = 1 + \epsilon^2$. (b) Show that for the choice of α determined in (a), the amplitude response at maxima exceeds unity and is given by $A_{max} = \sqrt{1 + \epsilon^2}$.

6-8 Using the tables in the text, determine the transfer function for a third-order Chebyshev low-pass filter with 3 dB passband ripple and a cutoff frequency of 5 kHz.

6-9 Using the tables in the text, determine the transfer function for a fourth-order Butterworth low-pass filter with a 3 dB cutoff frequency of 1 kHz.

6-10 Determine the transfer function for a band-pass filter with the following characteristics: (a) 4 poles, (b) Butterworth response, (c) geometric center frequency = 10 kHz, (d) 3 dB bandwidth = 1 kHz.

6-11 Determine the transfer function for a band-rejection filter with the following characteristics: (a) 4 poles, (b) Butterworth response, (c) geometric center of rejection band = 10 kHz, (d) 3 dB width of rejection band = 1 kHz.

6-12 Determine the transfer function for a fourth-order Butterworth high-pass filter with a 3 dB cutoff frequency of 1 kHz.

6-13 A low-pass filter is desired to satisfy the following requirements: (a) Response flat within 3 dB from dc to 5 kHz. (b) Attenuation ≥ 30 dB for $f \geq 10$ kHz. Determine the minimum orders for both a Butterworth filter and a Chebyshev filter that will realize the specifications.

6-14 A low-pass filter is desired to satisfy the following requirements: (a) Response flat within 1 dB from dc to 10 kHz. (b) Attenuation ≥ 40 dB for $f \geq 25$ kHz. Determine the minimum order of a filter that will realize the specifications, and specify the type.

6-15 A band-pass filter is desired to satisfy the following requirements: (a) Response flat within 3 dB over the range 100 kHz $\leq f \leq$ 105 kHz (b) Attenuation at 3 times 3 dB bandwidth ≥ 38 dB. Determine the minimum order of the *band-pass* filter that will satisfy the requirements, and specify the type.

6-16   Consider an amplitude-modulated signal of the form $x(t) = A(1 + m \cos \omega_m t) \cos \omega_c t$, where m is the modulation factor, which is bounded by $0 \leqslant m \leqslant 1$, ω_m is the modulating frequency, and ω_c is the carrier frequency. Assume the signal passes through an analog filter having phase delay and group delay at ω_c given by $T_p(f_c)$ and $T_g(f_c)$. Show that the carrier of the output signal is delayed by $T_p(f_c)$, and the envelope is delayed approximately by $T_g(f_c)$. Assume that $\omega_c \gg \omega_m$ and that the phase is reasonably well behaved in the vicinity of ω_c.

6-17   Derive equations (6-56) and (6-57).

6-18   The form of the step response of the ideal low-pass filter was illustrated in Fig. 6-6. Assuming that the impulse response has a delay of τ, determine an expression for the step response in two steps: (a) First, determine the impulse response $g(t)$. (b) Next, set up an expression for the step response involving integration of the result of (a). (Note: This integral requires numerical evaluation, so you are not asked to complete the problem.)

6-19   Assume that $x(f)$ represents some approximation to a desired frequency function $\bar{x}(f)$. Let $y(f) = \bar{x}(f) - x(f)$ represent the difference (or error) between the two functions. The quantity $x(f)$ will be defined as a *maximally flat* approximation to $\bar{x}(f)$ of order m at $f = f_0$ if

$$y(f_0) = 0$$

$$\frac{d^i y(f_0)}{df^i} = 0 \text{ for } 1 \leqslant i \leqslant m$$

$$\neq 0 \text{ for } i = m + 1$$

(a) Show that this definition is equivalent to having the coefficients of all terms up to and including the term $(f - f_0)^m$ in the power series expansion about f_0 vanish. (b) Show that if $x(f)$ is maximally flat approximation to $\bar{x}(f)$ of order m at $f = f_0$, then $1/x(f)$ is a maximally flat approximation to $1/\bar{x}(f)$ of the same order and at the same point.

6-20   Assume that the amplitude-squared low-pass approximation to an ideal filter function is given by

$$A^2(f) = \frac{1 + c_1 \omega^2 + c_2 \omega^4 + \cdots + c_i \omega^{2i}}{1 + d_1 \omega^2 + d_2 \omega^4 + \cdots + d_k \omega^{2k}}$$

where $k > i$, and the ideal response in the passband is represented as

$$\overline{A^2(f)} = 1$$

Making use of the results of Prob. 6-19, show that the conditions for maximal flatness at $f = 0$ are

$$c_n = d_n \qquad \text{for } 1 \leqslant n \leqslant i$$

$$d_n = 0 \qquad \text{for } i < n < k$$

$$d_k \neq 0$$

(Note that the requirement $d_k \neq 0$ is necessary in order that the function represent a low-pass filter. Otherwise the response would degenerate to a constant of unity!)

6-21 Using the results of Prob. 6-19, show that the Butterworth function of equation (6-17) is a maximally flat function of order $2k-1$ at $f = 0$.

6-22 Using the results of Prob. 6-19, show that the inverted Chebyshev function of equation (6-33) is a maximally flat function of order $2k-1$ at $f = 0$.

6-23 Demonstrate that the inverted Chebyshev amplitude response can be derived from the normal Chebyshev amplitude response by application of the following two steps: (a) Subtract the normal Chebyshev response from unity. Sketch the result and show that it is a high-pass function with equiripple stopband behavior and a monotonically increasing passband behavior. (b) Utilize the low-pass to high-pass transformation of Sec. 6-9 to obtain the final response.

6-24 Show that the high-frequency amplitude response of the inverted Chebyshev filter becomes asymptotic to a curve with slope -6 dB/octave for k odd.

6-25 Show that when k is even, the high-frequency amplitude-squared function for the inverted Chebyshev filter becomes asymptotic to the constant value $\epsilon^2/(1 + \epsilon^2)$.

6-26 Assume that the minimum stopband dB attenuation (expressed as a positive number) for an inverted Chebyshev filter is specified as R, in which the maximum amplitude response is used as the reference. Show that the required value of ϵ^2 is given by

$$\epsilon^2 = \frac{1}{10^{(R/10)} - 1}$$

7

INFINITE IMPULSE RESPONSE DIGITAL FILTER DESIGN

7-0 INTRODUCTION

The primary objective in this chapter is the development and application of some of the basic methods for designing digital filters of the infinite impulse response type. A digital filter may be defined as a computational process or algorithm that converts one sequence of numbers representing an input signal into another sequence of numbers representing an output signal, and in which the conversion changes the character of the signal in some prescribed fashion. In many applications, the processing operation may take the form of steady-state frequency-domain filtering such as was discussed for analog systems in Chapt. 6. In other cases, a digital filter may perform functions such as differentiation, integration, or estimation.

A linear time-invariant digital filter is designed by determining the coefficients of the input-output algorithm by some approximation process. The major strategy in this chapter will be that of forcing the digital filter to behave very closely to some reference analog filter. This concept permits the use of well-developed analog approximating functions and design data for developing digital filters. The three general procedures developed in this chapter are the bilinear transformation method, the step-invariance method, and the impulse-invariance method. In addition, special forms of the bilinear transformation will be given for designing digital band-pass, band-rejection, and high-pass filters.

166

7-1 GENERAL CONSIDERATIONS _____

An important process in this chapter and the next is that of determining a discrete transfer function or difference equation that will achieve a prescribed signal filtering requirement. In Chapts. 4 and 5, various discrete-time system analysis methods were discussed in detail, but in all cases the transfer function or difference equation was given. In this chapter, the situation is reversed in the sense that we are usually given a set of specific requirements, and we must determine a discrete-time system that will accomplish the chore.

Most of the concepts to be developed in this chapter and in Chapt. 8 apply to discrete-time systems in general as well as to sampled-data continuous-time systems. However, due to the widespread usage of the term, and in view of the principal area of interest intended for this book, we will use the term *digital filter* to refer to the end result of a given design procedure. The associated discrete transfer function will often be referred to as a *digital transfer function*. Thus, the general problem is that we are given a set of specific design requirements, and we must determine a digital filter to satisfy these requirements. The final digital filter may be in the form of a discrete or digital transfer function, a difference equation, or an impulse response.

The overall philosophy of digital filter design depends on the types of design criteria that could be used in actual applications. At the outset, it should be emphasized that most of the design concepts and criteria utilized in this book reflect the familiar frequency-domain approach in terms of steady-state amplitude and/or phase behavior. This approach has long dominated the design procedures for most analog filters, and it is only natural that most of the newer digital filter design procedures should follow in the same strong tradition. On the other hand, the digital filter has made possible new approaches that were previously unattainable or, at best, quite difficult to implement with analog filters. Such concepts as time-variable, adaptive, and nonlinear filters are possibilities with digital systems.

Since the frequency response concept plays the same powerful role in digital filter design as it does in analog design, it is only natural to classify many digital filters according to their frequency response characteristics. Digital filters designed on a frequency response basis can thus be classified as *low-pass, high-pass, band-pass,* and *band-rejection* types, as illustrated by the ideal models in Fig. 7-1. (Only the positive frequency ranges are shown.) It should be observed that such characteristics are actually periodic in nature, and the reference behavior is applied only with respect to the range from dc to the folding frequency f_0. As long as the sampling rate is sufficiently high, the filter behaves

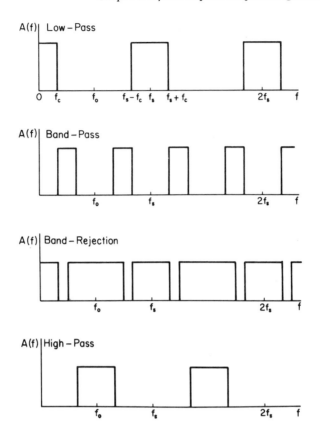

Figure 7-1 Ideal amplitude response models for digital filters.

in the manner for which it is designed, but the overall periodic nature of the response is still a property that must be considered.

It was shown in Chapt. 4 that the input-output difference equation for a DTLTI system can be expressed in the form

$$y(n) = \sum_{i=0}^{k} a_i x(n-i) - \sum_{i=1}^{k} b_i y(n-i) \qquad (7\text{-}1)$$

In the z-domain, (7-1) can be represented by the discrete transfer function

$$H(z) = \frac{N(z)}{D(z)} = \frac{\displaystyle\sum_{i=0}^{k} a_i z^{-i}}{1 + \displaystyle\sum_{i=1}^{k} b_i z^{-i}} \qquad (7\text{-}2)$$

where $N(z)$ is the numerator polynomial and $D(z)$ is the denominator polynomial.

The problem in digital filter design is to determine the set of coefficients a_i and b_i so that the filter will have the desired behavior. This concept is very similar to the approximation problem in analog filter design, for which some of the various approximations were discussed in the preceding chapter. Fortunately, as we will see later, use may be made of these analog functions in developing digital filter designs.

Digital filters of the DTLTI nature are classified both from the standpoint of the *duration of the impulse response* and from the standpoint of the *type of realization*. The impulse response duration characteristics can be divided into two broad classes:

(a) *Infinite Impulse Response (IIR)*. An IIR filter is one in which the impulse response $h(n)$ has an infinite number of samples. Thus, $h(n)$ is nonzero at an infinite number of points in the range $n_1 \le n \le \infty$.

(b) *Finite Impulse Response (FIR)*. An FIR filter is one in which the impulse response $h(n)$ is limited to a finite number of samples defined over the range $n_1 \le n \le n_2$, where n_1 and n_2 are both finite.

The possible realization procedures can be divided into three broad classes:

(a) *Recursive Realization*. A recursive realization is one in which the present value of the output depends both on the input (present and/or past values) and previous values of the output. A recursive filter is usually recognized by the presence of both a_i and b_i terms in a realization of the form of (7-1).

(b) *Nonrecursive (Direct Convolution) Realization*. A nonrecursive or direct convolution realization is one in which the present value of the output depends only on the present and past values of the input. This usually means that all values of $b_i = 0$ in a realization of the form of (7-1).

(c) *Fast Fourier Transform (FFT) Realization*. This type of realization is achieved by transforming the input signal with the FFT, filtering the spectrum as desired, and performing an inverse transformation. This procedure is more closely related to the material in Chapters 9 and 10, and discussion will be postponed until then.

In general, an *IIR filter* is usually more easily implemented by a *recursive realization,* and an *FIR filter* is usually more easily implemented by either *nonrecursive realization* or an *FFT realization*. For that reason, there are strong associations in *usage* between the terms *IIR* and *recursive* and between the terms *FIR* and *nonrecursive*. In much of the earlier literature, the terms recursive and nonrecursive were employed to describe digital filters from the standpoints of both impulse response duration and realization, as suggested by these associations. However, it has been established that both FIR and IIR functions may be implemented by either recursive or nonrecursive techniques. This suggests the need for clarification from both the standpoints of impulse response duration and realization. Typical realizations of third-order recursive filters are compared in Fig. 7-2.

This chapter will be devoted to the discussion of some of the most important methods for designing IIR filters. Many of these techniques utilize an analog transfer function as a prototype function, and by means of a suitable transformation, it is converted into a digital filter having similar characteristics. In most cases, a discrete transfer func-

Recursive Realisation

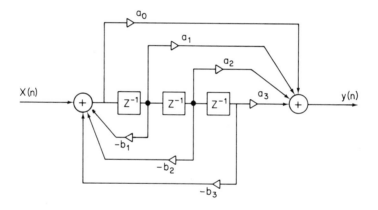

Nonrecursive Realisation

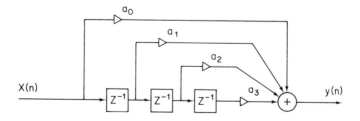

Figure 7-2 Typical recursive and nonrecursive realizations of digital filters.

tion of the form of (7-1) is obtained directly by such a process. In all cases within this chapter, the resulting impulse responses can be shown to have infinite duration.

7-2 DISCUSSION OF NOTATION

A short discussion concerning the notation employed in developing digital filter designs will be presented here so the reader will not feel that we are arbitrarily changing notation without reason. In some of the earlier chapters, where we were concerned with a given single transfer function, the variables s, ω, and f ($\omega = 2\pi f$), were used to denote, respectively, the complex Laplace variable, the steady-state radian frequency, and the steady-state cyclic frequency of the transfer function.

In this chapter, we will continue to reserve these same variables to describe the response of the actual final transfer function, which in this case will be a digital filter. However, some of these procedures require that we begin with an analog reference or prototype function, which will be converted into a digital function. We will always reserve the variables s, ω, and f (and the normalized frequency v) for the final function. In order to avoid confusion, therefore, it will often be necessary to introduce dummy or reference variables for the analog filter prototype. This means that in some cases we will be taking analog transfer functions from the tables and data from the curves in Chapt. 6 and changing the variables to dummy variables so that they may be converted to digital form.

The important point to remember is that dummy variables are introduced whenever necessary in order that the final Laplace variable of the digital filter can be designated as s and the final steady-state frequency can be designated as ω or f without ambiguity.

7-3 BILINEAR TRANSFORMATION METHOD

The bilinear transformation method appears to be one of the best procedures currently available for designing many *IIR* filters with respect to the following two criteria: (a) It is desired that the frequency response be similar to that of some reference analog filter. (b) Relative simplicity of design is desirable. Because of its importance, we will explore this method in some depth before discussing other procedures.

The following notation will be employed in this section:

p = *analog* prototype Laplace variable

s = *digital* final Laplace variable

λ = steady-state radian frequency corresponding to p $(p = j\lambda)$

ω = steady-state radian frequency corresponding to s $(s = j\omega)$

f = cyclic frequency corresponding to $\omega (f = \omega/2\pi)$

v = normalized frequency (with respect to folding frequency) = f/f_0

$G(p)$ = *analog* prototype transfer function

$H(z)$ = *discrete* or *digital* transfer function

Note that z is related to the final Laplace variable by the equation

$$z = \epsilon^{sT} \tag{7-3}$$

in accordance with the work of Chapt. 4.

The desired digital transfer function $H(z)$ is obtained by replacing p in $G(p)$ by an equation expressing p in terms of z. The bilinear transformation relating the prototype variable p to the discrete variable z is given by

$$p = \frac{C(1 - z^{-1})}{(1 + z^{-1})} \tag{7-4}$$

where C is a mapping constant to be discussed later. Substituting (7-3) in (7-4), we obtain the relationship between the prototype variable p and the final s variable.

$$p = \frac{C(1 - \epsilon^{-sT})}{(1 + \epsilon^{-sT})} = C \tanh \frac{sT}{2} \tag{7-5}$$

The relationships between the p, z, and s-planes are illustrated in Fig. 7-3. A careful study of the mapping geometry leads to the conclusion that some of the distortion between the z- and s-planes is compensated for, in part, by the relationship between the z- and p-planes. The overall result is that the p-plane and the s-plane have somewhat similar characteristics, at least over a portion of the s-plane.

These properties can be deduced by noting that the left-hand half of the p-plane corresponds to the left-hand half of the s-plane, and the imaginary axis of the p-plane corresponds to the imaginary axis of the s-plane. The primary difference is that the behavior in the p-plane over the infinite range $-\infty < \lambda < \infty$ maps to a principal value range in the s-plane of $-\pi < \omega T < \pi$. This means that the frequency response of the reference analog filter will be reproduced in the digital filter, but the frequency scale on which this response occurs will be compressed

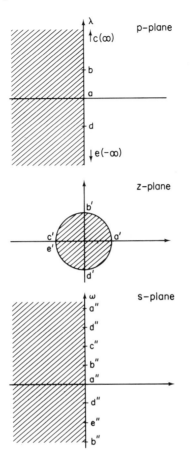

Figure 7-3 Relationships between the *p*, *z*, and *s*-planes.

from an infinite interval in the analog filter to a finite interval in the digital filter. The value $\omega T = \pi$ corresponds to $f = 1/2T = f_0$, the folding frequency. Thus, the behavior of the analog prototype function over an infinite frequency range is mapped into the range from dc to f_0 in the digital filter. This corresponds to the range $0 \leqslant v \leqslant 1$ on the normalized frequency scale.

The relationship between the steady-state frequencies of the prototype response and the final design response can be seen more clearly by letting $p = j\lambda$ and $s = j\omega$ in (7-5). Recognition of the fact that tanh $jx = j \tan x$ and cancellation of the *j*'s result in

$$\lambda = C \tan \frac{\omega T}{2} \qquad\qquad (7\text{-}6)$$

In terms of the folding frequency f_0 and the normalized frequency v, (7-6) can be expressed as

$$\lambda = C \tan \frac{\pi}{2} \frac{f}{f_0} = C \tan \frac{\pi}{2} v \qquad (7\text{-}7)$$

The relationship of (7-7) is shown in Fig. 7-4 over a portion of the positive frequency range.

The nature of the frequency mapping can now be observed. For relatively low frequencies compared to the folding frequency, i.e., $f/f_0 \ll 1$, there is an approximate linear relationship between the reference frequency scale and the actual frequency scale. This means that the relative behavior of the actual filter could correspond very closely to the behavior of the prototype filter in the low-frequency range. However, as the frequency begins to approach the folding frequency, the actual frequency "quickly" covers the behavior of the prototype all the way to $\lambda = \infty$.

The forms for the amplitude characteristics of the analog prototype and the final digital function are compared for a typical case in Fig. 7-5. This particular example represents a low-pass function. Note that the digital response is low-pass only for frequencies less than the folding frequency. Thus, if the input signal contained a frequency com-

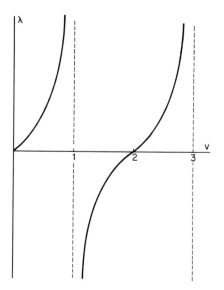

Figure 7-4 Relationship between frequency variables of the analog and digital functions.

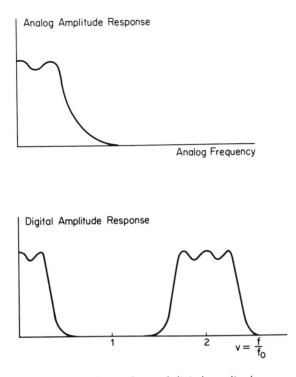

Figure 7-5 Forms for analog and digital amplitude response.

ponent in the vicinity of $2f_0$ (or for that matter near any integer multiple of f_0), it would *not* be rejected by the filter since it would fall in one of the periodic passband regions produced by the nature of the sampling process. Such a component would be greater in frequency than f_0 and would be in violation of the sampling theorem. Since the sampling rate is inadequate, it would be impossible to distinguish this component at the output from a low-frequency signal within the intended passband. This situation illustrates further the problem of aliasing, which results when the sampling rate is too low. As long as the sampling rate is known to be greater than twice the highest frequency of the signal, the passband regions above f_0 need cause no concern. Unless otherwise stated, we will assume adequate sampling in subsequent discussions, and this will normally mean that we need to display the response only over the range $0 \leqq v \leqq 1$.

The constant C is chosen so that the frequency scale of the desired filter is scaled to the proper range for the desired application. We will discuss two different strategies for determining this constant. Each strategy is characterized by a somewhat different criterion, so that the final constants obtained may differ.

The first approach is that of achieving exact correspondence at *a particular frequency* in the behavior of the digital filter with respect to a particular frequency of the reference prototype analog filter. Quite often, for low- and high-pass filters, this will be the cutoff frequency of the filters, and one is able to precisely control the location of this frequency using this approach. Let λ_r represent any particular reference analog frequency, and let ω_r represent the particular reference digital filter frequency at which the response is required to be the same. Let $v_r = f_r/f_0$. Substitution of these values into (7-6) or (7-7) and solution for C yield

$$C = \lambda_r \cot \frac{\omega_r T}{2} = \lambda_r \cot \frac{\pi f_r}{2 f_0} = \lambda_r \cot \frac{\pi}{2} v_r \qquad (7\text{-}8)$$

Using this approach, it is neither necessary nor particularly desirable in most cases to scale the analog transfer function to the proper frquency range, as scaling is automatically accomplished in the process. The major advantage in this approach is that exact equality in the responses at a particular reference analog frequency and a particular desired digital frequency is quickly established.

The second approach results in reasonably good *low-frequency correspondence* between the prototype analog filter and the actual digital filter. It was observed in Fig. 7-4 that λ and ω have nearly a linear relationship for low frequencies. This is further illustrated by utilizing the approximation $\tan \theta \approx \theta$ for small θ in (7-6) and (7-7). The constant C can then be determined so that

$$C = \frac{2}{T} = 2f_s = 4f_0 \qquad (7\text{-}9)$$

Using this latter approach, we can say that the low-frequency behavior of the analog prototype filter is approximately the same as that of the digital filter, but no exact behavior at any particular frequency can be stipulated (except dc and f_0) without further calculation. It is necessary with this procedure that the analog filter be scaled to the proper frequency range prior to making the transformation, so that the frequency scales will have the required correspondence.

If the reference frequency of the digital filter in the first procedure is quite small compared with the folding frequency, the resulting-z-domain transfer functions employing either of the procedures will be approximately the same. (The constant C in the two cases would be approximately the same if the prototype transfer function were scaled to the proper frequency range in both cases before determining C.

However, since it is not necessary to do this with the first procedure, the constants may be quite different.) If the reference frequency in the first procedure is not very small compared with the folding frequency, the resulting z-domain transfer functions employing the separate procedures may be quite different.

After the constant C is determined, the transfer function H(z) is obtained by substituting p in terms of z in G(p). Thus,

$$H(z) = G(p)]_{p = \frac{C(1-z^{-1})}{1+z^{-1}}} \qquad (7\text{-}10)$$

Observe that the number of poles (or order) of the digital filter will be the same as that of the reference analog filter.

The procedure of (7-10) is straightforward in concept, but the actual manipulations can become tedious. To assist in this step, some expressions relating the coefficients of the discrete transfer function to those of the analog transfer function have been worked out and tabulated. Assume that the transfer function of the reference analog function is given by

$$G(p) = \frac{A_0 + A_1 p + A_2 p^2 + \cdots + A_k p^k}{B_0 + B_1 p + B_2 p^2 + \cdots + B_k p^k} \qquad (7\text{-}11)$$

The transfer function of the digital filter will be of the form

$$H(z) = \frac{a_0 + a_1 z^{-1} + a_2 z^{-2} + \cdots + a_k z^{-k}}{1 + b_1 z^{-1} + b_2 z^{-2} + \cdots + b_k z^{-k}} \qquad (7\text{-}12)$$

Formulas for determining the coefficients of (7-12) in terms of the coefficients of (7-11) and the mapping constant C are tabulated for $k = 1$ through $k = 5$ in Tables 7-1 through 7-5. It should be understood that this data may be used only for filters designed with the form of the

Table 7-1
Bilinear transformation digital filter coefficients in terms of analog filter coefficients (1st order).

A	$B_0 + B_1 C$
a_0	$(A_0 + A_1 C)/A$
a_1	$(A_0 - A_1 C)/A$
b_1	$(B_0 - B_1 C)/A$

Table 7-2
Bilinear transformation digital filter coefficients in terms of analog filter coefficients (2nd order).

A	$B_0 + B_1 C + B_2 C^2$
a_0	$(A_0 + A_1 C + A_2 C^2)/A$
a_1	$(2A_0 - 2A_2 C^2)/A$
a_2	$(A_0 - A_1 C + A_2 C^2)/A$
b_1	$(2B_0 - 2B_2 C^2)/A$
b_2	$(B_0 - B_1 C + B_2 C^2)/A$

bilinear transformation used in this section and with the design process indicated by (7-10).

Although these data could be extended to higher order functions, the resulting expressions tend to become unwieldly, and it is felt that data relating to such higher order functions would not be particularly useful. The reason is based on the practical tendency to realize higher order systems as cascade or parallel combinations of lower order functions.

In considering the problem of decomposing a digital filter into cascade and parallel sections, the bilinear transformation method has the interesting property that the decomposition may first be applied to the prototype function before the transformation is applied. Assume that the prototype function is represented in cascade form as

$$G(p) = G_1(p) G_2(p) \cdots G_l(p) \qquad (7\text{-}13)$$

Table 7-3
Bilinear transformation digital filter coefficients in terms of analog filter coefficients (3rd order).

A	$B_0 + B_1 C + B_2 C^2 + B_3 C^3$
a_0	$(A_0 + A_1 C + A_2 C^2 + A_3 C^3)/A$
a_1	$(3A_0 + A_1 C - A_2 C^2 - 3A_3 C^3)/A$
a_2	$(3A_0 - A_1 C - A_2 C^2 + 3A_3 C^3)/A$
a_3	$(A_0 - A_1 C + A_2 C^2 - A_3 C^3)/A$
b_1	$(3B_0 + B_1 C - B_2 C^2 - 3B_3 C^3)/A$
b_2	$(3B_0 - B_1 C - B_2 C^2 + 3B_3 C^3)/A$
b_3	$(B_0 - B_1 C + B_2 C^2 - B_3 C^3)/A$

Table 7-4
Bilinear transformation digital filter coefficients in terms of analog filter coefficients
(4th order).

A	$B_0 + B_1 C + B_2 C^2 + B_3 C^3 + B_4 C^4$
a_0	$(A_0 + A_1 C + A_2 C^2 + A_3 C^3 + A_4 C^4)/A$
a_1	$(4A_0 + 2A_1 C - 2A_3 C^3 - 4A_4 C^4)/A$
a_2	$(6A_0 - 2A_2 C^2 + 6A_4 C^4)/A$
a_3	$(4A_0 - 2A_1 C + 2A_3 C^3 - 4A_4 C^4)/A$
a_4	$(A_0 - A_1 C + A_2 C^2 - A_3 C^3 + A_4 C^4)/A$
b_1	$(4B_0 + 2B_1 C - 2B_3 C^3 - 4B_4 C^4)/A$
b_2	$(6B_0 - 2B_2 C^2 + 6B_4 C^4)/A$
b_3	$(4B_0 - 2B_1 C + 2B_3 C^3 - 4B_4 C^4)/A$
b_4	$(B_0 - B_1 C + B_2 C^2 - B_3 C^3 + B_4 C^4)/A$

Then the resulting discrete transfer function can be represented as

$$H(z) = H_1'(z)H_2'(z) \cdots H_l'(z) \qquad (7-14)$$

where

$$H_i'(z) = G_i(p)]_{p = \frac{C(1-z^{-1})}{1+z^{-1}}} \qquad (7-15)$$

Now assume that the prototype function is represented in parallel
form as

$$G(p) = G_1(p) + G_2(p) + \cdots + G_r(p) \qquad (7-16)$$

Then H(z) can be represented as

$$H(z) = H_1'(z) + H_2'(z) + \cdots + H_r'(z) \qquad (7-17)$$

where a given $H_i'(z)$ is defined in the same form as in (7-15), but now
with respect to the parallel functions.

The significance of the preceding results is that almost all of the
decomposition can take place on the analog function, for which more
tabulated information is usually available, and for which the manipu-
lative steps of decomposition are usually easier. The bilinear transformation is then applied to each of the individual functions.

In actual practice, it may be desirable to modify the terms of (7-14)
and (7-17) in different ways. In (7-14), it may be desirable to factor out

Table 7-5
Bilinear transformation digital filter coefficients in terms of analog filter coefficients (5th order).

A	$B_0 + B_1 C + B_2 C^2 + B_3 C^3 + B_4 C^4 + B_5 C^5$
a_0	$(A_0 + A_1 C + A_2 C^2 + A_3 C^3 + A_4 C^4 + A_5 C^5)/A$
a_1	$(5A_0 + 3A_1 C + A_2 C^2 - A_3 C^3 - 3A_4 C^4 - 5A_5 C^5)/A$
a_2	$(10A_0 + 2A_1 C - 2A_2 C^2 - 2A_3 C^3 + 2A_4 C^4 + 10A_5 C^5)/A$
a_3	$(10A_0 - 2A_1 C - 2A_2 C^2 + 2A_3 C^3 + 2A_4 C^4 - 10A_5 C^5)/A$
a_4	$(5A_0 - 3A_1 C + A_2 C^2 + A_3 C^3 - 3A_4 C^4 + 5A_5 C^5)/A$
a_5	$(A_0 - A_1 C + A_2 C^2 - A_3 C^3 + A_4 C^4 - A_5 C^5)/A$
b_1	$(5B_0 + 3B_1 C + B_2 C^2 - B_3 C^3 - 3B_4 C^4 - 5B_5 C^5)/A$
b_2	$(10B_0 + 2B_1 C - 2B_2 C^2 - 2B_3 C^3 + 2B_4 C^4 + 10B_5 C^5)/A$
b_3	$(10B_0 - 2B_1 C - 2B_2 C^2 + 2B_3 C^3 + 2B_4 C^4 - 10B_5 C^5)/A$
b_4	$(5B_0 - 3B_1 C + B_2 C^2 + B_3 C^3 - 3B_4 C^4 + 5B_5 C^5)/A$
b_5	$(B_0 - B_1 C + B_2 C^2 - B_3 C^3 + B_4 C^4 - B_5 C^5)/A$

the a_{0i} term from each function and lump them all together. The resulting decomposition will then be of the form

$$H(z) = a_0 H_1(z) H_2(z) \cdots H_l(z) \qquad (7\text{-}18)$$

In (7-17), the various functions initially may have the same negative degree for both numerator and denominator polynomials. It may be desirable to extract constants from these different functions so that the resulting highest negative degree for each numerator is lower than the highest negative degree for the corresponding denominator. The resulting decomposition will then be of the form

$$H(z) = A + H_1(z) + H_2(z) + \cdots + H_r(z) \qquad (7\text{-}19)$$

7-4 BILINEAR TRANSFORMATION DESIGN EXAMPLES

This entire section will be devoted to the presentation and discussion of several design examples using the bilinear transformation procedure of the last section. Most of the calculations and the plots of the frequency response functions will be made in terms of the normalized frequency $v = f/f_0$. The reader should carefully observe the generality that this approach provides in each case. For example, suppose a given sampling frequency is 200 Hz and the cutoff frequency of a particular digital filter is 20 Hz. Since $f_0 = f_s/2 = 100$ Hz, the normalized cutoff frequency is $v_c = 20/100 = 0.2$. If the frequency response is plotted in terms of v, the curve would apply to any digital filter of the same type (identical coefficients) as long as the same ratio of cutoff frequency to folding frequency holds. Thus, if the sampling frequency were changed to 1400 Hz, the value $v_c = 0.2$ now corresponds to 140 Hz, and the normalized curve still applies without change.

The bilinear transformation method may be used to design low-pass, high-pass, band-pass, and band-rejection filters. However, the basic form of the transformation as presented in the last section is easiest to apply directly to a low-pass function. Consequently, all the examples presented in this section will be restricted to functions having a low-pass nature. In later sections of the chapter, special forms of the bilinear transformation will be developed for simplifying the specification and design of band-pass, band-rejection, and high-pass filters.

Example 7-1

Design a low-pass digital filter derived from a second-order Butterworth analog filter with a 3 dB cutoff frequency of 50 Hz. The sampling rate of the system is 500 Hz.

Solution

The normalized analog transfer function of the Butterworth filter is obtained from Table 6-2. using the dummy variable p, the function is

$$G(p) = \frac{1}{1 + 1.4142136p + p^2} \qquad (7\text{-}20)$$

The frequency $\lambda_r = 1$ rad/s in the prototype must correspond to $f_r = 50$ Hz in the digital filter, so that the design should be based on exact correspondence at these frequencies. The folding frequency is $f_0 = 500/2 = 250$ Hz, and $v_r = 50/250 = 0.2$. The constant C is determined from (7-8) as

$$C = \cot \frac{\pi}{2} (0.2) = \cot \frac{\pi}{10} = 3.0776835 \qquad (7\text{-}21)$$

The required transformation is

$$p = 3.0776835 \frac{(1-z^{-1})}{1+z^{-1}} \qquad (7\text{-}22)$$

Substitution of (7-22) into (7-20) or use of Table 7-2 yields

$$H(z) = \frac{0.0674553\,(1+2z^{-1}+z^{-2})}{1-1.14298z^{-1}+0.412802z^{-2}} \qquad (7\text{-}23)$$

The amplitude response of this digital filter expressed as a magnitude is shown as curve A in Fig. 7-11. The decibel form of the response is shown as curve A in Fig. 7-12. The other curves on each of the figures represent different approaches for the same function and will be discussed in later examples.

Example 7-2

The sampling rate in a certain digital processing system is 2000 Hz. It is desired to program a digital filter within the system to behave approximately like a simple first-order low-pass filter with a 3 dB frequency in the neighborhood of (but not necessarily equal to) 400 Hz. Rather, the major criterion is that the low-frequency response of the digital filter be close to that of the reference analog filter.

Solution

The requirements suggest the use of the bilinear transformation with the mapping constant selected to give good low-frequency correlation. The normalized low-pass analog transfer function with a cutoff frequency of 1 rad/s is

$$G_1(p) = \frac{1}{p+1} \qquad (7\text{-}24)$$

In this case, it is necessary to scale the analog filter to the proper frequency range before applying the transformation. This is achieved by replacing p by $p/(2\pi \times 400)$, as discussed in Chapt. 6. Letting $G_2(p)$ represent the resulting analog transfer function, we have

$$G_2(p) = G_1\left(\frac{p}{800\pi}\right) = \frac{800\pi}{p+800\pi} \qquad (7\text{-}25)$$

The bilinear transformation constant is obtained from (7-9) as

$$C = 2 \times 2000 = 4000 \qquad (7\text{-}26)$$

The transformation is

$$p = 4000 \frac{1 - z^{-1}}{1 + z^{-1}} \qquad (7\text{-}27)$$

Substitution of (7-27) into (7-25) yields

$$H(z) = \frac{0.385870(1 + z^{-1})}{1 - 0.228261 z^{-1}} \qquad (7\text{-}28)$$

The reader is invited to verify by the use of (7-7) that the actual 3 dB frequency of the digital filter is about 357 Hz. An alternative approach to this problem would be to design for exact correspondence between the digital and analog filters at 400 Hz (Prob. 7-8). Since the cutoff frequency is 40% of the folding frequency, this latter approach would result in some difference between the analog and digital responses at very low frequencies.

Example 7-3

The transfer function of one unit within a particular analog control system is given by

$$G(p) = \frac{2}{(p + 1)(p + 2)} \qquad (7\text{-}29)$$

The system is to be interfaced to a process control digital computer, and it is desired to replace many of the units within the system by software realizations. Determine the transfer function $H(z)$ of a possible replacement for the given analog unit. The sampling rate used in the system is 10 Hz.

Solution

Since the gain at dc is unity and since there are two zeros at $p = \infty$, it seems reasonable that an approximation emphasizing good correlation in the general low-frequency range would be suitable. Thus, the bilinear transformation method will be used, and the mapping constant will be selected according to (7-9). Note that the given transfer function is already scaled to the proper range, so the transformation is simply

$$p = \frac{20(1 - z^{-1})}{1 + z^{-1}} \tag{7-30}$$

Substitution of (7-30) in (7-29) yields

$$H(z) = \frac{0.0043290043(1 + z^{-1})^2}{1 - 1.7229437z^{-1} + 0.74025974z^{-2}} \tag{7-31}$$

In Ex. 7-1, the steady-state amplitude response of the digital filter was considered to be the major function of interest. As an illustration of a different type of criterion in this case, we will compare the step response of (7-31) to that of the analog filter. These results are summarized in Table 7-6. The additional data represent different approaches for approximating the same function and will be discussed later.

Example 7-4

Various specifications and parameters for a certain low-pass filter requirement are given as follows:

   A. Bilinear transformation design with Butterworth type response.
   B. Attenuation$\leq$ 3 dB for $0 \leqslant f \leqslant 25$ Hz
   C. Attenuation $\geqslant$ 38 dB for $f \geqslant 50$ Hz
   D. Sampling frequency = 200 Hz

   (a) Determine a single transfer function H(z) that will realize the requirements.
   (b) Determine a cascade system of transfer functions, none of which exceeds second order, that will realize the requirements.

Solution

(a) It is first necessary to determine the order of a transfer function that will meet the attenuation specifications. The folding frequency is $f_0 = 200/2 = 100$ Hz, and the normalized reference digital cutoff frequency is $v_r = 25/100 = 0.25$. The mapping constant will be chosen so

Table 7-6
Step responses for filters of Examples 7-3, 7-7, and 7-9. (Note: Results are shown only at every fourth point up to n = 76.)

n	Bilinear Transformation	Impulse Invariance	Analog Response and Step Invariance
0	0	0	0
4	0.1310	0.1295	0.1087
8	0.3273	0.3262	0.3032
12	0.5087	0.5075	0.4883
16	0.6526	0.6512	0.6370
20	0.7591	0.7575	0.7476
24	0.8349	0.8332	0.8268
28	0.8877	0.8860	0.8821
32	0.9240	0.9223	0.9201
36	0.9487	0.9470	0.9461
40	0.9655	0.9638	0.9637
44	0.9768	0.9751	0.9756
48	0.9844	0.9827	0.9836
52	0.9895	0.9878	0.9890
56	0.9929	0.9913	0.9926
60	0.9953	0.9936	0.9950
64	0.9968	0.9951	0.9966
68	0.9978	0.9962	0.9977
72	0.9985	0.9969	0.9985
76	0.9990	0.9973	0.9990
∞	1	1	1

that this frequency corresponds to $\lambda_r = 1$ rad/s in the analog prototype function. Hence,

$$C = \lambda_r \cot \frac{\pi}{2} v_r = \cot \frac{\pi}{8} = 2.4142136 \qquad (7\text{-}32)$$

Let $v_a = 50/100 = 0.5$ represent the lowest frequency at which the stopband attenuation requirement must be met. The corresponding analog reference frequency λ_a determined from (7-7) as

$$\lambda_a = C \tan \frac{\pi}{2} v_a = 2.4142136 \tan \frac{\pi}{4} = 2.4142136 \qquad (7\text{-}33)$$

Inspection of the curves of Fig. 6-23 reveals that at a normalized frequency of about 2.41, the attenuation of a 5-pole Butterworth filter is about 38 dB.

The analog prototype transfer function is obtained from Table 6-2 as

$$G(p) = \cfrac{1}{\begin{array}{c}(1 + 3.2360680p + 5.2360680p^2 \\ + 5.2360680p^3 + 3.2360680p^4 + p^5)\end{array}} \qquad (7\text{-}34)$$

The required transformation is then

$$p = 2.4142132 \frac{(1 - z^{-1})}{1 + z^{-1}} \qquad (7\text{-}35)$$

The formulas given in Table 7-5 may be used to simplify the transformation process. After considerable manipulation, the overall digital transfer function is

$$H(z) = \cfrac{3.279216 \times 10^{-3}(1 + 5z^{-1} + 10z^{-2} + 10z^{-3} + 5z^{-4} + z^{-5})}{\begin{array}{c}(1 - 2.4744163z^{-1} + 2.8110065z^{-2} - 1.7037724z^{-3} \\ + 0.5444328z^{-4} - 0.07231569z^{-5})\end{array}} \qquad (7\text{-}36)$$

(b) A cascade decomposition may be obtained through the aid of Table 6-3 by first expressing $G(p)$ in analog cascade form. Let

$$G(p) = G_1(p) \, G_2(p) \, G_3(p) \qquad (7\text{-}37)$$

where

$$G_1(p) = \frac{1}{1 + p} \qquad (7\text{-}38)$$

$$G_2(p) = \frac{1}{1 + 0.6180340p + p^2} \qquad (7\text{-}39)$$

$$G_3(p) = \frac{1}{1 + 1.618034p + p^2} \qquad (7\text{-}40)$$

Assume that the digital transfer function is to be expressed as

$$H(z) = a_0 H_1(z) H_2(z) H_3(z) \qquad (7\text{-}41)$$

The bilinear transformation may now be applied individually to each of the three analog functions. The constant a_0 is found by factoring out the respective a_{0i} constant for each function and forming the product. The results are

$$a_0 = 3.279216 \times 10^{-3} \qquad (7\text{-}42)$$

$$H_1(z) = \frac{1 + z^{-1}}{1 - 0.4142136 z^{-1}} \qquad (7\text{-}43)$$

$$H_2(z) = \frac{1 + 2z^{-1} + z^{-2}}{1 - 1.1606108 z^{-1} + 0.6413515 z^{-2}} \qquad (7\text{-}44)$$

$$H_3(z) = \frac{1 + 2z^{-1} + z^{-2}}{1 - 0.8995918 z^{-1} + 0.2722149 z^{-2}} \qquad (7\text{-}45)$$

It can be verified that the product of the preceding four terms yields (7-36). Note how much simpler in form the three individual transfer functions of the cascade realization are than the overall system function. The cascade form here would probably be a much more desirable form for implementation than the direct form involving (7-36).

The amplitude response $A(v)$ is shown in Fig. 7-6, and $A_{db}(v)$ is shown in Fig. 7-7.

Example 7-5

A low-pass digital IIR signal filter is desired to satisfy the following specifications:

    A. Attenuation $\leqslant 1$ dB for $0 \leqslant f \leqslant 5$ Hz
    B. Attenuation $\geqslant 40$ dB for $f \geqslant 10$ Hz

The sampling rate of the system is 100 Hz. Determine the type and order of a filter that will satisfy the requirements. (The actual filter design will not be done here, but will be left as exercises in Probs. 7-9 and 7-10).

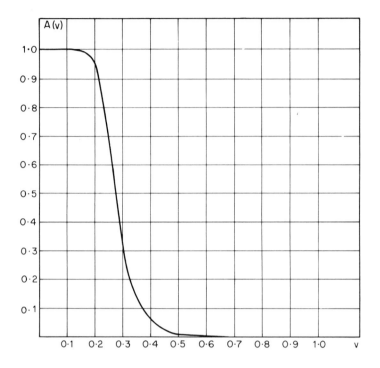

Figure 7-6 Amplitude response $A(v)$ for Example 7-4.

Solution

The folding frequency is $f_0 = 100/2 = 50$ Hz. We will restrict our consideration to the types of filters for which design data have been given in the text. The form of the passband specifications suggests the use of a 1 dB Chebyshev filter, and the bilinear transformation method will be employed. The normalized reference frequency is $v_r = 5/50 = 0.1$, which will correspond to $\lambda_r = 1$ rad/s in the pertinent analog prototype filter of Chapt. 6. Let $v_a = 10/50 = 0.2$ represent the frequency at which the attenuation must be at least 40 dB, and let λ_a represent the corresponding analog prototype frequency.

The mapping constant is determined to be

$$C = \cot \frac{\pi}{2}(0.1) = 6.3137515 \qquad (7\text{-}46)$$

The frequency λ_a is determined from (7-7) as

$$\lambda_a = 6.3137515 \tan \frac{\pi}{2} (0.2) = 2.0514622 \qquad (7\text{-}47)$$

From the curves of Fig. 6-25, it is seen that at a normalized frequency of about 2.05, the lowest order at which the attenuation exceeds 40 dB is a 5-pole filter. In fact, the attenuation at this frequency for a 5-pole filter actually exceeds 46 dB, so the requirement is met with some reserve.

Actually, the excess attenuation suggests the possibility that the passband ripple could be reduced, while still meeting the stopband

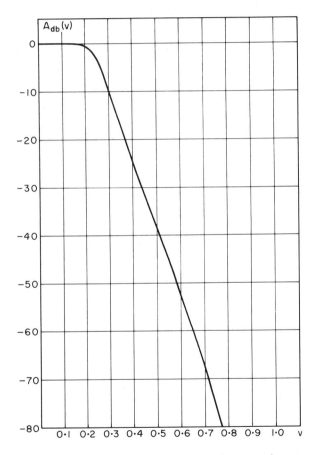

Figure 7-7 Amplitude response $A_{db}(v)$ for Example 7-4.

requirement. Indeed, inspection of Fig. 6-24 reveals that a 0.5 dB ripple filter with 5 poles would have about 43 dB attenuation at $v_a = 0.2$. The choice between these alternatives would depend on whether it would be more important to reduce the passband ripple further or to provide additional stopband attenuation beyond the given requirements.

7-5 NUMERICAL INTERPRETATION OF BILINEAR TRANSFORMATION

In this section, we will consider an alternative interpretation of the bilinear transformation as seen from a numerical analysis point of view. Consider a continuous signal $x(t)$ from which a sampled signal $x(n)$ is derived at multiples of $t = nT$. Suppose that it is desired to perform an approximate numerical integration on the sampled version of the signal. Of course, there are different approaches to this problem, with varying degrees of accuracy depending on the nature of the signal, the time interval, etc. However, assume that the trapezoidal algorithm is applied. This rather basic integration scheme assumes that the variation between successive points is linear as illustrated in Fig. 7-8. The resulting integration is achieved by summing the areas contained in a sequence of rectangles.

The trapezoidal algorithm may be expressed as

$$y(n) = y(n - 1) + \frac{T}{2}[x(n) + x(n - 1)] \qquad (7\text{-}48)$$

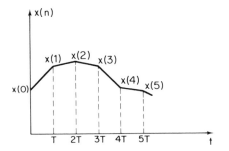

Figure 7-8 Integration using the trapezoidal algorithm.

Taking the z-transforms of both sides of (7-48) and solving for the transfer function, we obtain

$$H(z) = \frac{T}{2} \frac{(1 + z^{-1})}{(1 - z^{-1})} \qquad (7\text{-}49)$$

Since integration in the time domain corresponds to division by the Laplace variable in the transform domain, we can establish a sort of equivalence between this operation and the z-domain operation representing an approximation to integration. To conform with previous notation concerning the reference analog domain, we will use p as the variable. Thus, in some approximate sense

$$\frac{1}{p} = \frac{T}{2} \frac{(1 + z^{-1})}{(1 - z^{-1})} \qquad (7\text{-}50)$$

or

$$p = \frac{2}{T} \frac{(1 - z^{-1})}{(1 + z^{-1})} \qquad (7\text{-}50a)$$

which was one form of the bilinear transformation as given earlier in the chapter.

Any analog transfer function can be represented as a complex combination of integrators and algebraic operations. If each of the integrators is replaced by the numerical operation implied by the trapezoidal algorithm, then a certain numerical approximation to the system will result. This is equivalent to replacing p in the transfer function by its equivalent z function as given by the bilinear transformation. Even if a constant other than $2/T$ is used (exact frequency correspondence), this approach would still be a trapezoidal approximation, but with a changed weighting of the areas. Thus, the bilinear transformation approach can be thought of as a discrete numerical approximation to a continuous system in which the process of integration is replaced by the trapezoidal algorithm approximation.

7-6 IMPULSE-INVARIANCE METHOD

The next approach considered for designing IIR digital filters is the impulse-invariance method. The criterion for this approach is that the impulse response of the discrete-time system be the same as (or proportional to) the corresponding impulse response of the reference analog filter at sampling points. This idea is illustrated in Fig. 7-9.

Let $G(p)$ represent the reference analog transfer function, and let $H(z)$ represent the desired discrete transfer function. A discrete sample $x(n)$ of any given random input signal $x(t)$ should actually be represented by an impulse with the weight $Tx(n)$ in order to approximate the response of the corresponding analog system due to that segment of the signal. This can best be accomplished by leaving $x(n)$ as it is and multiplying the transfer function by T. The required transfer function can then be expressed as

$$H(z) = T \, 3 \, [g(t)] = TG(z) \qquad (7\text{-}51)$$

where $G(z)$ is the z-transform of the sampled representation of the continuous signal $g(t)$.

From the properties of a sampled signal as developed in Chapt. 3, the frequency response corresponding to (7-51) can be considered to be the reference analog frequency response plus an infinite number of shifted versions of this response centered in integer multiples of the sampling frequency. This means that if the original analog filter displays only a moderate rolloff rate, the frequency aliasing error using this approach may be significant. On the other hand, if the original analog filter is sharply bandlimited, and if the sampling rate is suf-

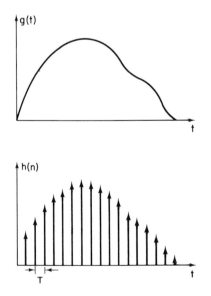

Figure 7-9 Illustration of the impulse-invariance concept.

ficiently high, there will be little or no aliasing error, and the resulting frequency response may be very close to the reference analog response. Consequently, the impulse-invariance method should be seriously considered only for filter functions having sharp cutoff characteristics.

The actual design of impulse-invariance filters is usually more difficult from a computational point of view than for filters designed with the bilinear transformation. In the impulse-invariance case, it is necessary to determine the z-transform corresponding to an analog transfer function (or impulse response), which can be a laborious process for relatively complex functions. Since the z-transform of a product is *not* the product of the separate transforms, the cascade decomposition property discussed in conjunction with equations (7-13) through (7-15) and (7-18) may not be easily applied in this case. However, since the z-transform of a sum is a linear operation, it may be possible to develop a parallel decomposition directly in some cases.

Example 7-6

Using the impulse-invariance method, design a low-pass filter according to the requirements stated in Example 7-1.

Solution

The normalized analog transfer function will be expressed as

$$G_1(p) = \frac{1}{1 + 1.4142136p + p^2} \tag{7-52}$$

Before taking the z-transform, it is necessary to change the frequency scale of $G_1(p)$ so that its 3 dB cutoff frequency is 50 Hz. This can be achieved by replacing p in (7-52) by $p/(2\pi \times 50)$. The resulting transfer function is

$$G(p) = G_1\left(\frac{p}{100\pi}\right) = \frac{9.8696044 \times 10^4}{p^2 + 444.28829p + 9.8696044 \times 10^4} \tag{7-53}$$

The impulse response $g(t)$ is

$$g(t) = 444.28829\,\epsilon^{-222.14415t}\sin(222.14415t) \tag{7-54}$$

The z-transform corresponding to the sampled version of (7-54) can be found from the use of transform pair ZT-6 of Table 4-1 and operation pair ZO-3 of Table 4-2. First, we apply ZT-6 to the sinusoidal part of (7-54) to obtain

$$3\left[\sin 222.14415t\right] = \frac{0.42981538z}{z^2 - 1.8058336z + 1} \qquad (7\text{-}55)$$

$G(z)$ is then obtained by applying ZO-3 to (7-55). $H(z)$ is obtained by multiplying by T. After arrangement in negative powers of z, the result is

$$H(z) = \frac{0.2449203z^{-1}}{1 - 1.1580459z^{-1} + 0.41124070z^{-2}} \qquad (7\text{-}56)$$

The amplitude response corresponding to (7-56) is shown as curve C in Figs. 7-11 and 7-12.

Example 7-7

Determine a possible digital filter for the system of Ex. 7-3 using the impulse-invariance method.

Solution

The impulse response $g(t)$ is determined from (7-29) as

$$g(t) = 2\epsilon^{-t} - 2\epsilon^{-2t} \qquad (7\text{-}57)$$

The z-transform of the sampled version of (7-57) is

$$G(z) = \frac{2}{1 - \epsilon^{-0.1}z^{-1}} - \frac{2}{1 - \epsilon^{-0.2}z^{-1}} \qquad (7\text{-}58)$$

The transfer function $H(z)$ is obtained by multiplying (7-58) by T. The result can be rearranged as

$$H(z) = \frac{0.017221333z^{-1}}{1 - 1.7235682z^{-1} + 0.74081822z^{-2}} \qquad (7\text{-}59)$$

The step response of this transfer function is tabulated at a number of sample points in Table 7-6.

7-7 STEP-INVARIANCE METHOD _____

The step-invariance method results from the criterion that the step response of the digital filter must be the same as the corresponding step response of the reference analog filter at sampling times. Let $h_s(n)$ represent the digital step response, and let $g_s(t)$ represent the analog step response. The concept is illustrated in Fig. 7-10.

It is required that

$$h_s(n) = g_s(t)]_{t=nT} \qquad (7\text{-}60)$$

Taking the z-transforms of both sides of (7-60), we have

$$H_s(z) = G_s(z) \qquad (7\text{-}61)$$

The digital step response $H_s(z)$ can be expressed in terms of the desired transfer function $H(z)$ as

$$H_s(z) = \frac{z}{z-1} H(z) \qquad (7\text{-}62)$$

The z-transform of the analog transfer function can be expressed as

$$G_s(z) = \mathbf{3}\left\{ \mathcal{L}^{-1}\left[\frac{G(p)}{p} \right] \right\} \qquad (7\text{-}63)$$

Note that the quantity in the inner brackets of (7-63) represents the Laplace transform of the step response, and its inverse represents the time-domain form of the step response. After substituting (7-62) and (7-63) in (7-61), the transfer function is obtained as

$$H(z) = \frac{z-1}{z} \mathbf{3}\left\{ \mathcal{L}^{-1}\left[\frac{G(p)}{p} \right] \right\} \qquad (7\text{-}64)$$

The development of one interesting interpretation of (7-64) is left as an exercise for the reader (Prob. 7-24), but a short discussion will be given here. Assume that an input signal $x(n)$ is applied to a zero-order holding circuit, which converts the discrete-time signal to a continuous-time signal consisting of a series of rectangles. If this signal is then applied to a continuous-time filter having a transfer function $G(p)$, the output signal at sample points will be equivalent to the discrete-time output of $H(z)$ in (7-64) when excited by $x(n)$. For this

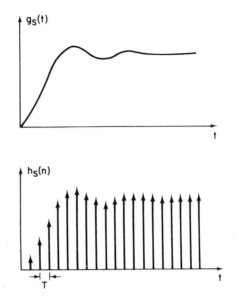

Figure 7-10 Illustration of the step-invariance concept.

reason, the step-invariance function has also been referred to as a *zero-order hold filter*.

Filters designed with the step-invariance method are subject to some of the same possible aliasing difficulties as with impulse-invariance filters if the amplitude response is not sharply bandlimited. However, the presence of the $1/p$ factor in the inner brackets of (7-64) provides an additional 6 dB/octave high-frequency attenuation, so for a given filter function, the aliasing errors are usually smaller with the step-invariance method.

Example 7-8

Using the step-invariance method, design a low-pass filter according to the requirements of Example 7-1.

Solution

The analog transfer function was scaled to the proper frequency range in Example 7-6, and the result was given in (7-53). Multiplication by $1/p$ yields the Laplace transform of the step response. We must now determine the z-transform corresponding to the sampled version of the continuous-time step response. First, we will determine the analog step response. The result is

$$g_s(t) = 1 - \epsilon^{-222.14415t} (\sin 222.14415t + \cos 222.14415t) \qquad (7\text{-}65)$$

The z-transform corresponding to (7-65) can be found from the use of transform pairs ZT-6 and ZT-7 of Table 4-1 and operation pair ZO-3 of Table 4-2. The result is

$$H_s(z) = \frac{z}{z-1} - \frac{z^2 - 0.30339071z}{z^2 - 1.1580459z + 0.41124070}$$

$$= \frac{0.14534481z^2 + 0.10784999z}{(z-1)(z^2 - 1.1580459z + 0.41124070)} \qquad (7\text{-}66)$$

The required transfer function $H(z)$ is now determined from (7-64). With final arrangement in negative powers of z, the result is

$$H(z) = \frac{0.14534481z^{-1} + 0.10784999z^{-2}}{1 - 1.1580459z^{-1} + 0.41124070z^{-2}} \qquad (7\text{-}67)$$

The amplitude response corresponding to (7-67) is shown as curve B in Figs. 7-11 and 7-12.

The reader can now compare the amplitude responses obtained using the three methods discussed in this chapter. In the passband, the three responses are all fairly close, with the exception that the gain of the impulse-invariance filter is slightly reduced. This problem is not serious since we could always adjust the overall gain level if desired. In the stopband, the bilinear transformation filter has the sharpest cutoff rate, and at the other extreme, the impulse-invariance filter exhibits relatively poor rolloff. In all fairness to the impulse-invariance filter, the analog filter in this problem was only a second-order function, so it was not sharply band-limited. Thus, both the impulse-invariance and the step-invariance filters display aliasing errors, although they are not as serious in the latter filter.

Example 7-9

Determine a possible digital filter for the system of Ex. 7-3, using the step-invariance method.

Solution

The step response $g_s(t)$ corresponding to (7-29) is

$$g_s(t) = 1 - 2\epsilon^{-t} + \epsilon^{-2t} \qquad (7\text{-}68)$$

The z-transform of the sampled version of (7-68) is

$$G_s(z) = \frac{z}{z-1} - \frac{2z}{z - \epsilon^{-0.1}} + \frac{z}{z - \epsilon^{-0.2}} \qquad (7\text{-}69)$$

$$= \frac{9.055917 \times 10^{-3} z^2 + 8.194133 \times 10^{-3} z}{(z-1)(z^2 - 1.7235682z + 0.74081822)}$$

The transfer function is then determined by multiplying (7-69) by $(z-1)/z$ according to (7-64). The result, arranged in negative powers of z, is

$$H(z) = \frac{9.055917 \times 10^{-3} (z^{-1} + 0.90483747z^{-2}}{1 - 1.7235682z^{-1} + 0.74081822z^{-2}} \qquad (7\text{-}70)$$

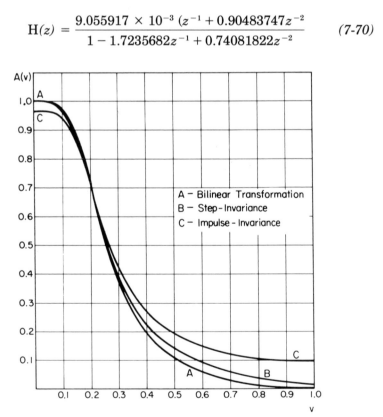

Figure 7-11 Amplitude response $A(v)$ for Examples 7-1, 7-6, and 7-8.

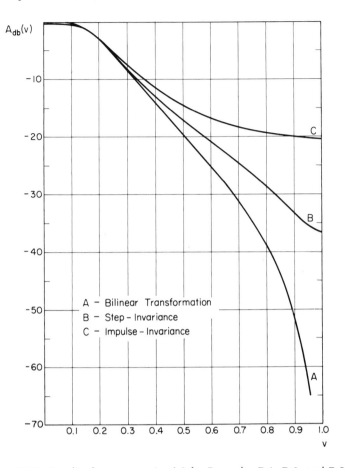

Figure 7-12 Amplitude response $A_{db}(v)$ for Examples 7-1, 7-6, and 7-8.

The step response corresponding to this function is tabulated in Table 7-6 along with the other step responses previously considered. As expected in this case, the filter designed by the step-invariance method has identical values at sample points as the reference analog function. This does not imply that this filter is necessarily better than those filters designed with other methods, as the step response is only one of a number of possible criteria that could be employed. However, it might suggest that if the transient response due to step type inputs is to be a very important criterion, and if it is desired that the response correlate very closely with that of the reference analog filter, this particular realization might be the best one in this case.

7-8 BAND-PASS DIGITAL FILTER DESIGN _____

In this section, we will develop a procedure for designing a *band-pass digital* IIR filter directly from a *low-pass analog* prototype transfer function, using a form of the bilinear transformation. This approach is based on a combination of the low-pass to band-pass analog transformation of Chapt. 6 and the bilinear transformation of this chapter.

Since there are two separate transformations involved, it is necessary to pay careful attention to notation in the development. The following quantities are defined:

p = *analog low-pass* reference Laplace variable

$\bar{s}$ = *analog band-pass* reference Laplace variable

s = *digital band-pass* final Laplace variable

λ = steady-state radian frequency corresponding to p ($p = j\lambda$)

$\bar{\omega}$ = steady-state radian frequency corresponding to $\bar{s}$ ($\bar{s} = j\bar{\omega}$)

$\bar{f}$ = $\bar{\omega}/2\pi$

ω = steady-state radian frequency corresponding to s ($s = j\omega$)

f = $\omega/2\pi$

λ_r = analog low-pass reference radian frequency (usually the cutoff frequency)

$\bar{\omega}_3, \bar{\omega}_1$ = analog band-pass radian frequencies corresponding to $\pm \lambda_r$ (usually the band-edge frequencies)

$\bar{\omega}_2$ = geometric center radian frequency of band-pass analog filter

ω_1 = lower radian frequency of digital band-pass filter corresponding to $-\lambda_r$ in analog low-pass filter and $\bar{\omega}_1$ in analog band-pass filter

ω_3 = upper radian frequency of digital band-pass filter corresponding to λ_r in analog low-pass filter and $\bar{\omega}_3$ in analog band-pass filter

ω_2 = radian frequency of digital band-pass filter corresponding to $\bar{\omega}_2$ in analog band-pass filter. (The quantity ω_2 will be called the "center frequency" even though it is usually not at the exact center of the band.)

f_1, f_2, f_3 = $\omega_1/2\pi$, $\omega_2/2\pi$, $\omega_3/2\pi$

B = $f_3 - f_1$ = reference bandwidth of digital band-pass filter

v_1, v_2, v_3 = normalized frequencies of digital filter relative to folding frequency = $f_1/f_0, f_2/f_0, f_3/f_0$

b = normalized reference bandwidth of digital band-pass filter relative to folding frequency = $(f_3 - f_1)/f_0 = v_3 - v_1$

Using the modified notation introduced in this section, the low-pass to band-pass transformation given by (6-41) can now be expressed as

$$p = \bar{s} + \frac{\bar{\omega}_2{}^2}{\bar{s}} \qquad (7\text{-}71)$$

The bilinear transformation of (7-4) now becomes

$$\bar{s} = \frac{C(1 - z^{-1})}{1 + z^{-1}} \qquad (7\text{-}72)$$

Substitution of (7-72) into (7-71) and some manipulation yield

$$p = \frac{C^2 + \bar{\omega}_2{}^2}{C} \left\{ \frac{1 - 2[(C^2 - \bar{\omega}_2{}^2)/(C^2 + \bar{\omega}_2{}^2)] z^{-1} + z^{-2}}{1 - z^{-2}} \right\} \qquad (7\text{-}73)$$

Before simplifying (7-73), several relationships will be developed. From the properties of the bilinear transformation developed in Sec. 7-3, the frequency scale $\bar{\omega}$ can be related to ω by the equation

$$\bar{\omega} = C \tan \frac{\omega T}{2} \qquad (7\text{-}74)$$

Application of (7-74) to (6-46) and (6-47), with suitable modifications in notation, results in the relationships

$$\tan^2 \frac{\omega_2 T}{2} = \tan \frac{\omega_1 T}{2} \tan \frac{\omega_3 T}{2} \qquad (7\text{-}75)$$

and

$$\tan \frac{\omega_3 T}{2} - \tan \frac{\omega_1 T}{2} = \frac{\lambda_r}{C} \qquad (7\text{-}76)$$

The preceding relationships may be expressed in terms of normalized frequencies as

$$\tan^2 \frac{\pi}{2} v_2 = \tan \frac{\pi}{2} v_1 \tan \frac{\pi}{2} v_3 \qquad (7\text{-}77)$$

and

$$\tan \frac{\pi}{2} v_3 - \tan \frac{\pi}{2} v_1 = \frac{\lambda_r}{C} \qquad (7\text{-}78)$$

The constant C can now be chosen so that $\bar{\omega}_2$ in the analog band-pass filter maps to ω_2 in the digital band-pass filter. From (7-8), C is determined to be

$$C = \bar{\omega}_2 \cot \frac{\omega_2 T}{2} \tag{7-79}$$

Using the preceding several equations and standard trigonometric identities, the constants appearing in (7-73) may be manipulated to yield simpler forms in which the digital center frequency and/or band-edge frequencies appear explicitly. The actual steps in this process will be left as an exercise for the reader (Prob. 7-17). The final form of the transformation will be given as

$$p = D \left[\frac{1 - Ez^{-1} + z^{-2}}{1 - z^{-2}} \right] \tag{7-80}$$

The constants D and E can be expressed in terms of the bandwidth and center frequency as

$$D = \lambda_r \cot \frac{\pi B}{2f_0} = \lambda_r \cot \left(\frac{\pi}{2} b \right) \tag{7-81}$$

$$E = 2 \cos \omega_2 T = 2 \cos \pi \frac{f_2}{f_0} = 2 \cos \pi v_2 \tag{7-82}$$

Alternatively, D and E can be expressed in terms of the band-edge frequencies as

$$D = \lambda_r \cot \frac{(\omega_3 - \omega_1)T}{2} = \lambda_r \cot \frac{\pi}{2} (v_3 - v_1) \tag{7-83}$$

$$E = \frac{2 \cos[(\omega_3 + \omega_1)T/2]}{\cos[(\omega_3 - \omega_1)T/2]} = \frac{2 \cos[(\pi/2)(v_3 + v_1)]}{\cos[(\pi/2)(v_3 - v_1)]} \tag{7-84}$$

In the design of a band-pass filter using this approach, it is necessary to specify either the center frequency and the band-edge frequencies. If the former quantities are specified, (7-81) and (7-82) may be used to determine the constants D and E. If the latter quantities are specified, (7-83) and (7-84) may be used to determine the constants. After the transformation is determined, the digital band-pass transfer function H(z) is determined from the analog low-pass transfer function G(p) by the relationship

$$H(z) = G(p)]_{p = D \left[\frac{1 - Ez^{-1} + z^{-2}}{1 - z^{-2}} \right]} \tag{7-85}$$

Observe that the number of poles (or order) of the band-pass digital filter will be twice that of the low-pass analog filter.

The frequency scale of the digital band-pass filter will now be expressed in terms of the analog low-pass filter. Since the $j\lambda$ axis of the p-plane maps to the $j\bar{\omega}$ axis of the $\bar{s}$-plane, and the $j\bar{\omega}$ axis of the $\bar{s}$-plane maps to the $j\omega$ axis of the s-plane, it follows that the $j\lambda$ axis of the p-plane can be directly related to the $j\omega$ axis of the s-plane. Letting $z = \epsilon^{j\omega T}$ and $p = j\lambda$ in (7-80), it can be shown (Prob. 7-18) that the following relationship is obtained:

$$\frac{\lambda}{D} = \frac{\cos \omega_2 T - \cos \omega T}{\sin \omega T}$$

$$= \frac{\cos \pi \upsilon_2 - \cos \pi \upsilon}{\sin \pi \upsilon} \qquad (7\text{-}86)$$

The function of (7-86) can be used in conjunction with the filter response curves in Chapt. 6 for designing digital band-pass filters to satisfy particular filtering requirements. This concept will be illustrated in Examples 7-10 and 7-11.

Example 7-10

A certain digital signal processing system has a sampling rate of 2 kHz. A digital band-pass filter is desired for the system, and the specifications are as follows:

(a) Range of passband is from 300 Hz to 400 Hz with attenuation permitted to be no greater than 3 dB at the two band-edge frequencies.

(b) Attenuation must be at least 18 dB at 200 Hz and 500 Hz.

(c) Butterworth type response is desired.

Solution

The folding frequency is $f_0 = f_s/2 = 1000$ Hz. The two frequencies 300 Hz and 400 Hz will be selected as the band-edge frequencies f_1 and f_3 respectively. For convenience, these quantities and all subsequent frequencies will be converted to normalized form. We have

$$\upsilon_1 = \frac{300}{1000} = 0.3$$

$$v_3 = \frac{400}{1000} = 0.4 \qquad (7\text{-}87)$$

$$b = \frac{400 - 300}{1000} = 0.1$$

The center frequency v_2 is determined from (7-77).

$$\tan^2 \frac{\pi}{2} v_2 = \tan \frac{\pi}{2} v_1 \tan \frac{\pi}{2} v_3$$

$$v_2 = 0.34797502 \qquad (7\text{-}88)$$

The transformation constants D and E may now be determined from (7-83) and (7-84) with the assumption that $\lambda_r = 1$ rad/s.

$$D = \lambda_r \cot(0.05\,\pi) = 6.31375152 \qquad (7\text{-}89)$$

$$E = \frac{2\cos(0.35\pi)}{\cos(0.05\pi)} = 0.91929910 \qquad (7\text{-}90)$$

We must now determine the minimum order required to satisfy the specifications. The reference bandwidth $b = 0.1$ will be related to the normalized Butterworth function at $\lambda_r = 1$. In order to determine the number of poles required, we must first determine the reference analog frequencies corresponding to $v_a = 200/1000 = 0.2$ and $v_b = 500/1000 = 0.5$, which are the two frequencies specified in the stopband. Letting λ_a and λ_b represent the two analog frequencies, we can determine these values from the frequency transformation function of (7-86).

$$\frac{\lambda_a}{D} = \frac{\cos 0.34797502\pi - \cos 0.2\pi}{\sin 0.2\pi}$$

$$\lambda_a = -3.7527638 \qquad (7\text{-}91)$$

$$\frac{\lambda_b}{D} = \frac{\cos 0.34797502\pi - \cos 0.5\pi}{\sin 0.5\pi}$$

$$\lambda_b = 2.9021131 \qquad (7\text{-}92)$$

Since the amplitude response of the analog filter is even, the negative sign in (7-91) is ignored in using Fig. 6-23. Because λ_a and λ_b are different, the attenuation at v_a and v_b will be different. If the low-pass analog response at λ_b is chosen to satisfy the requirements, the response at λ_a will more than meet the specifications. Thus, we must require that the low-pass reference function be down at least 18 dB at a normalized frequency of about 2.9 in Fig. 6-23. It can be seen that a 2-pole Butterworth analog low-pass function will accomplish the task. The response at a normalized frequency of 3.75 is down about 23 dB.

The required digital filter will be a 4-pole transfer function and can be obtained by the application of (7-85). After some manipulation, the result is

$$H(z) = \frac{0.020083366\,(1 - z^{-2})^2}{(1 - 1.63682036z^{-1} + 2.23760739z^{-2} - 1.30711515z^{-3} + 0.64135154z^{-4})} \qquad (7\text{-}93)$$

The amplitude response $A_{db}(v)$ is shown in Fig. 7-13.

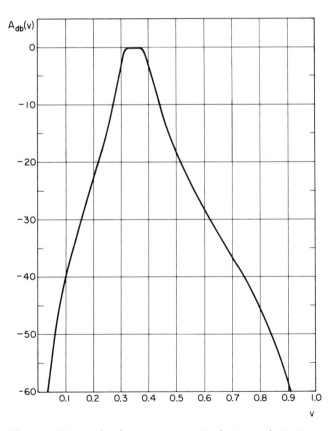

Figure 7-13 Amplitude response $A_{db}(v)$ for Example 7-10.

Example 7-11

Determine the type and order of a digital band-pass filter having a sampling rate of 200 Hz that will satisfy the following requirements:

   (a) Attenuation $\leqslant$ 1 dB for 19 Hz $\leqslant f \leqslant$ 21 Hz
   (b) Attenuation $\geqslant$ 30 dB for $f \leqslant$ 18 Hz and $f \geqslant$ 20 Hz

Solution

The folding frequency is f_0 = 100 Hz. The band-edge frequencies are f_1 = 19 Hz and f_3 = 21 Hz. The normalized values are

$$v_1 = \frac{19}{100} = 0.19$$

$$v_3 = \frac{21}{100} = 0.21 \qquad\qquad (7\text{-}94)$$

$$b = \frac{21 - 19}{100} = 0.02$$

The center frequency v_2 is determined from

$$\tan^2 \frac{\pi}{2} v_2 = \tan \frac{\pi}{2} v_1 \tan \frac{\pi}{2} v_3$$

or $\qquad\qquad\qquad\qquad\qquad\qquad\qquad\qquad\qquad\qquad (7\text{-}95)$

$$v_2 = 0.19978361$$

The constant D is determined from (7-83) with the assumption that λ_r = 1 rad/s.

$$D = \cot \frac{\pi}{2} (0.02) = 31.820516 \qquad\qquad (7\text{-}96)$$

The analog low-pass prototype frequencies corresponding to 18 Hz and 20 Hz may now be determined by means of the frequency transformation function of (7-86). Letting λ_a and λ_b represent these quantities, we have

$$\frac{\lambda_a}{D} = \frac{\cos (0.19978361\pi) - \cos (0.18\pi)}{\sin (0.18\pi)}$$

or $\qquad\qquad\qquad\qquad\qquad\qquad\qquad\qquad\qquad\qquad (7\text{-}97)$

$$\lambda_a = -2.0732504$$

$$\frac{\lambda_b}{D} = \frac{\cos{(0.19978361\pi)} - \cos{(0.22\pi)}}{\sin{(0.22\pi)}}$$

or

$$\lambda_b = 1.9420640 \tag{7-98}$$

We must ensure that the attenuation requirement is met at the lowest (in magnitude) analog low-pass frequency, which is λ_b. Choosing the 1 dB Chebyshev function of Fig. 6-25, we must determine the lowest order at which the response is down at least 30 dB at a normalized frequency of about 1.94. It is seen that a 4-pole function satisfies the requirement with over 2 dB to spare. At $\lambda_a = 2.07$, corresponding to the lower band-edge in the band-pass filter, the response is down over 35 dB. The final digital band-pass filter will thus have 8 poles.

7-9 BAND-REJECTION DIGITAL FILTER DESIGN _____

In this section, the transformation developed in the last section will be modified to permit the design of a *band-rejection digital* IIR filter directly from a *low-pass analog* prototype transfer function. The notation introduced at the beginning of the last section will be used except for the following modifications:

(a) The variables $\bar{s}$ and s represent the Laplace variables for the analog and digital band-rejection functions.

(b) The frequencies ω_1, ω_2, and ω_3 now represent frequencies associated with the rejection band.

The details of this development follow a similar pattern to those of the last section, with the exception that here the analog low-pass to band-rejection transformation of (6-53) is combined with the bilinear transformation. The details will be left as exercises for the reader (Probs. 7-19 and 7-20), and the results will be summarized here.

The general form of the transformation is

$$p = \frac{D_1(1 - z^{-2})}{1 - E_1 z^{-1} + z^{-2}} \tag{7-99}$$

The constants D_1 and E_1 can be expressed in terms of the bandwidth and center frequency as

$$D_1 = \lambda_r \tan{\frac{\pi}{2}\frac{B}{f_0}} = \lambda_r \tan{\frac{\pi}{2}b} \tag{7-100}$$

$$E_1 = 2 \cos \omega_2 T = 2 \cos \frac{\pi f_2}{f_0} = 2 \cos \pi v_2 \qquad (7\text{-}101)$$

Alternately, D_1 and E_1 can be expressed in terms of the band-edge frequencies as

$$D_1 = \lambda_r \tan \frac{(\omega_3 - \omega_1)T}{2} = \lambda_r \tan \frac{\pi}{2}(v_3 - v_1) \qquad (7\text{-}102)$$

$$E_1 = \frac{2 \cos\left[(\omega_3 + \omega_1)T/2\right]}{\cos\left[(\omega_3 - \omega_1)T/2\right]} = \frac{2 \cos\left[(\pi/2)(v_3 + v_1)\right]}{\cos\left[(\pi/2)(v_3 - v_1)\right]} \qquad (7\text{-}103)$$

It can be readily shown that ω_1, ω_2, and ω_3 may be related by

$$\tan^2 \frac{\omega_2 T}{2} = \tan \frac{\omega_1 T}{2} \tan \frac{\omega_3 T}{2} \qquad (7\text{-}104)$$

or

$$\tan^2 \frac{\pi}{2} v_2 = \tan \frac{\pi}{2} v_1 \tan \frac{\pi}{2} v_3 \qquad (7\text{-}105)$$

The frequency scale of the digital band-rejection filter is related to the frequency scale of the analog low-pass prototype by

$$\frac{\lambda}{D_1} = \frac{\sin \omega T}{\cos \omega T - \cos \omega_2 T}$$

$$= \frac{\sin \pi v}{\cos \pi v - \cos \pi v_2} \qquad (7\text{-}106)$$

The number of poles (or order) of the band-rejection digital filter will be twice that of the low-pass analog filter.

Example 7-12

A certain digital signal processing system operating at a sampling rate of 1 kHz is subjected to an undesirable interfering component at a frequency close to 100 Hz. A simple band-rejection algorithm is desired to eliminate the component. It appears that the following specifications will perform the task:

(a) 3 dB band-edge frequencies = 95 Hz and 105 Hz
(b) Two poles in final transfer function

Solution

Since the final transfer function is to contain two poles, the analog prototype filter is the simple one-pole function

$$G(p) = \frac{1}{1+p} \tag{7-107}$$

in which the reference 3 dB frequency is $\lambda_r = 1$ rad/s. The folding frequency is $f_0 = 500$ Hz, and the various normalized frequencies are

$$v_1 = \frac{95}{500} = 0.19$$

$$v_3 = \frac{105}{500} = 0.21 \tag{7-108}$$

$$b = \frac{105 - 95}{500} = 0.02$$

The various constants required in the transformation are computed as follows:

$$D_1 = \tan \frac{\pi}{2}(0.02) = 0.031426266 \tag{7-109}$$

$$E_1 = \frac{2 \cos((\pi/2)(0.4))}{\cos((\pi/2)(0.02))} = 1.61883279 \tag{7-110}$$

Substituting these constants in (7-99) and applying this transformation to (7-107), the transfer function is determined to be

$$H(z) = \frac{0.96953125\,(1 - 1.6188328z^{-1} + z^{-2})}{1 - 1.5695090z^{-1} + 0.9390625z^{-2}} \tag{7-111}$$

7-10 HIGH-PASS DIGITAL FILTER DESIGN

An inverted form of the bilinear transformation given in Sec. 7-3 may be used to design a *digital high-pass* filter directly from an *analog low-pass* prototype function. The same general conventions on notation established in Sec. 7-3 will be utilized here. The transformation is

$$p = \frac{C_1(1 + z^{-1})}{1 - z^{-1}} \tag{7-112}$$

The development of the results that follow will be left as exercises for the reader (Probs. 7-21 and 7-22).

The analog reference radian frequency λ is related to the digital frequency variables by

$$|\lambda| = C_1 \cot \frac{\omega T}{2} = C_1 \cot \frac{\pi}{2} \frac{f}{f_0} = C_1 \cot \frac{\pi}{2} v \qquad (7\text{-}113)$$

The mapping constant C_1 can be determined from the stipulation that the low-pass amplitude response at λ_r be the same as the high-pass amplitude response at ω_r. Of course, in the low-pass case λ_r is at the upper end of the passband, but in the high-pass case ω_r is at the lower end of the passband. The constant is determined as

$$C_1 = \lambda_r \tan \frac{\omega_r T}{2} = \lambda_r \tan \frac{\pi}{2} v_r \qquad (7\text{-}114)$$

The digital high-pass filter will have the same number of poles (or order) as the analog low-pass filter.

Example 7-13

Design a high-pass digital filter derived from a second-order Butterworth analog filter with a 3 dB cutoff frequency of 200 Hz. The sampling rate of the system is 500 Hz.

Solution

The low-pass analog prototype function is the same as was used in Ex. 7-1, so reference will be made to equation (7-20) for this function. The analog frequency $\lambda_r = 1$ rad/s must map to $f_r = 200$ Hz. The folding frequency is 250 Hz, so $v_r = 200/250 = 0.8$. The constant C_1 is determined as

$$C_1 = \tan \frac{\pi}{2} (0.8) = 3.0776835 \qquad (7\text{-}115)$$

The transformation is

$$p = 3.0776835 \frac{(1 + z^{-1})}{(1 - z^{-1})} \qquad (7\text{-}116)$$

Substitution of (7-116) into (7-20) yields

$$H(z) = \frac{0.0674553\,(1 - 2z^{-1} + z^{-2})}{1 + 1.14298z^{-1} + 0.412802z^{-2}} \qquad (7\text{-}117)$$

Notice the similarity of this high-pass transfer function having a cutoff frequency of $v_c = 0.8$ with the low-pass transfer function of (7-23) having a cutoff frequency of $v_c = 0.2$. This similarity is more than coincidental, and the interested reader is referred to Prob. 7-23 for more details.

PROBLEMS

7-1 The sampling rate in a certain digital system is 100 Hz. It is desired to program a computer within the system to simulate the analog transfer function

$$G(s) = \frac{10}{s\,(s + 10)}$$

Good correspondence at low frequencies is a desirable criterion. Determine a single discrete transfer function using the bilinear transformation method.

7-2 Determine a discrete transfer function for the system of Prob. 7-1 using the impulse-invariance method.

7-3 Determine a discrete transfer function for the system of Prob. 7-1 using the step-invariance method.

7-4 Using the bilinear transformation method, design a low-pass digital filter derived from a second-order Chebyshev filter with 1 dB passband ripple. The 1 dB "cutoff frequency" is 20 Hz, and the sampling rate of the system is 100 Hz.

7-5 Using the impulse-invariance method, design a filter to satisfy the requirements of Prob. 7-4.

7-6 Using the step-invariance method, design a filter to satisfy the requirements of Prob. 7-4.

7-7 Using the bilinear transformation, design a third-order low-pass Butterworth digital filter with a 3 dB cutoff frequency at 10 Hz. The sampling rate of the system is 200 Hz.

7-8 Determine the digital transfer function for the system of Ex. 7-2 if the major criterion is that the amplitude response of the digital function be the same as the analog function at 400 Hz.

7-9   Determine a single transfer function utilizing the 1 dB Chebyshev function that will meet the requirements of Ex. 7-5.

7-10   Repeat Prob. 7-9 utilizing a cascade system of transfer functions, none of which exceeds second order.

7-11   Determine the minimum order of a digital low-pass filter having a sampling rate of 2 kHz that will satisfy the following requirements:

     (a) Bilinear transformation design based on a Chebyshev analog prototype function.

     (b) Attenuation ≤ 2 dB for $0 \leq f \leq 250$ Hz

     (c) Attenuation ≥ 70 dB for $f \geq 500$ Hz.

7-12   Determine the type and the minimum order of a digital band-pass filter having a sampling rate of 2 kHz that will satisfy the following requirements:

     (a) Bilinear transformation design based on a Chebyshev analog prototype function.

     (b) Attenuation ≤ 3 dB for 790 Hz $\leq f \leq$ 810 Hz

     (c) Attenuation ≥ 16 dB for $f \leq 780$ Hz and $f \geq 820$ Hz.

7-13   Determine the minimum order of a high-pass filter having a sampling rate of 200 Hz that will satisfy the following requirements:

     (a) Bilinear transformation design based on a Butterworth analog prototype function.

     (b) Attenuation ≤ 3 dB for $f \geq 20$ Hz

     (c) Attenuation ≥ 36 dB for $f \leq 5$ Hz.

7-14   Determine a digital transfer function for a system satisfying the requirements of Prob. 7-12.

7-15   Determine the digital transfer function for a system satisfying the requirements of Prob. 7-13.

7-16   Design a band-rejection filter satisfying the following requirements:

     (a) Two poles in final digital transfer function

     (b) Sampling frequency = 2 kHz

     (c) 3 dB band-edge frequencies of rejection band = 250 Hz and 300 Hz.

7-17   Verify the results of the analog low-pass to digital band-pass transformation given by equations (7-80) through (7-84). You can start with equation (7-73) and make use of any results developed up through equation (7-79) along with standard trigonometric identities.

7-18 Derive equation (7-86).

7-19 Using the bilinear transformation in conjunction with the analog low-pass to band-rejection transformation, derive the general form of the transformation given by equation (7-99) for designing band-rejection digital filters. Verify the results of equations (7-101) through (7-103). The development follows essentially the same pattern as for the band-pass case of Sec. 7-8.

7-20 Verify equation (7-106).

7-21 Derive equation (7-113).

7-22 Derive equation (7-114).

7-23 Consider a low-pass digital transfer function $H_{lp}(\bar{z})$, where $\bar{z}$ is momentarily used to denote the z-transform variable. Assume that the normalized cutoff frequency is $\bar{v}_c$. Consider the transformation

$$z = -\bar{z}$$

(a) Show that the resulting transfer function represents a *high-pass* digital filter having a cutoff frequency v_c which is related to $\bar{v}_c$ by

$$v_c = 1 - \bar{v}_c$$

This means that a high-pass digital transfer function $H_{hp}(z)$ may be derived from a low-pass transfer function by means of the transformation

$$H_{hp}(z) = H_{lp}(-z)$$

(b) Use the results of (a) and the low-pass transfer function of Ex. 7-1 to determine the high-pass transfer function of Ex. 7-13.

7-24 Consider the system shown in Fig. P7-24. The input is a discrete-time signal and is converted to a continuous time signal by means of the zero-order holding circuit. This signal is then applied to a continuous-time filter having a transfer function $G(p)$, and the output is sampled.

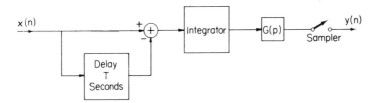

Figure P7-24

Show that the discrete transfer function $H(z)$ of this system is equivalent to the form derived in equation (7-64) using the step-invariance criteria.

Hint: $$\mathfrak{Z}\left\{\mathcal{L}^{-1}[\epsilon^{-pT}\,F(p)\,]\right\} = z^{-1}F(z)$$

7-25 Assume that it is desired to create a digital filter with *ramp-invariance,* i.e., the response due to a ramp input should be the same for the digital filter as for some prototype analog filter. Let $G(p)$ represent the prototype function and let $H(z)$ represent the desired discrete transfer function. Show that

$$H(z) = \frac{(z-1)^2}{Tz}\,\mathfrak{Z}\left\{\mathcal{L}^{-1}\left[\frac{G(p)}{p^2}\right]\right\}$$

7-26 Consider a digital band-pass filter designed with the procedure of Sec. 7-8 having a center frequency at half the folding frequency, i.e., $v_2 = 0.5$.

(a) Show that the amplitude response in this case has perfect arithmetic symmetry about the center frequency.

(b) Show that the transformation reduces to

$$p = D\left[\frac{1+z^{-2}}{1-z^{-2}}\right]$$

FINITE IMPULSE
RESPONSE DIGITAL
FILTER DESIGN

8-0 INTRODUCTION

The primary objective in this chapter is the development of the basic properties of the finite impulse response (FIR) digital filter. FIR filters have both advantages and disadvantages as compared with infinite impulse response (IIR) filters considered in the last chapter, so it is important that these various properties be considered in determining the requirements for a particular application. Among the advantages of FIR filters are the possible achievement of ideal linear phase characteristics and less susceptibility of the actual implementation to parameter quantization effects. Among the disadvantages are possible long time delays, the necessity for higher-order functions to achieve prescribed filtering requirements, and the lack of simpler design procedures that would permit direct attainment of filter specifications.

It appears that FIR filters will experience increasing usage in the future, so it is expected that simpler design procedures will evolve. In this chapter, we will develop the fundamental properties of FIR filter functions, and some of the basic design concepts will be explored. Additional FIR filter design concepts will be discussed in Chapt. 10 in conjunction with the fast Fourier transform.

8-1   GENERAL DISCUSSION _____

The basic differences between the IIR digital filter and the FIR digital
filter were discussed at the beginning of Chapt. 7, and various approximation procedures for IIR filters were subsequently developed in that
chapter. We will now direct our major efforts to the properties and
design concepts of FIR filters.

An FIR filter is one in which the impulse response $h(n)$ is limited
to a finite number of points. The impulse response can be expressed as

$$h(n) = a_n \text{ for } 0 \le n \le k$$
$$= 0 \text{ elsewhere} \tag{8-1}$$

In some cases, it is desirable to express $h(n)$ in the form

$$h(n) = \sum_{i=0}^{k} a_i \delta(n - i) \tag{8-2}$$

which is equivalent to (8-1). The transfer function corresponding to
(8-1) or (8-2) can be expressed in the form

$$H(z) = \sum_{m=0}^{k} a_m z^{-m}$$
$$= a_0 + a_1 z^{-1} + a_2 z^{-2} + \cdots + a_k z^{-k} \tag{8-3}$$

The integer k represents the *order* of the function.

Note that if no coefficients in (8-1) are missing, there will be
$k + 1$ terms in the impulse response for a function of order k. The values
of $h(n)$ at these points are readily determined from either of the forms
(8-1), (8-2), or (8-3). We observe that $h(0) = a_0$, $h(1) = a_1$, $h(2) = a_2$,
etc.

Many authors refer to the function of (8-3) as having only zeros
and no poles. While this terminology is widely used in the literature,
actually $H(z)$ has a pole of order k at $z = 0$. This is readily seen by
multiplying numerator and denominator of (8-3) by z^k.

The difference equation relating the output to the input in (8-3)
can be readily expressed as

$$y(n) = \sum_{i=0}^{k} a_i x(n - i) = \sum_{i=0}^{k} h(i)x(n - i) \tag{8-4}$$

Equation (8-4) describes a *nonrecursive* realization for the FIR transfer function. However, we also observe that since the difference equation involves only the input and the impulse response, it can be considered as a convolution summation between these two functions. This property was not encountered with IIR filters, since the input-output difference equation and convolution summation equation were quite different in form in that case. Thus, a nonrecursive realization of an FIR filter is equivalent to a direct convolution between the input and output from an implementation point of view.

As in the case of IIR filters, the basic design problem is to determine the constants in the transfer function (or impulse response) that will satisfy the given requirements. Since there are only numerator coefficients present in the transfer function of an FIR filter, the problem is somewhat more restricted now. The various transformations used in the preceding chapter cannot be used here since they usually yield IIR functions. Different procedures must be utilized for FIR filters, and it will be seen that the design process is usually more difficult in this case.

Some of the general properties of FIR filters are summarized as follows:

(a) Implementation is readily achieved by means of a nonrecursive or direct convolution type of realization. This type of implementation does not require feedback, so the direct form 1 and direct form 2 realizations are identical.

(b) Implementation is also possible by high-speed convolution using the Fast Fourier transform or by recursive techniques.

(c) Errors arising from quantization, roundoff, and coefficient inaccuracies are usually less critical in nonrecursive realizations of FIR filters than for IIR filters. This advantage is primarily due to the lack of feedback in FIR nonrecursive realizations.

(d) The transfer function of an FIR filter with a nonrecursive implementation has all of its poles at the origin and is always stable.

(e) FIR filters with ideal linear phase characteristics may be designed. This is seldom possible with IIR design procedures.

(f) A higher-order FIR filter is normally required to obtain the same sharpness of amplitude response control as compared with an IIR filter.

(g) The amount of time delay increases with the number of terms and can become quite large for a filter of relatively high order.

(h) In general, the overall approximation problem for FIR filters is somewhat more difficult than with the methods used for IIR filters. One of the primary problems is that the specification of such parameters as passband and stopband ripple bounds is more complicated for FIR filters. (Computer programs have been developed to assist in this process.)

8-2   FOURIER SERIES METHOD

In this section, we will consider the Fourier series method for approximating an FIR amplitude response. This approach is rather basic in the sense that all other methods for FIR filter response utilize much of the same underlying theory. The Fourier series method is relatively straightforward in concept, so it will be used as the primary basis for the efforts of this chapter. The major disadvantage is that one cannot easily specify in advance the exact levels for passband and stopband ripple levels, so it may be necessary to investigate several alternate designs to obtain a suitable function for a given filter requirement.

In actual practice, the Fourier series method is best used in conjunction with a "window function." To simplify the overall presentation, the basic concepts will be developed in this section without regard to such a function. In the next section, the theory of the window function will be discussed, and it will be related to the work of this section.

The key to the Fourier series method is the fact that the amplitude response $A(f)$ corresponding to a DTLTI impulse response $h(n)$ is a periodic function of *frequency* and as such can be expanded in a Fourier series in the *frequency domain*. (Note that the most common application of Fourier series in signal analysis is that of expanding a periodic *time* function in a Fourier series in the *time* domain, so the senses of time and frequency are somewhat reversed in the present application.) The coefficients obtained from the Fourier series can then be related to the impulse response, and the desired coefficients of the FIR transfer function can then be obtained.

A significant advantage of FIR filter functions is the capability of obtaining linear phase (or constant time delay). In order to obtain constant time delay easily, it is necessary that the Fourier series have either cosine terms only or sine terms only, but not both at the same time.

Since the amplitude response is generally regarded as an even function of frequency, the concept of expanding it in a cosine series seems reasonable. On the other hand, the reader may be puzzled as to how a sine series, which normally arises in the expansion of an odd function, could be used to expand the amplitude response. The answer to this dilemma lies in the fact that we normally *interpret* the steady-state transfer function to have an *even amplitude* response and an *odd phase* response. In some applications it is desirable to interpret these quantities in an opposite sense, i.e., an *odd amplitude* response and an *even phase* response.

To illustrate this concept with a simple example, consider the steady-state transfer function of the analog differentiator, which is

$$G(j\omega) = j\omega \qquad (8\text{-}5)$$

The usual manner for interpreting the amplitude and phase is

$$A(f) = |\omega| \text{ for } -\infty < \omega < \infty$$
$$\beta(f) = -90° \text{ for } -\infty < \omega < 0 \qquad (8\text{-}6)$$
$$= +90° \text{ for } 0 < \omega < \infty$$

This interpretation results in an even amplitude function and an odd phase function. On the other hand, we may write

$$A(f) = \omega \text{ for } -\infty < \omega < \infty$$
$$\beta(f) = +90° \text{ for } -\infty < \omega < \infty \qquad (8\text{-}7)$$

This latter interpretation results in an odd amplitude function and an even phase function. Yet, the combination of the two functions in (8-6) produces the same overall transfer function as the combination in (8-7). As far as the present application is concerned, this would suggest that the usual interpretation of even amplitude and odd phase would be used in the case of a cosine series expansion, but the opposite interpretation could be made in the case of a sine series expansion. The choice of which type of expansion to use in a given application will be discussed later.

Consider first the case of a *cosine series* representation. Let $A_d(f)$ denote some *desired* amplitude response. We will assume that this function is even and that it is periodic in f with a period f_s. (Note that $f_s = 1/T$ is the sampling frequency.) Let $A(f)$ represent the *approximation* to $A_d(f)$ that will result when the series is terminated after M terms. A representative case is illustrated in Fig. 8-1. The form of the finite series is

$$A(f) = \frac{\alpha_0}{2} + \sum_{m=1}^{M} \alpha_m \cos 2\pi m \, Tf \qquad (8\text{-}8)$$

From the basic properties of Fourier series (including the symmetry associated with an even function), the reader is invited to show (Prob. 8-1) that an expression for determining the coefficients is

$$\alpha_m = \frac{4}{f_s} \int_0^{f_s/2} A_d(f) \cos 2\pi m \, Tf \, df \qquad (8\text{-}9)$$

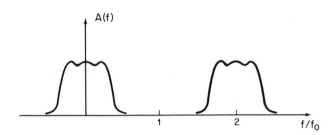

Figure 8-1 Fourier series approximation for even amplitude response.

In exponential form, (8-8) can be expressed as

$$A(f) = \sum_{m=-M}^{M} c_m \epsilon^{j\,2\pi\,m\,Tf} \qquad (8\text{-}10)$$

where

$$c_m = c_{-m} = \frac{\alpha_m}{2} = \frac{2}{f_s} \int_0^{f_s/2} A_d(f)\,\cos 2\pi\,m\,Tf\,df \qquad (8\text{-}11)$$

Equation (8-10) can be considered as the evaluation of some un-known discrete transfer function on the unit circle in the z-plane. To perform such an evaluation, we normally let $z = \epsilon^{j\omega T} = \epsilon^{j\,2\pi Tf}$. In this case, we can reverse the process and replace $\epsilon^{j\,2\pi Tf}$ by z. Denoting this initial series by $H_1(z)$ and turning it around for later convenience, we have

$$H_1(z) = \sum_{m=M}^{-M} c_m z^m \qquad (8\text{-}12)$$

The form of (8-12) represents an FIR transfer function, but it is *noncausal* in that it has positive powers of z. This implies that the filter would produce an output even before it would receive the input, which is impossible. This difficulty can be alleviated by permitting the final transfer function $H(z)$ to delay the signal for a sufficiently long time. We define

$$H(z) = z^{-M} H_1(z) = z^{-M} \sum_{m=M}^{-M} c_m z^m \qquad (8\text{-}13)$$

The reader is invited to verify (Prob. 8-3) that this result can then be expressed in the form

$$H(z) = \sum_{i=0}^{2M} a_i z^{-i} \qquad (8\text{-}14)$$

where

$$a_i = c_{M-i} \qquad (8\text{-}15)$$

The FIR transfer function of (8-14) is of order 2M, which implies that there will be 2M delays in a direct implementation. Letting τ represent the length of the impulse response, we have

$$\tau = 2MT \qquad (8\text{-}16)$$

The amplitude response is completely unaffected by the time shift and is still $A(f)$. On the other hand, the additional time delay introduces a phase shift $\beta(f)$ for $H(z)$ which, in radians, is given by

$$\beta(f) = -MT\omega = -2\pi MTf \qquad (8\text{-}17)$$

Observe that the phase is a linear function of frequency representing a constant time delay of MT seconds. The delay increases linearly with the order of the filter.

Consider next the case of a *sine series* representation. In this case, it is necessary that the amplitude response $A_d(f)$ be an odd periodic function with a period f_s. Again, let $A(f)$ represent the approximation resulting from M terms. The form of the response in a typical case is illustrated in Fig. 8-2. The form of the finite series is

$$A(f) = \sum_{m=1}^{M} \beta_m \sin 2\pi m\, Tf \qquad (8\text{-}18)$$

The reader is invited to show (Prob. 8-2) that the following expression can be obtained:

$$\beta_m = \frac{4}{f_s} \int_0^{f_s/2} A_d(f) \sin 2\pi m\, Tf\, df \qquad (8\text{-}19)$$

In exponential form, (8-18) can be expressed as

$$A(f) = \sum_{m=-M}^{M} \frac{d_m}{j} \, \epsilon^{j\, 2\pi m\, Tf} \qquad (8\text{-}20)$$

where

$$d_m = \frac{\beta_m}{2} = \frac{2}{f_s} \int_0^{f_s/2} \mathrm{A}_d(f) \sin 2\pi\, m\, Tf\, df \qquad (8\text{-}21)$$

and

$$d_{-m} = -d_m \qquad (8\text{-}22)$$

Before we can convert (8-20) to a z-domain function, it is necessary to investigate the significance of the imaginary j factor in the denominator. This factor was not present for the cosine series, and there was no delay or phase shift at this stage of the development. Certainly, we want to eliminate any complex or imaginary factors before obtaining the final transfer function, since we have dealt only with real coefficients in that form.

The problem is rectified by the requirement that the phase must be even when the amplitude is assumed to be odd. Let $\beta_1(f)$ represent the phase corresponding to the initial transfer function. Thus, instead of $\mathrm{A}(f)$, we actually need $\mathrm{A}(f) \ \underline{/\beta_1(f)}$ before changing to the z-plane function, and it is necessary that $\beta_1(f)$ be even. A phase shift $\beta_1(f) = \pi/2$, corresponding to a j factor in the numerator, will serve the purpose. Thus,

$$\mathrm{A}(f) \ \underline{/\beta_1(f)} = \sum_{m=-M}^{M} d_m \epsilon^{j\, 2\pi\, m\, Tf} \qquad (8\text{-}23)$$

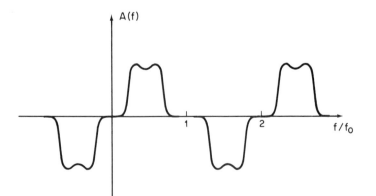

Figure 8-2 Fourier series approximation for odd amplitude response.

Replacing $\epsilon^{j\,2\pi\,Tf}$ by z and turning the series around, we have

$$H_1(z) = \sum_{m=M}^{-M} d_m z^m \qquad (8\text{-}24)$$

As in the case of the cosine series, the initial result of (8-24) is a noncausal function. Again, we multiply by z^{-M} to obtain the required causal function. The reader is invited to verify (Prob. 8-4) that the result can be expressed as

$$H(z) = \sum_{i=0}^{2M} a_i z^{-i} \qquad (8\text{-}25)$$

where

$$a_i = d_{M-i} \qquad (8\text{-}26)$$

The resulting transfer function is of order 2M. Note that the middle term in (8-25) is missing in this case, i.e., $a_M = 0$. This property arises from the absence of a dc term in the sine series expansion.

As in the case of the cosine series, the amplitude response is unaffected by the delay and is simply $A(f)$. However, the resulting phase response $\beta(f)$ will be a combination of the phase associated with the noncausal function and the additonal phase due to the added delay. The net result in radians is

$$\beta(f) = \frac{\pi}{2} - MT\omega = \frac{\pi}{2} - 2\pi MTf \qquad (8\text{-}27)$$

The choice as to whether a given function should be expanded in cosine or sine terms usually depends on whether the phase shift should be an exact linear phase of the form of (8-17) or a constant 90° phase shift plus a linear phase term of the form of (8-27). If the desired response is a filter function whose passband exhibits a constant amplitude response, the cosine series is normally the form that would be used. The sine series is used primarily in special cases where the amplitude response is asymptotic at low frequencies to ω^k, with k odd. An example of this type is a digital differentiator. (The reader might wish to momentarily look ahead to Fig. 8-10 for an illustration of this function.)

Before leaving this section, we will present simplified alternative forms for obtaining the impulse response coefficients when the frequency response is expressed in terms of the normalized frequency

$v = f/f_0$, where $f_0 = f_s/2$ is the folding frequency. Let $A_d(v)$ represent the desired amplitude response, and let $A(v)$ represent the approximation. With this approach, the period must always be selected as 2 units on the v scale.

For the *cosine* series, expressions for $A(v)$ and c_m are

$$A(v) = \sum_{m=-M}^{M} c_m \epsilon^{jm\pi v} \qquad (8\text{-}28)$$

$$c_m = \int_0^1 A_d(v) \cos m\pi v \, dv \qquad (8\text{-}29)$$

For the *sine* series, expressions for $A(v)$ and d_m are

$$A(v) = \sum_{m=-M}^{M} \frac{d_m}{j} \epsilon^{jm\pi v} \qquad (8\text{-}30)$$

$$d_m = \int_0^1 A_d(v) \sin m\pi v \, dv \qquad (8\text{-}31)$$

The procedure for determining $H(z)$ is essentially the same as before. In this case, the noncausal form of the transfer function is obtained by substituting z for $\epsilon^{j\pi v}$. From that point on, the process is the same as discussed earlier. The primary advantage of using the normalized form is that the results are independent of the actual values of the frequencies involved, being dependent only on the relative frequencies with respect to the folding or sampling frequency.

Example 8-1

A low-pass FIR digital filter is to be designed using the Fourier series approach. The desired amplitude response is

$A_d(f) = 1$ for $0 \leq f < 125$ Hz

$\qquad = 0$ elsewhere in the range $0 \leq f \leq f_0$

The sampling frequency is 1 kHz, and the impulse response is to be limited to 20 delays. Determine the transfer function using the techniques of this section.

Solution

The appropriate representation for the desired amplitude response is as an even function of frequency as shown in Fig. 8-3. The curve in (a) is

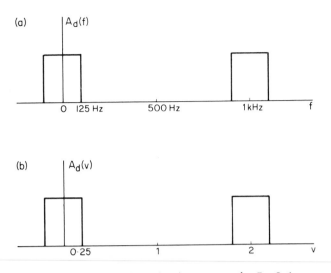

Figure 8-3 Desired amplitude response for Ex. 8-1.

shown in terms of the actual frequency scale, while the curve in (b) corresponds to a normalized frequency scale. Note that the folding frequency is $f_0 = 500$ Hz. For convenience, the problem will be developed in terms of the normalized frequency. Thus, the desired response can be restated for expansion purposes as

$$A_d(v) = 1 \text{ for } -0.25 < v < 0.25$$

$$= 0 \text{ elsewhere in the range } -1 < v < 1$$

The coefficients c_m can be determined from (8-29). We have

$$c_m = \int_0^{0.25} (1) \cos m \pi v \, dv = \left. \frac{\sin m \pi v}{m \pi} \right]_0^{0.25}$$

$$= \frac{\sin 0.25 \, m \pi}{m \pi}$$

(8-32)

The requirement that the impulse response be limited to 20 delays implies that the order of the transfer function should be 20. There could be as many as 21 terms in the impulse response, since one component need not be delayed. The necessary coefficients may be obtained by evaluating (8-32) for $m = 0$ through $m = 10$. The various values are

$$c_0 = 0.25 \qquad\qquad c_1 = 0.22507908$$
$$c_2 = 0.15915494 \qquad\qquad c_3 = 0.07502636$$

$$c_4 = 0 \qquad\qquad c_5 = -0.04501582$$
$$c_6 = -0.05305165 \qquad c_7 = -0.03215415 \qquad (8\text{-}33)$$
$$c_8 = 0 \qquad\qquad c_9 = 0.02500879$$
$$c_{10} = 0.03183099$$

The initial form of the transfer function is of the form of (8-12) with coefficients for negative i determined by $c_{-m} = c_m$. To make this function causal, we must multiply by z^{-10}. The final result can be expressed as

$$H(z) = \sum_{i=0}^{20} a_i z^{-i} \qquad (8\text{-}34)$$

where $a_i = c_{10-i}$. This result will be discussed in more detail and extended in Ex. 8-2 at the end of Sect. 8-3. The final array of a_i coefficients in (8-34) may be observed in the column "Rectangular" in Table 8-1.

8-3 WINDOW FUNCTIONS

All of the window functions that will be considered share this property: they are even functions of time when centered at the origin. For that reason, it is desirable to momentarily return to the noncausal form of the filter impulse response to study the effects produced. After the impulse response has been appropriately modified, the required delay may be inserted to make the final result causal.

Table 8-1
Digital filter coefficients for Exs. 8-1 and 8-2.

		Rectangular	Triangular	Hanning	Hamming	Kaiser ($\theta = 2\pi$)
a_0	a_{20}	0.03183099	0	0	0.00254648	0.00036542
a_1	a_{19}	0.02500879	0.00250088	0.00061201	0.00256375	0.00113712
a_2	a_{18}	0	0	0	0	0
a_3	a_{17}	-0.03215415	-0.00964624	-0.00662721	-0.00866936	-0.00637990
a_4	a_{16}	-0.05305165	-0.02122066	-0.01832889	-0.02110671	-0.01698822
a_5	a_{15}	-0.04501582	-0.02250791	-0.2250791	-0.02430854	-0.02092616
a_6	a_{14}	0	0	0	0	0
a_7	a_{13}	0.07502636	0.05251845	0.05956287	0.06079995	0.05758099
a_8	a_{12}	0.15915494	0.12732395	0.14395700	0.14517283	0.14168986
a_9	a_{11}	0.22507908	0.2025717	0.21957100	0.22001165	0.21867619
	a_{10}	0.25	0.25	0.25	0.25	0.25

The results that follow will be developed in terms of the c_m coefficients of the cosine series. Should the series be a sine series, one need only replace the c_m coefficients by the d_m coefficients, and the results are equally valid.

Consider, then, the noncausal FIR transfer function

$$H_1(z) = \sum_{m=-M}^{M} c_m z^{-m} \qquad (8\text{-}35)$$

The impulse response corresponding to (8-35) is

$$h_1(n) = \sum_{m=-M}^{M} c_m \delta(n-m) \qquad (8\text{-}36)$$

The resulting impulse response is centered at the origin and is an even function of n in the case of the cosine series. (It would be an odd function of n for a sine series.)

If the coefficients of the FIR filter are determined from the procedure of the last section, a particular difficulty arises that has not yet been considered. The coefficients of the transfer function were obtained by terminating the Fourier series expansion of the desired frequency function with a finite number of terms. It will be recalled from the familiar Gibbs phenomenon that abrupt termination may result in poor convergence of the resulting series, particularly in the vicinity of discontinuities.

This problem is illustrated in Fig. 8-4. A hypothetical impulse response $h_d(n)$ with an infinite number of terms is shown in (a). For purposes of discussion, assume that this series will converge uniformly to represent the desired amplitude response $A_d(f)$ shown in (b). (Only a portion of one period of the response is shown.) In (c), the series is terminated abruptly without modifying any of the coefficients. This terminated series $h_1(n)$ fails to converge uniformly at all points, so that the resulting amplitude response $A_1(f)$ shown in (d) suffers from oscillations and poor convergence.

The process of terminating the series after a finite number of terms can be thought of as multiplying the infinite-length impulse response by a finite-width *window function*. In a sense, the window function determines how much of the original impulse response that we can "see," so the term "window" is quite descriptive. In the case where the series is abruptly terminated without modification of any coefficients, we may consider the window function to be *rectangular*. The rectangular window function can be considered as the source of some of the convergence difficulties, as will be seen shortly.

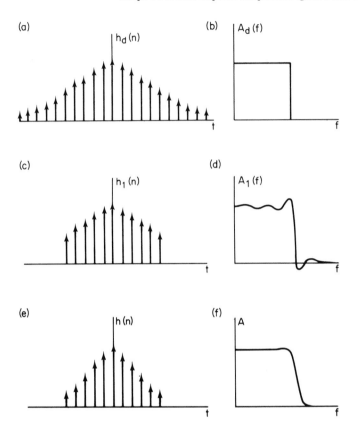

Figure 8-4 Illustrations for window function discussion.

Since it is necessary to terminate the series with a finite number of terms, the question arises whether there might be a better window function for this purpose. We can gain some insight into this concept by considering again that the terminated series can be represented as the product of the infinite-length impulse response and a window function. Since multiplication in the time-domain corresponds to convolution in the frequency-domain, the actual frequency response may be considered as the convolution of the desired frequency response and the frequency response (Fourier transform) of the window function. The Fourier transform of the rectangular window function exhibits significant oscillations and poor high-frequency convergence. When this spectrum is convolved with the desired amplitude response, poor convergence of the resulting amplitude response may result.

We will now investigate the use of other possible window functions that minimize some of the difficulties encountered with the rectangular function. In order for the spectrum of the window function to have minimal effect on the desired amplitude response when the two functions are convolved, it is necessary that the window spectrum approximate an impulse function in some sense. This means that as much of its energy as possible should be concentrated at the center of the spectrum. Obviously, an ideal impulse spectrum is impossible since this would require an infinitely long window.

In general, the spectrum of a window function consists of a *main lobe* representing the middle of the spectrum and various *side lobes* located on either side of the main lobe. It is desired that the window function satisfy the two criteria (a) the main lobe should be as narrow as possible, and (b) the maximum side lobe level should be as small as possible relative to the main lobe.

It turns out that both of these criteria cannot be simultaneously optimized, so that most usable window functions represent a suitable compromise between the two factors. A window function in which minimization of the main lobe width is the primary objective would tend to have a sharper cutoff but might suffer from some oscillations in the passband and significant ripple of the stopband. Conversely, a window function in which minimization of the side lobe level is the primary objective would tend to have a smooth amplitude response and very low ripple in the stopband, but the sharpness of cutoff might not be as great.

Referring again to Fig. 8-4, the impulse response $h(n)$ shown in (e) represents the function obtained by multiplying the impulse response in (a) by a more desirable window function than the rectangular window. The modified response $A(f)$ shown in (f) is now smoother and has a lower ripple level in the stopband.

All window functions that will be considered are even functions of n when centered at the origin. Let w_m represent the various coefficients of a particular window function, and let c_m' represent the coefficients of the modified transfer function. The modification is simply

$$c_m' = w_m c_m \qquad (8\text{-}37)$$

The modified noncausal transfer function $H_1'(z)$ is then

$$H_1'(z) = \sum_{m=-M}^{M} c_m' z^{-m} \qquad (8\text{-}38)$$

The resulting function may be made causal by multiplying by z^{-M}, and the final result is

$$H(z) = \sum_{i=0}^{2M} a_i z^{-i} \qquad (8\text{-}39)$$

where

$$a_i = c'_{M-i} \qquad (8\text{-}40)$$

For a sine series, the various c_m terms in the preceding development should be replaced by d_m terms.

We will now discuss some of the window functions that either have been or could be used in designing FIR filters. It is appropriate to mention at this point that these same window functions may be used in spectral analysis in conjunction with the discrete Fourier transform, so that reference to them will be made again in Chapt. 10.

For convenience in development and presentation, all functions will be presented in continuous-time form as a function of the variable t. To apply these functions to a discrete-time function, the variable t should be replaced by nT, and the variable n can then assume values from 0 to M. All functions are even and are assumed to have a width τ, which is the desired width of the filter impulse response. Because of the even nature of these functions, the window coefficients in the range from -1 to $-M$ are readily obtained from those in the positive range.

In each case, we shall let $w(t)$ denote the time-domain window function and $W(f)$ represent its Fourier transform. Because of the number of curves involved and the application to spectral analysis in Chapt. 10, the window functions and their transforms are given in the Appendix. Figure numbers beginning with the letter A in the remainder of this section refer to curves in the Appendix.

In studying the amplitude frequency response of window functions, it is desirable to employ a decibel scale. All of the amplitude response curves will be presented in terms of a decibel function $W_{db}(f)$. In each case, the decibel response is normalized with respect to the dc value $W(0)$. The function $W_{db}(f)$ is then defined as

$$W_{db}(f) = 20 \log_{10} \frac{|W(f)|}{W(0)} \qquad (8\text{-}41)$$

We will now consider some common window functions.

Rectangular Window. The rectangular window will be considered primarily as a basis for reference in studying other functions. The rectangular function is simply

$$w(t) = 1 \text{ for } |t| < \frac{\tau}{2}$$
$$= 0 \text{ elsewhere} \qquad (8\text{-}42)$$

The Fourier transform is

$$W(f) = \frac{\tau \sin \pi f \tau}{\pi f \tau} \qquad (8\text{-}43)$$

The function $w(t)$ is one of the curves shown in Fig. A-1, and $W_{db}(f)$ is shown in Fig. A-2, both located in the Appendix.

Triangular Window. The triangular window function is defined as

$$w(t) = 1 - \frac{2|t|}{\tau} \text{ for } |t| \leq \frac{\tau}{2} \qquad (8\text{-}44)$$
$$= 0 \text{ elsewhere}$$

We leave as an exercise (Prob. 8-16) for the reader to show that the Fourier transform of (8-44) is

$$W(f) = \frac{\tau}{2} \left[\frac{\sin (\pi f \tau / 2)}{(\pi f \tau / 2)} \right]^2 \qquad (8\text{-}45)$$

The function $w(t)$ is shown along with the rectangular window in Fig. A-1, and $W_{db}(f)$ is shown in Fig. A-3, both in the Appendix. The width of the main lobe of the triangular window function is about twice as wide as that of the rectangular window, but the side lobe level is much lower.

Hanning Window. The Hanning, or cosine-squared, window function is defined as

$$w(t) = \cos^2 \frac{\pi t}{\tau} = \frac{1}{2} \left(1 + \cos \frac{2\pi t}{\tau} \right) \text{ for } |t| \leq \frac{\tau}{2} \qquad (8\text{-}46)$$
$$= 0 \text{ elsewhere}$$

We leave as an exercise (Prob. 8-17) for the reader to show that

$$W(f) = \frac{\tau}{2} \frac{\sin \pi f \tau}{\pi f \tau} \left[\frac{1}{1 - (f\tau)^2} \right] \qquad (8\text{-}47)$$

The function $w(t)$ is shown in Fig. A-4, and $W_{db}(f)$ is shown in Fig. A-5, in the Appendix.

Hamming Window. The Hamming window function is defined as

$$w(t) = 0.54 + 0.46 \cos \frac{2\pi t}{\tau} \text{ for } |t| \leq \frac{\tau}{2}$$
$$= 0 \text{ elsewhere} \tag{8-48}$$

We leave as an exercise (Prob. 8-18) for the reader to show that

$$W(f) = \frac{\tau \sin \pi f \tau}{\pi f \tau} \left[\frac{0.54 - 0.08(f\tau)^2}{1 - (f\tau)^2} \right] \tag{8-49}$$

The function $w(t)$ is shown in Fig. A-6, and $W_{db}(f)$ is shown in Fig. A-7.

Kaiser Windows. A family of flexible window functions can be described by the equation.

$$w(t) = \frac{I_0[\theta \sqrt{1 - (2t/\tau)^2}]}{I_0(\theta)} \text{ for } |t| \leq \frac{\tau}{2} \tag{8-50}$$

where I_0 is the modified Bessel function of the first kind and of order zero, and θ is a parameter. By varying the parameter θ, the tradeoff between the main lobe width and the side lobe level can be adjusted. Large values of θ correspond to wider main lobe widths and smaller side lobe levels. Several typical Kaiser functions are shown in Fig. A-8.

The Fourier transform corresponding to (8-50) can be expressed as

$$W(f) = \frac{\tau \sin [\sqrt{(\pi f \tau)^2 - \theta^2}]}{I_0(\theta)\sqrt{(\pi f \tau)^2 - \theta^2}} \tag{8-51}$$

When the expression under the radical in (8-51) is negative, the function can be expressed in terms of the hyperbolic sine function (Prob. 8-19). Curves of $W_{db}(f)$ corresponding to the three cases given in Fig. A-8 are shown in Figs. A-9, A-10, and A-11.

Other Window Functions. Other window functions include the *Blackman window* and the *Dolph-Chebyshev* window. The Blackman window consists of a constant and two cosine terms. (See Prob. 8-20.) The peak amplitude of the side lobe level of the Blackman window spectrum is more than 80 dB down from the main lobe level, but the main lobe has a width triple that of the rectangular window. The Dolph-Chebyshev window is optimum in the sense that the main-lobe width is as small as possible for a given side-lobe peak ripple level.

Example 8-2

Compare the various FIR digital filter designs for the response of Ex. 8-1 using each of the following window functions: (a) rectangular, (b) triangular, (c) Hanning, (d) Hamming, (e) Kaiser ($\theta = 2\pi$).

Solution

In each of the cases that follow, the coefficients representing the terms of the various transfer functions are listed in Table 8-1. The coefficients represent the product of the original unmodified transfer function (which corresponds to the coefficients of the rectangular window) and the window function for the particular case according to (8-37).

(a) *Rectangular Window.* This is the initial form obtained in Ex. 8-1, and it represents no modification in the original coefficients. The decibel amplitude response corresponding to this case is shown in Fig. 8-5. Note that while the response displays a reasonably sharp rate of cutoff, the sidelobe ripple level is rather high.

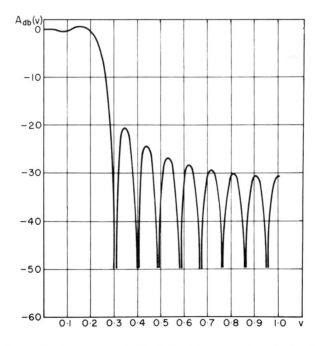

Figure 8-5 Amplitude response for Ex. 8-2 with rectangular window function.

(b) *Triangular Window.* The coefficients of the triangular window are obtained in this case by setting $t = m\,T$ and $\tau = 20T$ in (8-44) with the result

$$w_m = 1 - \frac{|m|}{10} \text{ for } |m| \leqslant 10 \qquad (8\text{-}52)$$

As previously discussed, the window coefficients are applied to the noncausal form of the transfer function centered at the origin. Of course, this is equivalent to considering the 10th coefficient in each column of Table 8-1 as the origin for this purpose.

The amplitude response is shown in Fig. 8-6. The sidelobe level has been reduced significantly, although the sharpness of cutoff is not as great.

(c) *Hanning Window.* The coefficients of the Hanning window function are obtained from (8-46) and are given by

$$w_m = \frac{1}{2}\left(1 + \cos\frac{m\pi}{10}\right) \text{ for } |m| \leqslant 10 \qquad (8\text{-}53)$$

The amplitude response is shown in Fig. 8-7.

(d) *Hamming Window.* The coefficients of the Hamming window function are obtained from (8-48) and are given by

$$w_m = 0.54 + 0.46 \cos\frac{m\pi}{10} \text{ for } |m| \leqslant 10 \qquad (8\text{-}54)$$

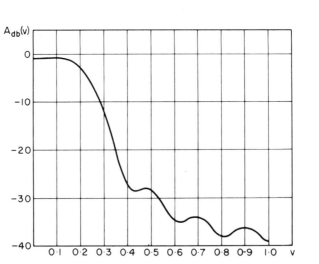

Figure 8-6 Amplitude response for Ex. 8-2 with triangular window function.

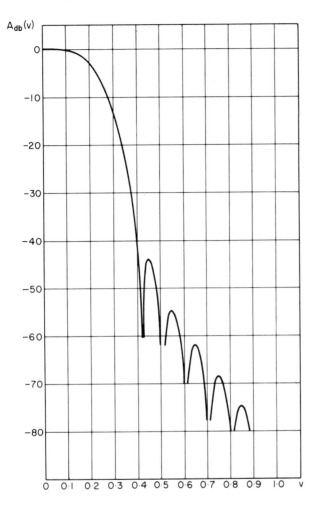

Figure 8-7 Amplitude response for Ex. 8-2 with Hanning window function.

The amplitude response is shown in Fig. 8-8.

(e) *Kaiser Window*. The coefficients of the Kaiser window function are obtained from (8-50) with $\theta = 2\pi$, and this results in

$$w_m = \frac{I_0[2\pi\sqrt{1 - (m/10)^2}]}{I_0(2\pi)} \text{ for } |m| \leqslant 10 \qquad (8\text{-}55)$$

The amplitude response is shown in Fig. 8-9.

Example 8-3

Design an FIR filter whose amplitude response approximates that of an ideal differentiator. The function is to be limited to a 12th order approximation, and the Hamming window function is to be used.

Solution

The amplitude response of an ideal analog differentiator is simply $A(f) = \omega$. The corresponding digital function must be periodic in nature. An odd function representation is the ideal choice in this case since an ideal differentiator should exhibit a constant 90° phase shift. The assumed form of the ideal amplitude response is shown in Fig. 8-10.

The frequency response expressed in terms of the actual frequency rather than the normalized form will be used in this case due

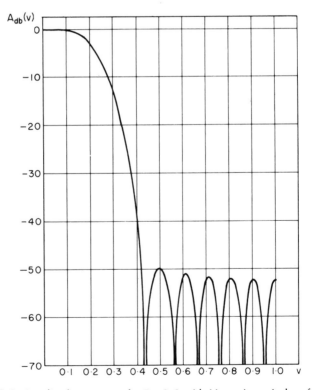

Figure 8-8 Amplitude response for Ex. 8-2 with Hamming window function.

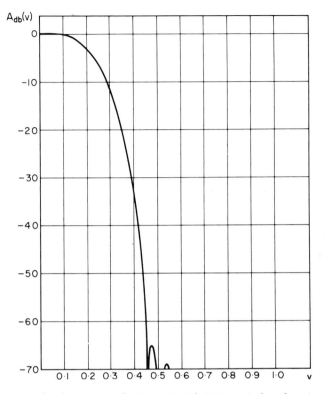

Figure 8-9 Amplitude response for Ex. 8-2 with Kaiser window function ($\theta = 2\pi$).

to the presence of the first-order variation with respect to the frequency. The desired response in one period can be written as

$$A_d(f) = \omega \text{ for } \frac{-f_s}{2} < f < \frac{f_s}{2} \tag{8-56}$$

The coefficients d_m are determined from (8-21) as

$$d_m = \frac{2}{f_s} \int_0^{f_s/2} \omega \sin 2\pi m\,Tf\,df$$

$$= \frac{4\pi}{f_s} \left[\frac{\sin 2\pi m\,Tf}{(2\pi m\,T)^2} - \frac{f \cos 2\pi m\,Tf}{2\pi m\,T} \right]_0^{f_s/2} \tag{8-57}$$

$$= -\frac{\cos m\pi}{m\,T} = \frac{(-1)^{m+1}}{m\,T}$$

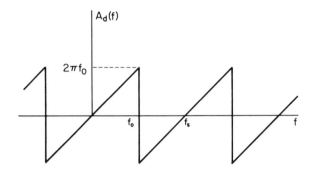

Figure 8-10 Desired amplitude response for FIR differentiator.

From the preceding result, it can be seen that the sample time T must be specified before the final values can be obtained. For the purpose of this example, we shall simply choose T = 1 s. Any other value would affect only the relative levels of the various c_m coefficients, not the shape of the resulting response. The noncausal basic coefficients are then

$$d_m = \frac{(-1)^{m+1}}{m} \text{ for } m \neq 0 \text{ and } -6 \leq m \leq 6 \qquad (8\text{-}58)$$

The Hamming window function coefficients are obtained from (8-48) with $t = n\,T$ and $\tau = 12T$. We have

$$w_m = 0.54 + 0.46 \cos\frac{m\pi}{6} \text{ for } |m| \leq 6 \qquad (8\text{-}59)$$

Table 8-2
Digital filter coefficients for Ex. 8-3.

		Original Coefficients	Modified by Hamming Window
a_0	a_{12}	-0.16666667	-0.01333333
a_1	a_{11}	0.20000000	0.02832566
a_2	a_{10}	-0.25000000	-0.07750000
a_3	a_9	0.33333333	0.18000000
a_4	a_8	-0.50000000	-0.38500000
a_5	a_7	1.00000000	0.93837169

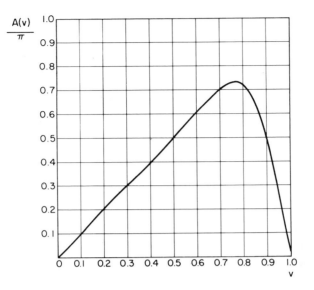

Figure 8-11 Actual amplitude response for 12th order FIR differentiator using Hamming window function.

After multiplication of the w_m coefficients by the d_m coefficients, the final coefficients a_i of the transfer function are obtained by the procedure outlined in (8-37) through (8-40), with c_m replaced by d_m in these equations. The coefficients before and after multiplication by the window function are listed in Table 8-2. The actual amplitude response is shown in Fig. 8-11.

This example was not necessarily intended to represent any particular optimum design for a digital differentiator. Rather, it was selected as a representative application for a sine series frequency response expansion. However, this result might be satisfactory for many applications in which approximate numerical differentiation is required. Various optimum differentiating digital filters of both the recursive and nonrecursive varieties have been developed.

_____ *PROBLEMS* _____

8-1 Derive equation (8-9).

8-2 Derive equation (8-19).

8-3 Verify that equations (8-14) and (8-15) are correct.

8-4 Verify that equations (8-25) and (8-26) are correct.

8-5 The transfer function of a certain FIR filter is given by

$$H(z) = \frac{1}{10}[1 + 2z^{-1} + 4z^{-2} + 2z^{-3} + z^{-4}]$$

(a) Determine the frequency response of the filter. Express in the form of an amplitude response and a phase response. (Hint: The amplitude response can be expressed as a cosine series in this case.)

(b) Determine the impulse response $h(n)$.

8-6 The filter of Prob. 8-5 is excited by the discrete-time step function

$$x(n) = u(n)$$

(a) Determine the response $y(n)$ using the transfer function approach.

(b) Determine the response using direct convolution. Carry out the convolution far enough so that the steady-state condition is reached.

8-7 Show that both the phase and group delay functions for a causal FIR filter derived from a *cosine* series are identical and constant.

8-8 Show that the phase and group delay functions for a causal FIR filter derived from a *sine* series are different. Furthermore, show that the group delay is constant, but that the phase delay is not.

8-9 The desired amplitude response of a certain low-pass FIR filter can be stated as

$$A_d(f) = 1 \text{ for } 0 \leq f \leq 500 \text{ Hz}$$
$$= 0 \text{ elsewhere in the range } 0 \leq f \leq f_0$$

The sampling rate is 2 kHz, and the impulse response is to be 30 ms long. Using a rectangular window function, determine the transfer function.

8-10 Repeat Prob. 8-9 if the desired amplitude response is

$$A_d(f) = 1 \text{ for } 0 \leq f \leq 50 \text{ Hz}$$
$$= 0 \text{ elsewhere in the range } 0 \leq f \leq f_0$$

All other quantities are unchanged.

8-11 A Hanning window function is to be used to smooth the coefficients in Prob. 8-9. Determine the modified transfer function.

8-12 A Hamming window function is to be used to smooth the coefficients in Prob. 8-10. Determine the modified transfer function.

8-13 The desired amplitude response of a certain band-pass FIR filter can be stated as

$$A_d(f) = 1 \text{ for } 250 \leqslant f \leqslant 750 \text{ Hz}$$
$$= 0 \text{ elsewhere in the range } 0 \leqslant f \leqslant f_0$$

The sampling rate is 2 kHz, and the impulse response is to be limited to 30 delays. Using a Hamming window function, determine the transfer function.

8-14 Repeat Prob. 8-13 if the desired amplitude response is

$$A_d(f) = 1 \text{ for } 450 \leqslant f \leqslant 550 \text{ Hz}$$
$$= 0 \text{ elsewhere in the range } 0 \leqslant f \leqslant f_0$$

All other quantities are unchanged.

8-15 The Fourier transforms of window functions containing trigonometric terms, such as the Hanning and Hamming functions, can be most easily derived by the procedure that follows: Consider $w(t)$ to be expressible as the product of a periodic trigonometric function $g(t)$, which extends to infinity in both directions, and a nonperiodic pulse $p(t)$ of width τ, i.e.

$$w(t) = p(t)g(t)$$

Assume that $g(t)$ can be expressed as

$$g(t) = \sum_n c_n \epsilon^{j2\pi nf_1 t}$$

Show that $W(f) = F[w(t)]$ can be expressed as

$$W(f) = \sum_n c_n P(f - nf_1)$$

where

$$P(f) = F[p(t)]$$

8-16 Derive the Fourier transform of the triangular window function, i.e., equation (8-45).

8-17 Derive the Fourier transform of the Hanning window function, i.e., equation (8-47). Hint: Consider the result of Prob. 8-15.

8-18 Derive the Fourier transform of the Hamming window function, i.e., equation (8-49). Hint: Consider the result of Prob. 8-15.

8-19 Show that when the quantity under the radical in equation (8-51) is negative, the function may be expressed as

$$W(f) = \frac{\tau}{I_0(\theta)} \frac{\sinh\left[\sqrt{\theta^2 - (\pi f \tau)^2}\right]}{\sqrt{\theta^2 - (\pi f \tau)^2}}$$

8-20 The Blackman window function is defined by

$$w(t) = 0.42 + 0.5 \cos\frac{2\pi t}{\tau} + 0.08 \cos\frac{4\pi t}{\tau} \text{ for } |t| \leq \frac{\tau}{2}$$

Using the results of Prob. 8-15, show that the Fourier transform $W(f)$ is

$$W(f) = \tau \frac{\sin\pi f\tau}{\pi f\tau}\left[0.42 + \frac{0.5\,(f\tau)^2}{1 - (f\tau)^2} - \frac{0.08\,(f\tau)^2}{4 - (f\tau)^2}\right]$$

9

DISCRETE AND FAST
FOURIER TRANSFORMS

9-0 INTRODUCTION

The primary objective in this chapter is the development of the basic theory and computational procedures for evaluating discrete Fourier transforms. The particular aspect of major importance is the so-called fast Fourier transform (FFT), which is a high-speed algorithm for computing the Fourier transform of a discrete-time signal. The FFT has made it possible to compute the Fourier transforms of signals containing thousands of points in a matter of milliseconds.

The material will emphasize various transform properties both from the analytical and the computational points of view. Various signal flow graphs and computer flow charts will be presented to enhance the design of FFT processing systems. Some of the possible applications of the FFT will be discussed in the next chapter, but the material in this chapter is necessary as a basis for understanding its use.

9-1 FORMS OF THE FOURIER TRANSFORM

In describing the properties of the Fourier transform and inverse transform, it is quite convenient to use the concepts of time and frequency, even though the transformation is applicable to a wide range of physical and mathematical problems having other variables. It is very instructive to see the variety of forms that the transform takes when the time and frequency variables assume combinations of continuous and discrete forms.

The following quantities are defined:

t = continuous-time variable

T = time increment between successive components when a time function is sampled

t_p = effective period for a time function when it is periodic

f = continuous-frequency variable

F = frequency increment between successive components when a frequency function is sampled

f_s = sampling rate or frequency when a time function is sampled, i.e., the number of samples per second

N = number of samples in the range $0 \leqslant t < t_p$ when the time function is sampled. N is also equal to the number of samples in the range $0 \leqslant f < f_s$ when the frequency function is sampled.

From the previous definitions, it can be seen that when the time function is sampled and the length of the signal is limited to t_p, we have

$$t_p = \text{NT} \qquad (9\text{-}1)$$

Similarly, when the frequency function is sampled and the width of the frequency function is limited to f_s, we have

$$f_s = \text{NF} \qquad (9\text{-}2)$$

We will now consider four possible forms that could be used in representing Fourier transform and inverse transform functions. These correspond to the four combinations obtained from successively assuming the time and frequency variables each to be continuous and discrete. In some cases, we will encounter functions previously used, but the notation chosen will be slightly different here for the sake of comparison with the other functions. The properties of these functions will be illustrated by a series of transform pairs shown in Figs. 9-1 through 9-4. The hypothetical functions actually shown in these figures were chosen purely for clarity in illustrating various properties and are not intended to represent any actual transform pairs.

1. *Continuous-Time and Continuous-Frequency.* This form was encountered in Chapt. 3 and was used there for describing the continuous spectrum of a nonperiodic time signal. The Fourier transform $X(f)$ of a continuous time function $x(t)$ can be expressed as

$$X(f) = \int_{-\infty}^{\infty} x(t)\, \epsilon^{-j\,2\pi ft}\, dt \qquad (9\text{-}3)$$

The inverse transform is

$$x(t) = \int_{-\infty}^{\infty} X(f)\, \epsilon^{j\,2\pi ft}\, df \qquad (9\text{-}4)$$

The forms for the time function and the transform function are illustrated in Fig. 9-1, which shows that *a nonperiodic continuous-time function corresponds to a nonperiodic continuous-frequency transform function.*

2. *Continuous-Time and Discrete-Frequency.* This is the form of the Fourier transform that is most often referred to as a Fourier series, and it was also encountered in Chapt. 3. Let $x(t)$ represent a periodic continuous-time function with period t_p. The Fourier transform of $x(t)$ is a discrete-frequency function, which we will denote here by $X(m\,F)$. The transform pair is given by

$$X(m\,F) = \frac{1}{t_p}\int_{t_p} x(t)\, \epsilon^{-j\,2\pi m Ft}\, dt \qquad (9\text{-}5)$$

and

$$x(t) = \sum_{-\infty}^{\infty} X(m\,F)\epsilon^{j\,2\pi m Ft} \qquad (9\text{-}6)$$

The integral in (9-5) is evaluated over one period of $x(t)$.

Some of the properties of these functions are illustrated in Fig. 9-2. In giving the transform relationships, it was stated that $x(t)$ was periodic. This property automatically forces the transform to be a discrete-frequency function. On the other hand, consider the possibility where $x(t)$ is originally not periodic, which leads to a continuous-frequency transform as shown in Fig. 9-1. Then assume that the transform is sampled. In effect, the process of sampling the spectrum leads to a periodic time function upon applying the inverse transform of (9-6). Thus, in one sense, it is immaterial whether the original time function was periodic or not if the spectrum is sampled. The sampling process itself forces the time function to be periodic if inversion is performed.

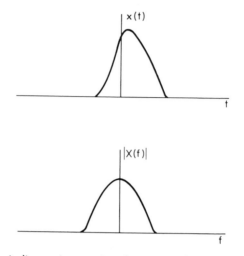

Figure 9-1 Nonperiodic continuous-time function and its Fourier transform, which is a nonperiodic continuous-frequency function.

The frequency increment F between successive spectral components is related to the time period t_p by

$$F = \frac{1}{t_p} \tag{9-7}$$

The conclusion is that a *periodic continuous-time function corresponds to a nonperiodic discrete-frequency transform function.*

3. *Discrete-time and Continuous-Frequency.* This form of the Fourier transform is equivalent to evaluating the z-transform and inverse transform on the unit circle. The relationships may be obtained by applying this concept to the z-transform pair given in Chapt. 4. Let $x(nT)$ represent the discrete-time signal, and let $X(f)$ represent the transform. We will leave as an exercise (Prob. 9-2) for the reader to show that the pertinent Fourier transform relationships are

$$X(f) = \sum_{0}^{\infty} x(nT)\,\epsilon^{-j\,2\pi nfT} \tag{9-8}$$

and

$$x(nT) = \frac{1}{f_s} \int_{f_s} X(f)\,\epsilon^{j\,2\pi nfT}\,df \tag{9-9}$$

The integral in (9-9) is evaluated over one period of $X(f)$.

Some of the properties of these functions are illustrated in Fig. 9-3. Sampling of the time function produces a periodic frequency function. By the same logic, if a frequency function is specified as being periodic, the resulting time function must be a discrete-time signal.

The period of the frequency function is simply the sampling rate f_s and is related to the sample time T by

$$f_s = \frac{1}{T} \qquad (9\text{-}10)$$

The conclusion is that a *nonperiodic discrete-time function corresponds to a periodic continuous-frequency transform function.*

4. *Discrete-Time and Discrete-Frequency.* We will now consider the fourth possibility, which is a situation that we have not yet encountered in any form in this text. This is the case where both the time and frequency variables are discrete. Let $x(nT)$ represent the discrete-time signal, and let $X(mF)$ represent the discrete-frequency transform function. A suitable Fourier transform pair is given by

$$X(mF) = \sum_n x(nT)\epsilon^{-j\,2\pi mn\,\text{FT}} \qquad (9\text{-}11)$$

$$x(nT) = \frac{1}{N}\sum_m X(mF)\epsilon^{j\,2\pi mn\,\text{FT}} \qquad (9\text{-}12)$$

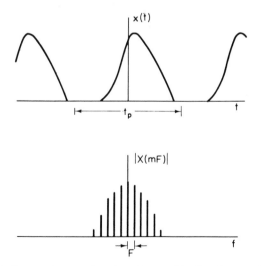

Figure 9-2 Periodic continuous-time function and its Fourier transform, which is a nonperiodic discrete-frequency function.

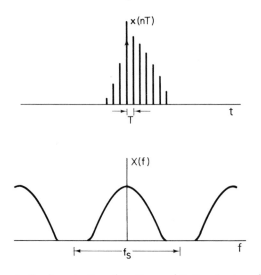

Figure 9-3 Nonperiodic discrete-time function and its Fourier transform, which is a periodic continuous-frequency function.

The summation in (9-11) is evaluated over one period of $x(nT)$, and the summation of (9-12) is evaluated over one period of $X(mF)$.

Equations (9-11) and 9-12) describe one form of the *discrete Fourier transform* (DFT) pair that constitutes an important basis for the work of this chapter. In the next section, this pair will be modified for convenience in digital computation, but for the moment, we will consider the forms as given. The basic properties of the time and frequency functions are illustrated in Fig. 9-4. Since the time function is sampled, the frequency function is periodic with a period f_s given by

$$f_s = \frac{1}{T} \qquad (9\text{-}13)$$

On the other hand, since the frequency function is sampled, the time function is periodic with a period t_p given by

$$t_p = \frac{1}{F} \qquad (9\text{-}14)$$

It can be seen, then, that *a periodic discrete-time signal corresponds to a periodic discrete-frequency transform function.*

By reviewing the preceding steps, several general conclusions can be made. If a function in one domain (either time or frequency) is periodic, then the corresponding transform in the other domain is a

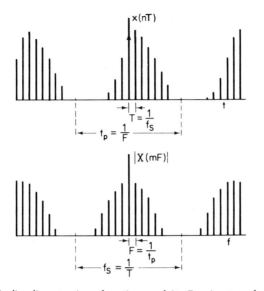

Figure 9-4 Periodic discrete-time function and its Fourier transform, which is a periodic discrete-frequency function.

sampled form, which means it is a function of a discrete variable. Conversely, if a function in one domain is sampled, then the function in the other domain becomes periodic. The period in one domain is always the reciprocal of the increment between samples in the other domain. Some of the preceding properties are summarized in Table 9-1.

When a function is evaluated by numerical procedures, it is always necessary to sample it in some fashion. This means that in order to fully evaluate a Fourier transform or inverse transform with digital operations, it is necessary that both the time and frequency functions be eventually sampled in one form or another. Thus, the last of the four possible Fourier pairs (DFT) is the one that is of primary interest in digital computation.

Table 9-1
Comparison of forms for Fourier transform pairs.

Time Function	Frequency Function
Non–Periodic and Continuous	Non–Periodic and Continuous
Periodic and Continuous	Non–Periodic and Discrete
Non–Periodic and Discrete	Periodic and Continuous
Periodic and Discrete	Periodic and Discrete

It is necessary that the implications of the sampling process in both the time and frequency domains be considered in order to ascertain that the data obtained by the discrete process represents the actual data desired. The fictitious transform pairs used for illustration in Figs. 9-1 through 9-4 were chosen to be both band- and time-limited within proper ranges. The sampling rate was assumed to be greater than twice the highest frequency, and the period of the time function was chosen to be longer than the time length of the signal, so no overlapping of time or frequency functions (aliasing) was observed in the illustrations. However, these properties are not always satisfied, so one must be very careful in applying discrete computational methods to evaluate the Fourier transforms of continuous functions. This problem will be discussed at some length in Chapt. 10.

9-2   DISCRETE FOURIER TRANSFORM

In this section, the Discrete Fourier transform pair introduced in the last section will be studied in more detail. Consider the transform pair introduced by Equations (9-11) and (9-12). The following modifications in notation and form will be made at this time:

(a) The time signal will be denoted simply as $x(n)$, with the sample time T understood.

(b) The frequency function will be denoted as $X(m)$, with the frequency increment F understood.

(c) The time domain interval will be shifted to the right so that the range of n corresponding to a period is $0 \leq n \leq N\text{-}1$. Note that the point $n = N$ actually corresponds to the beginning of a new period.

(d) The frequency domain interval of interest will be shifted to the right so that the range of m corresponding to a period in the frequency domain is $0 \leq m \leq N\text{-}1$. Note that the point $m = N$ corresponds to the beginning of a new period.

In addition to the preceding changes, let us inspect the arguments of the exponential appearing in (9-11) and (9-12). Using (9-1) and (9-14), the quantity FT can be expressed as

$$FT = \frac{1}{N} \qquad\qquad (9\text{-}15)$$

We will now define a quantity W_N as

$$W_N = \epsilon^{-j(2\pi/N)} \tag{9-16}$$

The reciprocal of W_N can be expressed as

$$W_N^{-1} = \epsilon^{j(2\pi/N)} \tag{9-17}$$

When the subscript N is omitted from W_N, it will be understood that we are dealing with an N-point signal. Thus, $W_N = W$ in some subsequent developments.

Using the relationships given by (9-15), (9-16), and (9-17), and the assumptions previously made, the discrete Fourier transform (DFT) pair can be stated as

$$X(m) = \sum_{n=0}^{N-1} x(n) W^{mn} \tag{9-18}$$

$$x(n) = \frac{1}{N} \sum_{m=0}^{N-1} X(m) W^{-mn} \tag{9-19}$$

This is the form of the DFT that will be employed in subsequent developments. In some cases, it is advantageous to express these operations in symbolic forms. The transformation of (9-18) will sometimes be denoted as

$$X(m) = D[x(n)] \tag{9-20}$$

The inverse transformation of (9-19) will sometimes be denoted as

$$x(n) = D^{-1}[X(m)] \tag{9-21}$$

Furthermore, there will be cases where the following notation is convenient in relating the various transforms pairs:

$$x(n) \rightleftharpoons X(m) \tag{9-22}$$

In studying the various properties of the DFT pair, it is convenient to think of the integers n and m as the variables rather than time and frequency (or whatever the actual physical variables are). In this sense, n represents a *time integer* and m represents a *frequency integer* whenever the physical variables are actually time and frequency. Thus, the actual time associated with an arbitrary time integer n is n T, and the actual frequency associated with an arbitrary frequency integer m is $m\,F$. As long as these points are understood, the complete problem can often be analyzed in terms of the integer variables.

Some of the properties of the transform pair in terms of these integer relationships are illustrated in Fig. 9-5. The hypothetical transform pair shown was sketched on the basis of N = 16. However, the results are labeled in terms of arbitrary N in order to make the results appear more general. Only one period of each function is shown, but both functions may actually be assumed to be periodic, as previously indicated. The time function in this case is assumed to be *real*.

In the time domain, one period corresponds to N points. The point $n = $ N actually corresponds to the beginning of a new period, and the points $n = 0$ though $n = $ N-1 are the N points contained in one period.

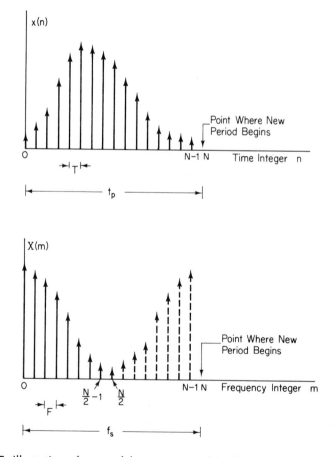

Figure 9-5 Illustration of some of the properties of the discrete Fourier transform.

Similar relationships hold in the frequency domain. A period may be assumed to correspond to the N points in the range from $m = 0$ through $m = $ N-1. The point $m = $ N corresponds to the beginning of a new period.

There is one important difference between the frequency and time functions when the time function is real, which is the most common case. Although the "period" in the frequency domain, as measured on a continuous-frequency scale, is f_s, the transform over half of the interval is related to the transform over the other half. Thus, the maximum unambiguous frequency range is $f_s/2$, which is the familiar folding frequency f_0. This concept is seen to be in perfect agreement with the results of earlier chapters.

In terms of the frequency integer, the maximum unambiguous integer when the time function is real is $(N/2)-1$, as illustrated in Fig. 9-5. Since $m = 0$ is the first integer, this means that there are $N/2$ unique transform components when the time signal has N points and is real. The point $m = N/2$ corresponds to the folding frequency for the given sampling rate. The components in the range $N/2 \le m \le $ N-1 are shown with dashed lines in Fig. 9-5.

To summarize these properties in terms of the integer variables, both $x(n)$ and $X(m)$ may be considered to be periodic functions of their respective arguments with a period N in each case. Thus,

$$x(n + kN) = x(n) \qquad (9\text{-}23)$$

and

$$X(m + kN) = X(m) \qquad (9\text{-}24)$$

for any integer k. In addition, if $x(n)$ is a real function, the transform is unique at only $N/2$ points.

Because we have stated the range of the integer variables in terms of positive values, it is convenient to redefine the concepts of even and odd functions in this case. It can be readily shown that the behavior of either $x(n)$ or $X(m)$ over the range of $N/2$ to N is identical to the behavior from $-N/2$ to 0. Thus, we can consider the interval from $N/2$ to N as a sort of "negative" time or frequency range in interpreting various even or odd properties of the transform functions.

Using this type of interpretation, the following definitions of even and odd functions will be made:

even function	$x(N-n) = x(n)$	$(9\text{-}25)$
odd function	$x(N-n) = -x(n)$	$(9\text{-}26)$

even function	$X(N-m) = X(m)$	*(9-27)*
odd function	$X(N-m) = -X(m)$	*(9-28)*

From the appearance of $|X(m)|$ in Fig. 9-5, it can be seen that this function is even. The magnitude spectrum satisfies this property when the time function is real. More general relationships will be developed shortly.

9-3· EVEN AND ODD PROPERTIES OF THE DFT

We will now investigate some of the even and/or odd properties of the DFT transform pair and how they relate to the real and/or imaginary parts of the transform functions. The casual reader who is interested only in using available Fourier transform programs may not need to pursue all of this section in great depth. However, it is felt that more efficient use of available programs and better interpretation of the results may be possible with a better understanding of these concepts.

As a starting point, some of the properties of W_N as defined by (9-16) will be listed. The quantity W_N^k can be readily shown to be a periodic function of k with a period N. Using this property, a number of additional properties of W_N^k can be readily derived, and these are tabulated in Table 9-2. The reader is encouraged to verify these results (Prob. 9-3.)

Assume now that we have a *real* sequence $x(n)$ with a DFT $X(m)$. Let

$$X(m) = X_r(m) + jX_i(m) \qquad (9-29)$$

where $X_r(m)$ is the real part of $X(m)$ and $X_i(m)$ is the imaginary part. Using the basic definition of the DFT and the expansion of W_N into its real and imaginary parts, we can write

$$X(m) = \sum_{n=0}^{N-1} x(n) \cos \frac{2\pi mn}{N} - j \sum_{n=0}^{N-1} x(n) \sin \frac{2\pi mn}{N} \qquad (9-30)$$

The real and imaginary parts of (9-29) can be equated to those of (9-30) to yield

$$X_r(m) = \sum_{n=0}^{N-1} x(n) \cos \frac{2\pi mn}{N} \qquad (9-31)$$

$$X_i(m) = -\sum_{n=0}^{N-1} x(n) \sin \frac{2\pi mn}{N} \qquad (9\text{-}32)$$

It can be seen from (9-31) that $X_r(-m) = X_r(N-m) = X_r(m)$. Similarly, it can be seen from (9-32) that $X_i(-m) = X_i(N-m) = -X_i(m)$. These results means that when $x(n)$ is real, $X_r(m)$ is an even function of m and $X_i(m)$ is an odd function of m. Thus, *when the time function is real, the real part of the frequency function is an even function of frequency, and the imaginary part is an odd function of frequency.*

Now let $x(n)$ represent a purely imaginary sequence with a DFT $X(m)$. (The reason why the time signal is represented as an imaginary sequence will be discussed later.) Using (9-29) as the definition of the transform again, it can be shown (Prob. 9-4) that now $X_r(m)$ is an odd function of m and $X_i(m)$ is an even function of m. Thus, *when the time function is purely imaginary, the real part of the frequency function is an odd function of frequency, and the imaginary part is an even function of frequency.*

Let $x_e(n)$ be a *real even* function of n. The reader is invited to show (Prob. 9-5) that the DFT is of the form

$$x_e(n) \rightleftharpoons X_r(m) \qquad (9\text{-}33)$$

where $X_r(m)$ is a *real even* function of m.

Let $x_o(n)$ be a *real odd* function of n. It can be shown (Prob. 9-6) that the DFT is of the form

$$x_o(n) \rightleftharpoons j X_i(m) \qquad (9\text{-}34)$$

Table 9-2
Properties of the quantity W.

$W_N^N = 1$	(a)
$W_N^{\frac{N}{2}} = -1$	(b)
$W_N^{\frac{N}{4}} = -j$	(c)
$W_N^{\frac{3N}{4}} = j$	(d)
$W_N^{KN} = 1$	(e)
$W_N^{KN+r} = W_N^r$	(f)
$W_{2N}^K = W_N^{\frac{K}{2}}$	(g)

where $j\,X_i(m)$ is an *imaginary odd* function of m. (Note that $X_i(m)$ itself is a real function.)

Properties opposite to those associated with (9-33) and (9-34) apply to the cases where $x(n)$ is a purely imaginary sequence with even and odd properties, respectively. All of the preceding properties are summarized in Table 9-3.

Assume now that the time function $x(n)$ is permitted to be *complex*. In effect, this means that two time sequences are represented by association with the real and imaginary parts, respectively. Let

$$x(n) = x_1(n) + jx_2(n) \qquad\qquad (9\text{-}35)$$

where $x_1(n)$ *and* $x_2(n)$ are both real sequences.
Let

$$x_1(n) \rightleftharpoons X_1(m) \qquad\qquad (9\text{-}36)$$

$$x_2(n) \rightleftharpoons X_2(m) \qquad\qquad (9\text{-}37)$$

It is readily shown that

$$x_1(n) + jx_2(n) \rightleftharpoons X_1(m) + j\,X_2(m) \qquad\qquad (9\text{-}38)$$

However, it should be noted that $X_1(m)$ and $X_2(m)$ are both complex. Therefore, in the right-hand side of (9-38), the overall real and imaginary parts are not directly identifiable.

Table 9-3
Even and odd properties of the DFT.

x (n)	X (m)
Real	Real Part is Even Imaginary Part is Odd
Imaginary	Real Part is Odd Imaginary Part is Even
Real and Even	Real and Even
Real and Odd	Imaginary and Odd
Imaginary and Even	Imaginary and Even
Imaginary and Odd	Real and Odd

We will next evaluate $X(m)$ in the "negative" frequency range and make use of the even and odd proponents of the real and imaginary parts of $X_1(m)$ and $X_2(m)$. Let $(\sim)$ denote the process of complex conjugation. We begin with

$$X(m) = X_1(m) + j X_2(m) \qquad (9\text{-}39)$$

Substituting $N-m$ for m, we have

$$X(N-m) = X_1(N-m) + j X_2(N-m) \qquad (9\text{-}40)$$

By earlier developments of this section, it can be deduced that the real parts of X_1 and X_2 are even and the imaginary parts are odd. This means that the imaginary parts of X_1 and X_2 in the negative frequency range are the negatives of the corresponding segments in the positive frequency range; this is equivalent to the imaginary parts being the complex conjugates in the negative frequency range of their values in the positive frequency range.

Thus, (9-40) can be expressed as

$$X(N-m) = \widetilde{X}_1(m) + j \widetilde{X}_2(m) \qquad (9\text{-}41)$$

Forming the complex conjugates of both sides of (9-41), we have

$$\widetilde{X}(N-m) = X_1(m) - j X_2(m) \qquad (9\text{-}42)$$

Now let us successively add and subtract (9-39) and (9-42) and solve for the functions $X_1(m)$ and $X_2(m)$, respectively. We obtain

$$X_1(m) = \frac{1}{2}[X(m) + \widetilde{X}(N-m)] \qquad (9\text{-}43)$$

$$X_2(m) = \frac{1}{2j}[X(m) - \widetilde{X}(N-m)] \qquad (9\text{-}44)$$

These results are rather significant in that they permit two real sequences $x_1(n)$ and $x_2(n)$ to be combined into a single complex function as indicated by (9-35). After the transform of the complex combination $X(m)$ is computed, the relationships of (9-43) and (9-44) permit the separation of the two distinct transforms $X_1(m)$ and $X_2(m)$. Thus, it is possible to obtain the transforms of two separate signals in one computational sweep using this approach.

9-4 FUNCTIONAL OPERATIONS WITH THE DFT _____

As has been the case with all previous transform pairs considered in the text, there are a number of operations pairs that are useful in dealing with the DFT. Some of the most useful of these are summarized in Table 9-4. Several of these will be derived, while others will be left as exercises for the reader. For clarity in presentation, the derivations given will be postponed until the end of the section and presented as example problems. Within this section, we will discuss some of the

Table 9-4

Discrete Fourier transform operation pairs.

$x(n)$	$X(m) = D\left[x(n)\right]$	
$ax_1(n) + bx_2(n)$	$aX_1(m) + bX_2(m)$	(DO–1)
$x(n-k)$	$W_N^{km}\, X(m)$	(DO–2)
$W_N^{-kn}\, x(n)$	$X(m-k)$	(DO–3)
$x(n)^* h(n) = \displaystyle\sum_{k=0}^{N-1} x(k)\,h(n-k)$	$X(m)\, H(m)$	(DO–4)
$\displaystyle\sum_{n=0}^{N-1} x(n)\,y(n-k)$	$X(m)\, \tilde{Y}(m)$	(DO–5)
$x(n)\, y(n)$	$\dfrac{1}{N} \displaystyle\sum_{k=0}^{N-1} X(k)\, Y(m-k)$	(DO–6)

basic interpretations of the various transform pairs. In some cases, more detailed explanations will be given in later sections, where they are actually applied to spectral analysis.

    1. *Linearity Property.* Consider the transform pairs

$$x_1(n) \rightleftharpoons X_1(m) \qquad (9\text{-}45)$$

$$x_2(n) \rightleftharpoons X_2(m) \qquad (9\text{-}46)$$

Let a and b represent two arbitrary constants. Then the following transform pair can be readily obtained from the basic definition:

$$ax_1(n) + bx_2(n) \rightleftharpoons aX_1(m) + bX_2(m) \qquad (9\text{-}47)$$

This property implies that the DFT is a linear operation and thus satisfies the superposition principle.

2. *Shifting Theorem.* The process of shifting a time signal k intervals to the right (or to the left for that matter) introduces a phase shift factor similar to that encountered in other transform pairs. This theorem, which will be derived in Ex. 9-1, reads

$$x(n-k) \rightleftharpoons W_N^{km} X(m) \qquad (9\text{-}48)$$

The factor W_N^{km} introduces additional phase shift only and does not modify the magnitude spectrum of the unshifted spectrum. The reader is invited to show (Prob. 9-7) that the phase introduced by this process is $2\pi km/N$ radians, which is a linear function of the frequency integer m.

3. *Modulation Theorem.* This operation will be referred to as the modulation theorem, since it corresponds to the product modulation operation obtained by multiplying a signal by a sinusoidal function. The reader is invited to derive this theorem (Prob. 9-8), which is

$$W_N^{-kn} x(n) \rightleftharpoons X(m-k) \qquad (9\text{-}49)$$

In effect, the spectrum is shifted to the right by k intervals when the time signal is multiplied by an exponential term of the form given.

Whenever we are dealing directly with real functions, a complex exponential in the time domain is usually accompanied by its complex conjugate. Using (DO-3), the reader is invited to show (Prob. 9-9) that two alternate forms of the modulation theorem applicable directly to cosine and sine functions may be expressed as follows:

$$x(n) \cos \frac{2\pi kn}{N} \rightleftharpoons \frac{1}{2}\,[X(m-k) + X(m+k)] \qquad (9\text{-}50)$$

$$x(n) \sin \frac{2\pi kn}{N} \rightleftharpoons \frac{1}{2j}\,[X(m-k) - X(m+k)] \qquad (9\text{-}51)$$

4. *Convolution in the Time Domain.* One of the most important applications of the DFT is in dealing with convolution products in the time domain. The convolution theorem will be derived in Ex. 9-2, and it reads

$$\sum_{k=0}^{N-1} x(k)h(n-k) \rightleftharpoons X(m)\,H(m) \qquad (9\text{-}52)$$

This theorem states that discrete convolution in the time domain is equivalent to forming the product of the DFT's in the frequency domain. Thus, a discrete convolution could be evaluated by evaluating the two DFT's, forming their product at all frequency integers in the proper range, and determining the inverse DFT of the result. However, there are some possible difficulties with this process, so a rather detailed discussion will be given in the next chapter.

5. *Lagged Products.* The computation of lagged products is an integral part of determining the discrete cross-correlation or autocorrelation functions of discrete-time signals. While this is similar in form to the convolution operation, there are some minor differences. The development of the transform relationship for this pair,

$$\sum_{n=0}^{N-1} x(n)y(n-k) \rightleftharpoons X(m)\,\widetilde{Y}(m) \qquad (9\text{-}53)$$

is left as an exercise (Prob. 9-10). Some discussion of the applications of this operation will be given in Chapt. 10.

6. *Multiplication in the Time Domain.* When two discrete-time signals $x_1(n)$ and $x_2(n)$ are multiplied in the time domain, the DFT of the product may be determined by performing a convolution between the respective DFT's. The development of the theorem is left as an exercise (Prob. 9-11). The result is

$$x(n)y(n) \rightleftharpoons \frac{1}{N}\sum_{k=0}^{N-1} X(k)\,Y(m-k) \qquad (9\text{-}54)$$

The various properties of convolution in the time domain apply in this case, but with the concepts of time and frequency reversed. Hence, the details of convolution to be discussed in Chapt. 10 may be readily applied to this operation as long as the time and frequency variables are interchanged.

Example 9-1

Derive operation pair DO-2 of Table 9-4.

Solution

The function $x(n-k)$ is shifted to the right by k sample points (assuming $k > 0$), so that the N points are assumed to be in the range

$k \leq n \leq N + k - 1$. Application of the DFT definition to the function yields

$$D[x(n-k)] = \sum_{n=k}^{N+k-1} x(n-k) W_N^{nm} \qquad (9\text{-}55)$$

Let $n - k = i$. Substituting this change of variables, we have

$$D[x(n-k)] = \sum_{i=0}^{N-1} x(i) W_N^{(i+k)m}$$

$$= W_N^{km} \sum_{i=0}^{N-1} x(i) W_N^{im} \qquad (9\text{-}56)$$

$$= W_N^{km} X(m)$$

Example 9-2

Derive operation pair DO-4 of Table 9-4.

Solution

Application of the DFT definition to the convolution definition yields

$$D[x(n)*h(n)] = \sum_{n=0}^{N-1} [\sum_{k=0}^{N-1} x(k)h(n-k)] W_N^{nm} \qquad (9\text{-}57)$$

The order of summation for the indices k and n will now be reversed. At the same time, it is desirable to change the range of summation for the inner function $h(n-k)$ due to its shifted nature. We have

$$D[x(n)*h(n)] = \sum_{k=0}^{N-1} x(k) [\sum_{n=k}^{k+N-1} h(n-k) W_N^{nm}] \qquad (9\text{-}58)$$

The quantity in the brackets of (9-58) has the same form encountered in Ex. 9-1 in relation to DO-2, namely, $W_N^{km} H(m)$. The quantity $H(m)$ may be factored out to yield

$$D[x(n)*h(n)] = [\sum_{k=0}^{N-1} x(k) W_N^{km}] H(m)$$
$$ \qquad (9\text{-}59)$$

$$= X(m) H(m)$$

9-5   FAST FOURIER TRANSFORM _____

This section will be devoted to a discussion of certain special algorithms that permit implementation of the discrete Fourier transform with considerable savings in computational time. The class of such algorithms is referred to as the *fast Fourier transform* (FFT). It should be pointed out that the FFT is not a different transform from the DFT, but rather it represents a means for computing the DFT with a considerable reduction in the number of computations. Of course, the development of these FFT algorithms represented the major step in the realization of modern high-speed digital Fourier analysis equipment.

Because of the intended level of this book, we will not attempt to present a rigorous development of the underlying analytical and computational theory of the FFT. Instead, we will first present a somewhat simplified overall discussion of the general computational approach. Next we will present several signal flow charts corresponding to several versions of the FFT. The emphasis will be on forms that are easier to follow computationally rather than those that are optimally organized.

While it is possible to develop FFT algorithms that work with any number of points, maximum efficiency of computation is obtained by constraining the number of time points to be an integer power of two. In fact, most of the available hardware has been designed around this concept. Consequently, this assumption will be made for all forms of the algorithms that are presented.

Let us now inspect the actual steps involved in the computation of the DFT. The operation described by (9-18) can be expressed by the array of equations

$$X(0) \quad = x(0)W^0 + x(1)W^0 + x(2)W^0 + \cdots + x(N-1)W^0$$

$$X(1) \quad = x(0)W^0 + x(1)W^1 + x(2)W^2 + \cdots + x(N-1)W^{N-1}$$

$$X(2) \quad = x(0)W^0 + x(1)W^2 + x(2)W^4 + \cdots + x(N-1)W^{2(N-1)}$$

$$\begin{array}{ccccc} \cdot & = & \cdot & \cdot & \cdot & \cdot \\ \cdot & & \cdot & \cdot & \cdot & \cdot \\ \cdot & & \cdot & \cdot & \cdot & \cdot \end{array} \qquad (9\text{-}60)$$

$$X(N-1) = x(0)W^0 + x(1)W^{N-1} + x(2)W^{2(N-1)} + \cdots + x(N-1)W^{(N-1)^2}$$

Since $W^0 = 1$, some simplification could be achieved in the array by making this substitution. However, it is conceptually convenient to leave the W^0 term in the array. With this assumption, it can be seen that the computation of any one particular spectral component requires about N complex multiplications and about N complex additions. Thus, there are about 2N complex arithmetic operations involved in computing a given frequency component. From the array, it would appear that we should compute N spectral components. However, if $x(n)$ is real, only N/2 components are unique, and a full expansion of the form expressed in (9-60) would necessitate computing only that many. This results in a minimum of about $2N \times (N/2) = N^2$ complex operations. Thus, it is convenient to state that the number of complex computations involved in obtaining the complete spectrum using the DFT is approximately N^2. For a reasonably long signal, this number can be very large, resulting in a prohibitively long computational time.

The array of (9-60) can be arranged in a matrix form as

$$
\begin{bmatrix}
X(0) \\
X(1) \\
X(2) \\
\cdot \\
\cdot \\
\cdot \\
X(N-1)
\end{bmatrix}
=
\begin{bmatrix}
W^0 & W^0 & W^0 & \cdots & W^0 \\
W^0 & W^1 & W^2 & \cdots & W^{N-1} \\
W^0 & W^2 & W^4 & \cdots & W^{2(N-1)} \\
\cdot & \cdot & \cdot & & \cdot \\
\cdot & \cdot & \cdot & & \cdot \\
\cdot & \cdot & \cdot & & \cdot \\
W^0 & W^{N-1} & W^{2(N-1)} & \cdots & W^{(N-1)^2}
\end{bmatrix}
\begin{bmatrix}
x(0) \\
x(1) \\
x(2) \\
\cdot \\
\cdot \\
\cdot \\
x(N-1)
\end{bmatrix}
\qquad (9\text{-}61)
$$

This can be expressed as

$$
\overline{X} = [W]\overline{x} \qquad (9\text{-}62)
$$

where $\overline{X}$ is the column vector defining the transform, $\overline{x}$ is the column vector defining the discrete time signal, and $[W]$ is the N by N square matrix.

The basis for the fast Fourier transform (FFT) is an algorithm presented by J. W. Cooley and J. W. Tukey in 1965 which can be thought of as a matrix factorization of (9-61) or (9-62). Assume that N is chosen as an integer multiple of 2, and define an integer L as

$$
L = \log_2 N \qquad (9\text{-}63)
$$

or

$$
N = 2^L \qquad (9\text{-}64)
$$

Then [W] can be factored into L matrices in the form

$$W = [W_1][W_2] \cdots [W_L] \qquad (9\text{-}65)$$

Each row of each of the individual matrices has the property that it contains only two nonzero terms: unity and W^k, where k is some integer.

Substitution of (9-65) into (9-62) yields the form

$$\overline{X}_s = [W_1]]W_2] \cdots [W_L]\overline{x} \qquad (9\text{-}66)$$

where the subscript on $\overline{X}_s$ is used only to denote the fact that the components of this vector appear in a different order than assumed in the original definition of X. At the outset $]W_L]$ operates on $\overline{x}$ to yield a new vector. Each component of the new vector may be obtained by one multiplication and one addition, since all but two elements on a given row of the matrix are zero. Since there are N components of $\overline{x}$, there will be N complex additions and N complex multiplications required in this process. The new vector is then operated on by $[W_{L-1}]$, and the process is repeated until (9-66) is completely satisfied. Thus, it initially appears that the number of operations is $NL = N \log_2 N$ complex additions and $N \log_2 N$ complex multiplications. However, by taking advantage of various symmetry properties and the fact that many of the W^k terms are unity, the actual number of complex computations can be reduced by one-half or more. As an approximate worst-case bound for comparison, we will state the value $N \log_2 N$ as the number of complex computations involved in the Cooley-Tukey FFT algorithm. Approximate ratios of the number of computations required for the FFT to the number required with direct use of the DFT definition are given in Table 9-5 for several possible cases.

There are a number of variations in the FFT algorithms indicated by (9-66), and some of these will be explored in Sec. 9-6. Most of these algorithms may be classified as either (a) *in-place* or (b) *natural input-output*. An in-place algorithm is one in which a given component of any intermediate vector may be stored in the same location occupied by the corresponding component of the preceding vector, thus reducing the total storage required. Unfortunately, most of the in-place algorithms result in either the output spectrum appearing in an unnatural order, or they require that the input data be rearranged before entering the computational array. The natural input-output algorithms, on the other hand, require more internal memory in order to maintain this natural order. Thus, if memory size is extremely critical, it would be desirable to use an in-place algorithm even though the input or output

Table 9-5

Comparison of approximate number of computations required for DFT and FFT.

N	N(DFT)	N(FFT)	N(FFT)/ N(DFT)
16	256	64	0.250
32	1024	160	0.156
64	4096	384	0.0938
128	16,384	896	0.0547
256	65,536	2048	0.0312
512	262,144	4608	0.0176
1024	1,048,576	10,240	0.0098
2048	4,194,304	22,528	0.0054
4096	16,777,216	49,152	0.0029

N = Number of Points in Time Sample.

N(DFT) = N^2 = Approximate Number of Complex Arithmetic Operations With DFT.

N(FFT) = N Log$_2$N = Approximate Number of Complex Arithmetic Operations With FFT.

data has to be reordered. This reordering process, will be referred to as a *scrambling* operation, and it will be discussed next.

The *scrambled value* of a given integer m will be denoted as $\widehat{m}$. Assume that m can be represented in binary form as

$$m = m_{N-1}m_{N-2} \cdots m_1 m_0 \qquad (9\text{-}67)$$

The scrambled value of m will be defined as

$$\widehat{m} = m_0 m_1 \cdots m_{N-2} m_{N-1} \qquad (9\text{-}68)$$

Thus, the scrambled value of a given integer is a new number obtained by reversing the order of all the bits in the binary representation of the given number. Note that if m is scrambled twice, the original value is obtained again, i.e.,

$$\widehat{\widehat{m}} = m \qquad (9\text{-}69)$$

For the sake of illustration, values of m and $\widehat{m}$ for N = 8 and 16 are given in decimal and binary form in Table 9-6.

With some of the in-place algorithms, the data must be scrambled either before or after processing. Using the output as a reference for

Table 9-6

Integers and their scrambled values for N = 8 and N = 16.

N = 8

m (decimal)	0	1	2	3	4	5	6	7
m (binary)	000	001	010	011	100	101	110	111
m̂ (binary)	000	100	010	110	001	101	011	111
m̂ (decimal)	0	4	2	6	1	5	3	7

N = 16

m (decimal)	0	1	2	3	4	5	6	7	8	9	10	11	12	13	14	15
m (binary)	0000	0001	0010	0011	0100	0101	0110	0111	1000	1001	1010	1011	1100	1101	1110	1111
m̂ (binary)	0000	1000	0100	1100	0010	1010	0110	1110	0001	1001	0101	1101	0011	1011	0111	1111
m̂ (decimal)	0	8	4	12	2	10	6	14	1	9	5	13	3	11	7	15

discussion, assume that the output registers are arranged in a natural order ranging from 0 to $N-1$. Then, at a particular location m, the component appearing at the output is not $X(m)$, but rather $X(\widehat{m})$. In this case, it would be necessary to go to location $\widehat{m}$ to obtain the component desired for the index m. The computer flow chart of an algorithm for performing the scrambling operation will be shown and discussed later in the chapter (Fig. 9-16).

9-6 SURVEY OF ALGORITHMS

At this point, we will inspect some of the variations of the basic FFT algorithm and their various computational structures. It must be stressed at the outset that the collection presented is not intended to be a complete set of such algorithms. Indeed, there have been many additional modifications depending on the particular requirements, the limitations of available hardware, and the ingenuity of the individual designer or programmer. Many applications of the FFT involve programming a general-purpose digital computer to solve a particular problem. In these cases, the efficiency of the program organization is not always of paramount importance. On the other hand, special-purpose FFT computers are rapidly increasing in appearance, and the designers of these machines must pay extremely close attention to optimum organization.

The particular layouts shown have been organized around the goal of clarity in presentation rather than optimum organization efficiency. It is a challenge for the programmer or system designer to finalize these layouts into the most practical form, subject to the particular constraints present.

For each variation of the algorithm presented, a signal processing layout referred to as a *signal flow graph* will be given. This terminology is used because of the close physical and mathematical similarity to a conventional signal flow graph as used in system theory. In all cases, the organizational layout of an 8-point system will be used to illustrate the flow graph. The general trends in each case may be observed from a close inspection of the 8-point system, so that the result may be generalized to any arbitrary number of points satisfying (9-63) and (9-64).

A total of eight signal flow graphs will be shown. The first four (Figs. 9-6 through 9-9) represent variations of the original Cooley-Tukey algorithm. These algorithms have been derived by a process called *decimation in time*. The second form (Figs. 9-10 through 9-13) represent variations of an algorithm developed independently by

Sande, Tukey, Stockham, and others. The derivations of these forms have been accomplished by a process called *decimation in frequency*. For convenience in discussion, we will refer to the decimation-in-time forms as *type 1* algorithms and the decimation-in-frequency forms as *type 2* algorithms. This terminology will be used in the remainder of the chapter.

In addition to the signal flow graphs, two *computer flow charts* (Figs. 9-14 and 9-15) will be presented corresponding to two particular type 1 algorithms. These flow charts are in forms from which computer programs can be readily written.

From the definitions of the DFT and inverse DFT as given by (9-18) and 9-19), it is seen that the only differences in form between the two functions are the presence of the $1/N$ factor in the inverse function and the replacement of W by W^{-1}. Actually, the exact forms given here are somewhat arbitrary, as a number of possible forms have been used. One common modification is the placement of the $1/N$ factor in the DFT rather than the inverse DFT, and this form appears extensively in the literature.

The signal flow graphs and computer charts have been organized around the computation of the DFT using the form of (9-18). The same layouts can be used to compute the inverse DFT using (9-19) with the following simple modifications: (1) The quantity $W = \epsilon(-j2\pi/N)$ is replaced by $W^{-1} = \epsilon(j2\pi/N)$. This is achieved by reversing the signs of all the sine terms. (2) All terms must be multiplied by $1/N$. This can be done at either the input or the output. (3) The input is now the transform $X(m)$, and the output is the time signal $x(n)$.

The procedure for reading the signal flow graphs will now be discussed. Refer to Fig. 9-6 for discussion. There are four columns, each containing eight entries. For the sake of clarity, the two-dimensional variable $y(\ell, m)$ will be used to denote the value of a given node in the array, where ℓ is the number of the column and m is the number of the component within the column. Note that in general, ℓ varies over the range $0 \leq \ell \leq L$, with $\ell = 0$ at the left, and m varies over the range $0 \leq m \leq N-1$, with $m = 0$ at the top.

The preceding does *not* imply that separate storage will have to be set aside for all of the elements of the two-dimensional variable $y(\ell, m)$. Indeed, with the in-place algorithms, the column $y(\ell + 1, m)$ is stored in the same array as $y(\ell, m)$. With other algorithms, it is usually necessary to maintain more internal storage, but it is rarely necessary to provide total storage for every variable in the process. Nevertheless, in our discussion it is very convenient to look at all the elements of the total array as a distinct set of variables. In this respect, the input $x(m)$ is stored in the location $y(0, m)$ when no scrambling is required there

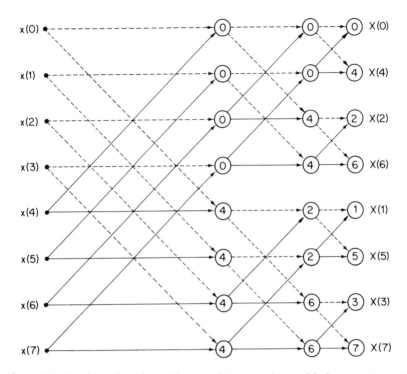

Figure 9-6 In-place algorithm with natural input and scrambled output (type 1).

and in the location $y(0,\widehat{m})$ when scrambling at the input is required. Likewise, the output $X(m)$ is obtained in the location $y(L,m)$ when no output scrambling is required and in the location $y(L,\widehat{m})$ when scrambling at the output is required.

The procedure that follows applies to the type 1 algorithms of Figs. 9-6 through 9-9. At the node corresponding to column ℓ and row m, the variable $y(\ell,m)$ is found from an equation of the form

$$y(\ell,m) = y(\ell-1,m_1) + W^r y(\ell-1,m_2) \qquad (9\text{-}70)$$

where m_1, m_2, and r are functions of the location within the array and the particular algorithm. In each case, the *dashed line* connecting the variable in row $\ell-1$ with row ℓ refers to the first term on the right-hand side of equation (9-70), i.e., the *nonweighted* term. The *solid* line refers to the second term on the right-hand side of (9-70), i.e., the *weighted* term. The number in the circle is the degree of W as indicated by the integer r in (9-70). The correctness of this signal flow graph will be illustrated for a particular component in Ex. 9-3.

The algorithm of Fig. 9-6 is one of the in-place forms, as will be illustrated later in the flow chart of Fig. 9-14. This means that when a particular column of data is calculated, the values can be stored in the same locations occupied by the previous column. Thus, storage for about N complex signal values is required.

In the preceding algorithm, the input signal appears in natural order and the output is scrambled. A modification in which the input is scrambled and the output appears in natural order is shown in Fig. 9-7.

The signal flow graph of a natural input-output algorithm is shown in Fig. 9-8. It can be shown that the in-place property no longer holds, so it is necessary to maintain storage for about 2N complex signal values in this case.

A rather interesting arrangement is shown in Fig. 9-9. In this form, the geometry of each stage is identical with that of other stages. This property might be advantageous in the design of certain systems. However, this form requires more internal storage, and the input data

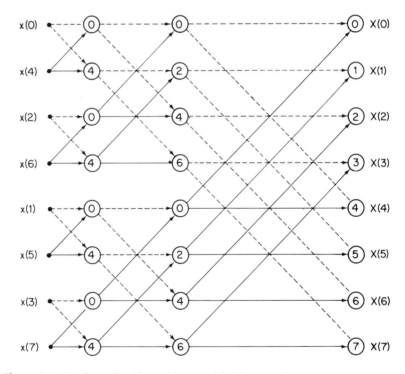

Figure 9-7 In-place algorithm with scrambled input and natural output (type 1).

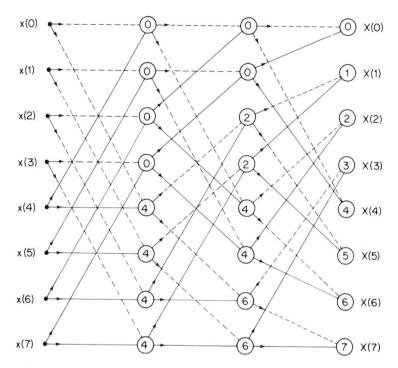

Figure 9-8 Natural input-output algorithm requiring more internal storage (type 1).

must be scrambled, so that the algorithm is neither an in-place nor a natural input-output version.

The signal flow graphs shown in Figs. 9-10 through 9-13 all represent type 2 algorithms. With all of these flow graphs, the equations relating successive columns have one of two possible forms, depending on the location within the array. One form is the equation

$$y(\ell,m) = y(\ell-1,m_1) + y(\ell-1,m_2) \qquad (9\text{-}71)$$

The other form is the equation

$$y(\ell,m) = W^r[y(\ell-1,m_1) - y(\ell-1,m_2)] \qquad (9\text{-}72)$$

where m_1, m_2, and r are functions of the location within the array and the particular algorithm.

Refer to Fig. 9-10 for illustration. Components that correspond to (9-71) are those with two *dashed* lines terminating on them. Components that correspond to (9-72) are those with two *solid* lines terminat-

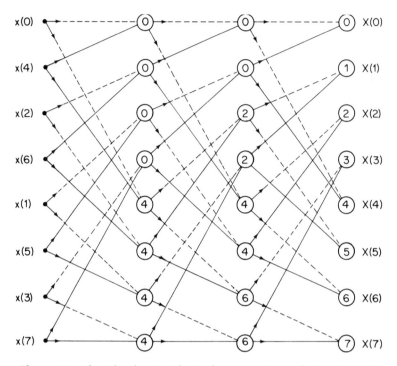

Figure 9-9 Algorithm having identical geometry in each stage (type 1).

ing on the pertinent circle. The integer in the circle is the degree of W as indicated by r in (9-72). The $(-)$ sign appears adjacent to the branch that is subtracted, always the lowest branch terminating on the given circle.

To further illustrate this graph, the equations corresponding to the first inner column of Fig. 9-10 are written as follows:

$$
\begin{aligned}
y(1,0) &= y(0,0) + y(0,4) \\
y(1,1) &= y(0,1) + y(0,5) \\
y(1,2) &= y(0,2) + y(0,6) \\
y(1,3) &= y(0,3) + y(0,7) \\
y(1,4) &= W^0[y(0,0) - y(0,4)] \\
y(1,5) &= W^1[y(0,1) - y(0,5)] \\
y(1,6) &= W^2[y(0,2) - y(0,6)] \\
y(1,7) &= W^3[y(0,3) - y(0,7)]
\end{aligned}
\qquad (9\text{-}73)
$$

The reader is invited to verify the correctness of this graph (Prob. 9-14) by writing the equations at the other columns and solving for some particular component. After a few exercises of this type, most readers

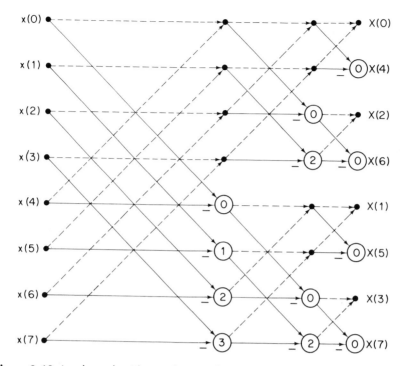

Figure 9-10 In-place algorithm with natural input and scrambled output (type 2).

will probably be content to accept the algorithms given in the text on faith!

The algorithm of Fig. 9-10 is an in-place form, and the output data is scrambled. A modified form in which the input data is scrambled and the output appears in natural order is shown in Fig. 9-11.

The signal flow graph of a natural input-output type 2 form is shown in Fig. 9-12. As in the case of the type 1 natural input-output version, more internal memory is required. Finally, an algorithm exhibiting identical geometry in each stage is shown in Fig. 9-13.

Two computer flow charts corresponding to two particular algorithms previously given are shown in Figs. 9-14 and 9-15, and a flow chart for performing the scrambling operation is shown in Fig. 9-16. The equations appearing on these flow charts represent a sort of mixture between normal algebraic equations and equations typically used in programming languages, with clarity in presentation sought as a primary goal. An equation of the form $x = x + y$ should be read as follows: "Add y to the value found in location x and store the result in location x." The integer m is shown on the flow chart in its natural

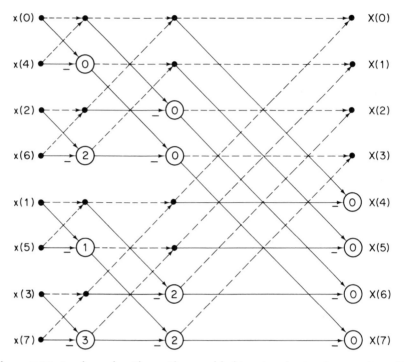

Figure 9-11 In-place algorithm with scrambled input and natural output (type 2).

range, i.e., $0 \leq m \leq N-1$. However, dimensioned variables in many programming languages accept only positive integers in arguments, so it may be necessary to shift such arguments by one unit in an actual program.

The flow chart of Fig. 9-14 corresponds to the in-place algorithm of Fig. 9-6. The integers L and N on the flow chart correspond to the definitions of (9-63) and (9-64) and are assumed to be constrained accordingly. The operation ($\frown$) over an integer refers to the scrambled value of that particular integer. A separate routine may be developed for performing the scrambling operation, and a flow chart for this purpose is shown in Fig. 9-16.

One of the operations shown in Fig. 9-14 is given by

$$I_e = \left[\frac{\widehat{I_c}}{I_a} \right] \qquad (9\text{-}74)$$

The operation [ ] is defined as the "integer part" of the quantity within the brackets. This refers simply to the process of rounding off the number to the largest integer equal to or smaller than the given

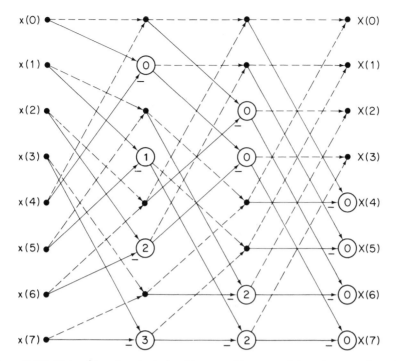

Figure 9-12 Natural input-output algorithm requiring more internal storage (type 2).

number. Thus, the integer parts of 2, 2.3, and 2.7 are all equal to 2. This operation is achieved in some programming languages by equating an integer variable on the left to the given quotient on the right. In the particular operation of (9-74), the resulting integer is scrambled in turn.

The computer flow chart corresponding to the natural input-output algorithm of Fig. 9-8 is shown in Fig. 9-15. As expected, the amount of internal storage for this form is about twice that of the in-place algorithms, since it is necessary to maintain the separate arrays $y_1(m)$ and $y_2(m)$ in this case. However, no scrambling is required, so that the overall organization is somewhat simpler.

Example 9-3

Illustrate the signal flow graph of Fig. 9-6 by solving for the particular component $X(3)$ in terms of the input components, and verify that the result is identical to the quantity obtained by direct application of the DFT definition.

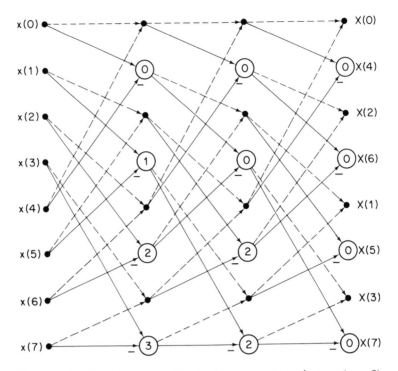

Figure 9-13 Algorithm having identical geometry in each stage (type 2).

Solution

In the results that follow, use will be made of the relationship

$$W^{kN+r} = W^r \tag{9-75}$$

where r and k are integers. This relationship was given in Table 9-2. From Fig. 9-6, the equations of column 1 are

$$
\begin{aligned}
y(1,0) &= y(0,0) + W^0 y(0,4) \\
y(1,1) &= y(0,1) + W^0 y(0,5) \\
y(1,2) &= y(0,2) + W^0 y(0,6) \\
y(1,3) &= y(0,3) + W^0 y(0,7) \\
y(1,4) &= y(0,0) + W^4 y(0,4) \\
y(1,5) &= y(0,1) + W^4 y(0,5) \\
y(1,6) &= y(0,2) + W^4 y(0,6) \\
y(1,7) &= y(0,3) + W^4 y(0,7)
\end{aligned}
\tag{9-76}
$$

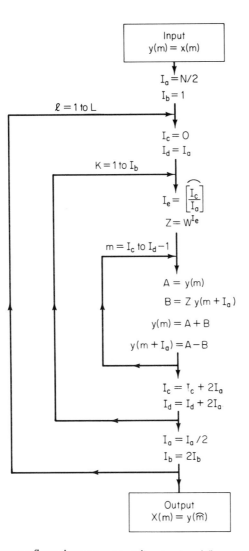

Input
$y(m) = x(m)$

$I_a = N/2$
$I_b = 1$

$\ell = 1 \text{ to } L$

$I_c = 0$
$I_d = I_a$

$K = 1 \text{ to } I_b$

$I_e = \left[\dfrac{I_c}{I_a} \right]$
$Z = W^{I_e}$

$m = I_c \text{ to } I_d - 1$

$A = y(m)$
$B = Z\, y(m + I_a)$
$y(m) = A + B$
$y(m + I_a) = A - B$

$I_c = I_c + 2I_a$
$I_d = I_d + 2I_a$

$I_a = I_a / 2$
$I_b = 2I_b$

Output
$X(m) = y(\widehat{m})$

Figure 9-14 Computer flow chart corresponding to signal flow graph of Figure 9-6.

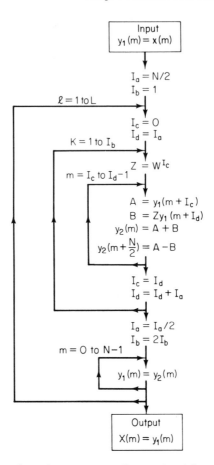

Figure 9-15 Computer flow chart corresponding to signal flow graph of Figure 9-8.

The equations of column 2 are

$$y(2,0) = y(1,0) + W^0 y(1,2)$$
$$y(2,1) = y(1,1) + W^0 y(1,3)$$
$$y(2,2) = y(1,0) + W^4 y(1,2)$$
$$y(2,3) = y(1,1) + W^4 y(1,3)$$
$$y(2,4) = y(1,4) + W^2 y(1,6)$$
$$y(2,5) = y(1,5) + W^2 y(1,7)$$
$$y(2,6) = y(1,4) + W^6 y(1,6)$$
$$y(2,7) = y(1,5) + W^6 y(1,7)$$

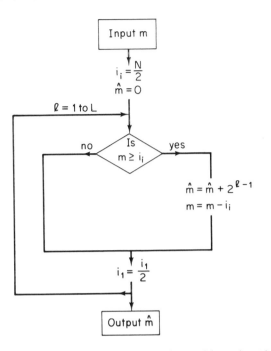

Figure 9-16 Computer flow chart of scrambling algorithm.

The equations of column 3 are

$$
\begin{aligned}
y(3,0) &= y(2,0) + W^0 y(2,1) \\
y(3,1) &= y(2,0) + W^4 y(2,1) \\
y(3,2) &= y(2,2) + W^2 y(2,3) \\
y(3,3) &= y(2,2) + W^6 y(2,3) \\
y(3,4) &= y(2,4) + W^1 y(2,5) \\
y(3,5) &= y(2,4) + W^5 y(2,5) \\
y(3,6) &= y(2,6) + W^3 y(2,7) \\
y(3,7) &= y(2,6) + W^7 y(2,7)
\end{aligned}
\qquad (9\text{-}78)
$$

By successive elimination, we can solve for either of the variables on the left-hand side of (9-78) in terms of the input data. The particular value desired is X (3) and this quantity actually corresponds to $y(3,6)$ in the array of (9-78), as can be seen in Fig. 9-6. From the expression for $y(3,6)$, it is seen that we must substitute in $y(2,6)$ and $y(2,7)$. However, the expressions for $y(2,6)$ and $y(2,7)$ in (9-77) require that we substitute in $y(1,4)$, $y(1,6)$, $y(1,5)$, and $y(1,7)$. Finally, each of these latter variables involve all eight values of the input data, as seen in (9-76). Carrying through this successive chain of substitutions, we obtain

$$y(3,6) = y(0,0) + W^3 y(0,1) + W^6 y(0,2) + W^9 y(0,3)$$
$$+ W^4 y(0,4) + W^7 y(0,5) + W^{10} y(0,6) + W^{13} y(0.7) \qquad (9\text{-}79)$$

If this expression is correct, the result should be $X(3)$. If we take the general DFT expression and expand it for $X(3)$, we initially obtain

$$X(3) = x(0) + W^3 x(1) + W^6 x(2) + W^9 x(3)$$
$$+ W^{12} x(4) + W^{15} x(5) + W^{18} x(6) + W^{21} x(7) \qquad (9\text{-}80)$$

Before comparing (9-79) and (9-80), we note that $y(0,m) = x(m)$ and $X(m) = y(L,\widehat{m})$. It can then be readily observed that the first four terms of (9-79) and (9-80) are equal. The last four terms are then seen to be equal by application of (9-75).

PROBLEMS

9-1   Suppose that we are given a certain continuous-time signal $x(t)$ having a continuous-frequency Fourier transform $X(f)$. The time signal has a duration of 2.048 seconds. The signal is then sampled at 256 equally spaced points.

    (a) Determine the increment in Hz between successive frequency components in the spectrum of the sampled signal.

    (b) Determine the "period" in Hz of the spectrum.

    (c) What is the highest frequency permitted in the spectrum of the signal if no aliasing is to occur?

9-2   Derive the form of the Fourier transform pair of equations (9-8) and (9-9) by evaluating the z-transform and inverse transform functions on the unit circle in the z-plane.

9-3   Verify all of the results of Table 9-2.

9-4   Prove that when $x(n)$ is purely imaginary, the real part of $X(m)$ is an odd function of m, and the imaginary part is an even function of m.

9-5   Prove that when the time function is a real even function of n, the frequency function is a real even function of m, as indicated by equation (9-33).

9-6 Prove that when the time function is a real odd function of n, the frequency function is an imaginary odd function of m, as indicated by equation (9-34).

9-7 Show from the shifting theorem as given by operation pair DO-2 that the amplitude spectrum is not affected by the shifting operation, but that a phase shift of $2\pi km/N$ radians is introduced in the spectrum.

9-8 Derive the form of the modulation theorem as given by operation pair DO-3.

9-9 Using the basic form of the modulation theorem as given by operation pair DO-3, derive equations (9-50) and (9-51).

9-10 Derive the DFT of a lagged product as given by operation pair DO-5.

9-11 Derive the DFT of the product of two signals as given by operation pair DO-6.

9-12 A certain long signal contains about 100,000 points. Assume that zeros are added to the end of the signal to make the total number of points be an integer power of two. Assuming that a program is available to transform the entire signal as a unit, determine the approximate ratio of the time required with the FFT to the time required for a direct DFT evaluation.

9-13 Compute a table of the forms given in Table 9-6 for N = 32.

9-14 The equations for the first column of Fig. 9-10 were outlined in (9-73). Write similar equations for the remaining columns on the right, and solve for X(3) in terms of the input data. Verify that this result is correct by solving directly for X(3) using the DFT definition.

10

GENERAL PROPERTIES OF THE DISCRETE FOURIER TRANSFORM

10-0 INTRODUCTION

The basic definition and forms of the discrete Fourier transform (DFT) were introduced in the last chapter. It was shown that this operation could be implemented by a fast Fourier transform (FFT) algorithm, which permits a considerable reduction in the number of computations required for evaluating a discrete spectrum. Some of the basic relationships and the computational procedures were discussed.

Possible applications of the FFT appear in almost all of the general areas of engineering, science, and mathematics. The variety of applications includes the analysis of mechanical and structural vibrations, the extraction of vital information from radar and sonar signals, analysis of statistical data, digital filtering, and many other applications.

The primary emphasis in this chapter will be on the consideration of the various properties of the DFT (or FFT) when utilized for general applications. The approximations involved when using the DFT in the analysis of continuous-time systems must be carefully understood. There are problems that arise in the process that may lead to erroneous results unless proper precautions are taken. These problems and means for alleviating them will be discussed, and some of the general applications will be considered.

10-1 APPROXIMATION OF CONTINUOUS-TIME TRANSFORMS WITH THE DFT _____

We have seen that the DFT pair can be considered as the combination of a periodic discrete-time function and a periodic discrete-frequency function, which are related through the processes of finite summations. Such summations can be performed on a digital computer with the special assistance of an FFT algorithm, which provides the means for high-speed spectral analysis.

While the mathematical properties of the DFT are exact, the DFT is seldom of interest as the end goal in most digital signal processing applications. Rather, it is usually employed to transform data which may arise from either an actual continuous-time process or perhaps a discrete-time process which is being analyzed from a continuous-time system approach. In this sense, then, the DFT is usually employed to approximate the Fourier transform of a continuous-time process, and it is necessary to understand some of the limitations inherent in this process. In studying these limitations, we will frequently refer back to the properties and equations developed in the preceding chapter.

By inspecting the differences between the continuous Fourier integral transform pair and the DFT pair, it can be deduced that the DFT pair has the form (but not the magnitude) of a zero-order approximation for the continuous integral pair. While this observation provides some qualitative insight, it does not tell us anything about the nature or magnitude of the error in the spectrum.

Assuming that the primary goal is to use the DFT to approximate the Fourier transform of a continuous-time signal, we will investigate three possible phenomena that result in errors between the computed and the desired transform. These three phenomena are (a) *aliasing*, (b) *leakage*, and (c) *the picket-fence effect*. These properties will be investigated individually.

(a) *Aliasing*. The phenomenon of aliasing has been discussed in some detail in earlier chapters, but will be reviewed here in reference to the DFT. Consider the continuous-time signal $x_1(t)$ shown in Fig. 10-1. The transform $X_1(f)$ is assumed to be bandlimited to $0 \leq f \leq f_h$ as shown. Assume now that the time signal is sampled at a rate f_s that is less than $2f_h$, and let $x_2(n)$ represent the sampled signal. Its transform $X_2(f)$ is characterized by spectral overlap, or aliasing, as can be seen. In effect, frequencies in the overlap region may be mistaken for other frequencies, so that it is impossible to recover the original signal. For example, if $f_h = 4$ kHz and if $f_s = 5$ kHz, a 4 kHz component could be mistaken as a 1 kHz component.

The only solution to the aliasing problem is to ensure that the

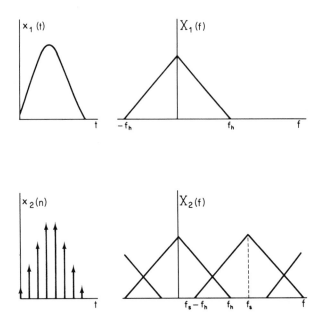

Figure 10-1 Illustration of how aliasing error arises when sampling rate is too low.

sampling rate is high enough to avoid any spectral overlap. This means that some prior knowledge of the nature of the spectrum is often required before the exact sampling rate is determined. In many cases, the signal may be filtered with a low-pass analog filter before sampling to ensure that no components higher than the folding frequency appear.

(b) *Leakage*. This problem arises because of the practical requirement that we must limit observation of the signal to a finite interval. To illustrate, consider the discrete-time $x_1(n)$ shown in Fig. 10-2, which is presumed to be infinite in extent. Assume for the sake of argument that the spectrum is of the form illustrated by $X_1(f)$. (Only a portion of one cycle of the periodic spectrum is shown.) Since we do not possess the capability, nor can we wait long enough, to sum an infinite number of terms, it is necessary to select a finite segment of the signal to observe.

The process of terminating the signal after a finite number of terms is equivalent to multiplying the signal by a *window function*. The problem is the same as was encountered in the design of finite impulse response digital filters in Chapt. 8. If the window function is a rectangular function, the series is abruptly terminated without modifying any coefficients within the window, as illustrated by $x_2(n)$. The

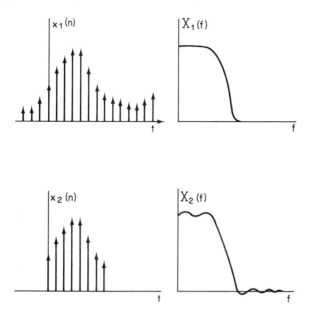

Figure 10-2 Illustration of leakage effect produced by abrupt termination of signal.

resulting transform can be considered as the convolution of the desired spectrum with the spectrum of the rectangular window. The net effect is a distortion of the spectrum, as illustrated by $X_2(f)$. There is a spreading or leakage of the spectral components away from the correct frequency, resulting in an undesirable modification of the total spectrum.

The leakage effect cannot always be isolated from the aliasing effect because leakage may also lead to aliasing. Since leakage results in a spreading of the spectrum, the upper frequency of the composite spectrum may move beyond the folding frequency, and aliasing may then result. This possibility is particularly significant in the case of a rectangular window function, since the tail of the window spectrum does not converge rapidly.

While the rectangular window may be acceptable in some applications, the best approach for alleviating the leakage effect is to choose a suitable window function that minimizes the spreading. The problem of selecting an appropriate window function is essentially the same as was encountered with FIR filter design, so the material in Sec. 8-3 and the Appendix are directly applicable to spectral analysis. To apply the notation of Sec. 8-3 and the Appendix for spectral analysis, the length

τ should be interpreted as the length of the signal for which the window is to be applied. In each case, the window function should be centered on the signal to be transformed, so it is necessary to either momentarily shift the signal to the left by $N/2$ points or shift the window to the right by the same amount before multiplying by the window coefficients.

(c) *Picket-Fence Effect.* This effect is produced by the inability of the DFT to observe the spectrum as a continuous function, since computation of the spectrum is limited to integer multiples of the fundamental frequency F. In a sense, then, observation of the spectrum with the DFT is analogous to looking at it through a sort of "picket-fence," since we can observe the exact behavior only at discrete points. The major peak of a particular component could lie between two of the discrete transform lines, and the peak of this component might not be detected without some additional processing.

One procedure for reducing the picket-fence effect is to vary the number of points in a time period by adding zeros at the end of the original record, while maintaining the original record intact. This process artificially changes the period, which in turn changes the locations of the spectral lines without altering the continuous form of the original spectrum. In this manner, spectral components originally hidden from view can be shifted to points where they can be observed.

When zeros are added to a signal for the purpose of artificially changing the period, the width of any window function used should *not* be changed. In other words, the window function should be selected around the true length of the data record rather than the longer length obtained from adding additional zeros.

Apart from the differences in the spectra of continuous-time and discrete-time functions previously discussed, a minor additional point of consideration is the manner in which the relative magnitudes are defined. There have been a number of variations appearing in the literature for continuous-time Fourier transforms and series, so this problem is nothing new.

For the sake of this discussion, assume that the definitions of the transforms of continuous-time nonperiodic signals are those given by (9-3) and (9-4) and that the definitions of the Fourier series for periodic signals are those given by (9-5) and (9-6). Computation of the DFT could be done as either an approximation to (a) the Fourier transform of a nonperiodic signal according to the definition of (9-3), or (b) the Fourier coefficients of a periodic signal according to the definition of (9-5).

If it is desirable to determine the Fourier transform of a nonperiodic signal, the approximation employed must involve sums of areas in the time domain. Assume that the basic DFT definition of

(9-18) is used. The proper magnitude level of the spectrum can then be obtained by multiplying all the components by T. This completes the process of representing the DFT as a zero-order integration approximation of the true integral.

Suppose now that we have a transform computed by the true integral transform definition of (9-3) or as computed by the DFT and modified by multiplying all components by T as indicated in the last paragraph. Assume that we wish to compute the time signal by an approximation to (9-4) obtained by using (9-19) with the $1/N$ factor included. In this case, the approximation must involve sums of areas in the frequency domain. The proper magnitude level is obtained by multiplying all of the resulting time signal components by $NF = f_s$. Note that in the whole cycle from time to frequency and back again as discussed here, we have multiplied by $T \times NF = 1$, so the magnitude level of the complete cycle has, of necessity, not been affected.

Slightly different forms for the scaling constants are required when it is desired to use the DFT to determine the approximate coefficients for the Fourier series of a periodic function. The usual expression for the coefficients of a Fourier series as given by (9-5) involve determining the average value of the integrand. The corresponding magnitude level using the DFT could be obtained by multiplying by T and dividing by t_p. However, $T/t_p = 1/N$. This suggests that the $1/N$ factor would be best associated with the transform rather than the inverse transform for this purpose. Hence, if it is desired to use the DFT for computing regular Fourier series using the standard definitions of (9-5) and (9-6), it is recommended that the DFT definitions be modified by placing the $1/N$ factor with the direct transform rather than with the inverse transform.

The process of scaling the levels may not really be necessary in many applications. In fact, the actual levels of the transform components are often not important; it is the *relative* levels between different components in the spectrum that determine the most significant properties, and these are preserved independently of the overall levels. This fact is illuminated by the variations in the literature concerning the magnitude levels of continuous-time transforms.

To summarize this section, the DFT algorithm can be used to approximate the transform of a continuous-time function, subject to the following limitations and difficulties.

(a) The signal must be bandlimited, and the sampling rate must be sufficiently high to avoid aliasing.

(b) If it is necessary to limit the length of the signal for computational purposes, the spectrum will be degraded somewhat by the leakage effect.

Leakage is most severe when the simple rectangular window function is used.

(c) Components lying between discrete frequency lines are subject to error in magnitude due to the "picket-fence" effect.

(d) The magnitude level may be different from that of the continuous-time transform due to the variation in definitions. This problem is readily resolved by multiplying all of the components by a simple constant, as discussed earlier, if it is necessary to force the levels to be compatible with those of the continuous-time definitions.

10-2 SELECTION OF DFT (OR FFT) PARAMETERS

The purpose of this short section is to summarize the important parameter relationships that must be considered in using the DFT. It is assumed that the actual discrete-time signal is either derived from a continuous-time function or at least referred to such a function for analysis purposes. The major parameters of interest will be reviewed here and are as follows:

T = increment between time samples (in seconds)

f_s = sampling rate (in hertz) = $1/T$

F = increment between frequency components (in hertz) = frequency resolution

t_p = record length (in seconds) = effective period of time signal = $1/F$

f_0 = folding frequency = $f_s/2$ (in hertz)

f_h = highest possible frequency in spectrum (in hertz)

N = number of samples in record

Assume that the function to be analyzed is a *baseband* signal. Such a signal is one in which the spectrum is primarily concentrated at lower frequencies and in which no translation of the spectrum has been performed.

In order to avoid aliasing, it is necessary that

$$f_s \geq 2f_h \qquad\qquad (10\text{-}1)$$

This result implies that T must be selected according to

$$T \leq \frac{1}{2f_h} \qquad\qquad (10\text{-}2)$$

The increment between spectral components F can also be thought of as the *frequency resolution*. For a desired frequency resolution, the minimum record length t_p must be selected according to

$$t_p = \frac{1}{F} \qquad (10\text{-}3)$$

A study of (10-2) and (10-3) leads to the conclusion that there is a tradeoff between the high-frequency capability and the frequency resolution between successive components. To increase the high-frequency capability, it is necessary that T be reduced. For a given N, this would shorten the record length and thus decrease the frequency resolution. Conversely, to improve the resolution, it is necessary to increase t_p. For a given N, this would increase T, which would decrease the high-frequency capability.

The only way in which either the high-frequency capability or the frequency resolution can be increased while holding the other constant is to increase the number of points N in a record length. If f_h and F are both specified, N must satisfy

$$N \geq \frac{2f_h}{F} \qquad (10\text{-}4)$$

The preceding relationships are minimum conditions that should be satisfied with a basic DFT (or FFT) processing algorithm with no special data modification techniques applied. Modifications in the basic procedures could alter these conditions. For example, the use of a special window function will broaden the widths of spectral components, so the frequency resolution may be degraded somewhat in this case. Consequently, it may be necessary to increase the record length in order to maintain a fixed resolution when a special window function is employed.

Example 10-1

An FFT processor is to be employed in the spectral analysis of a random real signal. Assume that the number of points permitted by the processor must be an integer power of two and that no special data modifications are used. The following specifications are given: (1) resolution between frequencies ≤ 5 Hz, (2) highest frequency in signal ≤ 1.25 kHz. Determine the following parameters: (a) minimum record length, (b) maximum time between samples, and (c) minimum number of points in a record.

Solution

(a) The desired resolution determines the minimum record length.

$$t_p = \frac{1}{F} = \frac{1}{5} = 0.2 \text{ seconds}$$

The record length t_p must then satisfy the equation

$$t_p \geq 0.2 \text{ seconds} \qquad (10\text{-}5)$$

(b) The highest frequency determines the maximum sample time.

$$T \leq \frac{1}{2f_h}$$

$$\frac{1}{2f_h} = \frac{1}{2 \times 1.25 \times 10^3} = 0.4 \times 10^{-3}$$

The sample time T is constrained by

$$T \leq 0.4 \text{ milliseconds} \qquad (10\text{-}6)$$

(c) The number of points must satisfy

$$N \geq \frac{0.2}{0.4 \times 10^{-3}} = 500$$

The minimum number is seen to be 500, so an appropriate number for the processor is

$$N = 512 \qquad (10\text{-}7)$$

10-3　CONVOLUTION WITH THE FFT

One of the most important applictions of the FFT is that of *high-speed convolution*, a process made possible by the simplicity of the ·corresponding relationships in the transform domain. The convolution of two signals $x(n)$ and $h(n)$ is denoted by $x(n) * h(n)$ and is defined as

$$x(n) * h(n) = \sum_{k=0}^{N-1} x(k) h(n-k) \qquad (10\text{-}8)$$

By the use of DFT operation pair DO-4 of Table 9-4, this expression is equivalent to

$$x(n)*h(n) \xrightarrow{\hspace{2cm}} X(m)\,H(m) \qquad\qquad (10\text{-}9)$$

If $x(n)$ and $h(n)$ are relatively long functions, the number of computations required to perform a direct convolution can become excessively large. However, according to (10-9), this operation is equivalent in the transform domain to simply multiplying the DFT's of the two signals.

There are actually three basic steps involved in using the DFT to perform high-speed convolution: (a) The DFT's of the two signals are computed using an FFT algorithm. (b) The transforms of the signals are multiplied together at all pertinent frequency points. (c) The inverse transform of the product is computed, again using an FFT algorithm.

Among the many possible applications of this concept is that of digital filtering, as illustrated in Fig. 10-3. It is desired to filter a certain input signal that may be in either analog or digital form (If it is analog, it must first be converted to digital form with an A/D converter.) The DFT of the input signal $x(n)$ is first computed. Next, the DFT is modified by the desired frequency response directly in the frequency domain. The inverse DFT $y(n)$ is then computed, and the result represents the filtered signal. This concept represents a rather interesting approach to digital filtering in the sense that frequency response functions completely unattainable with rational transfer functions may be applied directly to the spectrum.

Before concluding that high-speed convolution is so straightforward, we must point out that there are some serious problems that must be considered, and it is necessary that these be understood before operation DO-4 can be blindly employed. In addition to the possible difficulties discussed in Sec. 10-1, which are always present in DFT analysis, there are some special problems that arise when transforming a convolution using the DFT. Finally, there are certain limitations

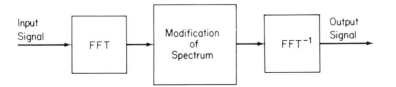

Figure 10-3 Digital filtering using the FFT.

concerning the type of frequency response weighting that can be applied to a spectrum when the DFT is used for digital filtering.

Discrete convolution may be applied directly to a purely discrete system, or it may be used as an approximation for a continuous-time convolution. For the moment, let us consider the latter case, since the nature of the approximation must be considered. Let $x_c(t)$ and $h_c(t)$ represent two continuous-time signals for which we desire a convolution, and let $y_c(t)$ represent the result. Assume that all of the signals are zero for $t < 0$. The desired response can be expressed in the form

$$y_c(t) = \int_0^t x_c(u)h_c(t - u)du \qquad (10\text{-}10)$$

The use of operation DO-4 to evaluate the integral is equivalent to approximating the area under the integrand curve by a zero-order numerical summation process. Assuming that the approximation is reasonable, let $x(n)$, $h(n)$, and $y(n)$ represent the discrete-time functions corresponding to the three continuous-time functions. Assume that N samples of $x(n)$ and $h(n)$ are used. The differential du in (10-10) becomes T, and the required function at sample points can be approximated by

$$y_c(nT) \approx y(n) = T \sum_{k=0}^{n} x(k)h(n - k) \qquad (10\text{-}11)$$

In effect, the desired continuous-time convolution has been approximated by a discrete-time convolution summation, which could be evaluated with the help of the DFT according to operation DO-4.

Everything up to this point appears in order, but there is one important point that may not be evident yet. In general, the input signal $x_c(t)$ and the impulse response $h_c(t)$ of the continuous-time system are not periodic. However, we have previously seen that the inverse DFT operation, resulting from sampling the spectrum, produces a periodic time signal. From the standpoint of using DO-4, this means that the inverse transform of $X(m)$ $H(m)$ is equivalent to having formed the convolution of the *periodic* versions of $x(n)$ and $h(n)$ rather than their true nonperiodic forms. This process is called *cyclical convolution*, and it is a direct result of the periodic character of the DFT.

Before discussing means of alleviating this difficulty, let us present a numerical example to clarify the concepts involved. For illustration, we will choose some functions far too simple to warrant use of the DFT, but appropriate for explaining the process. Consider the two

4-point nonperiodic functions $x(n)$ and $h(n)$ shown in Fig. 10-4, for which the convolution is desired. Using impulse notation, the two signals can be written as

$$x(n) = 2[\delta(n) + \delta(n-1) + \delta(n-2) + \delta(n-3)] \qquad (10\text{-}12)$$

$$h(n) = \delta(n) + 2\delta(n-1) + 3\delta(n-2) + 4\delta(n-3) \qquad (10\text{-}13)$$

The operation we desire is

$$y(n) = x(n)*h(n) = \sum_{k=0}^{n} x(k)h(n-k) \qquad (10\text{-}14)$$

Whether or not (10-14) represents a reasonable approximation to some continuous-time process is unimportant for this illustration.

The various steps involved with this convolution are illustrated in Fig. 10-4. The actual discrete variable n is first replaced with a dummy variable k in $x(n)$ as shown in (c). The quantity $h(n-k)$ is generated by first replacing n by $-k$ as shown in (d) and then replacing $-k$ by $n-k$ as shown in (e). In theory, it would be necessary to consider a separate figure for each value of n, but with proper insight to the process, this need not be done. The particular case shown is for $n = 1$. Next, the product function $x(k)h(n-k)$ is formed as shown in (f). Finally, the sum of the product terms is computed to yield $y(n)$ for that particular value of n. This process is repeated for all pertinent values of n. Note that the product function is zero for $n < 0$ and for $n > 6$, so only a finite number of terms is involved.

The preceding function is the result that would be obtained if a direct convolution summation were performed, and it is the result that we would like to obtain using the DFT. However, what actually happens is that the DFT assumes that both $x(n)$ and $h(n)$ are periodic, and the resulting convolution may be quite different. Assume that the record length for both $x(n)$ and $h(n)$ is held to the four points previously indicated and that no additional points are added. This means that the two signals are equivalent, as far as the DFT is concerned, to the periodic signals $x_a(n)$ and $h_a(n)$ shown in Fig. 10-5. (Note that we will interpret $x_a(n)$ to have a period of 4 because of the way it is defined.)

To illustrate what the inverse DFT would produce, we will actually convolve the two signals. The various steps involved are shown in (c) through (g). Note that in (f) and (g), we have shown the output over one period only, but these results are periodic. Clearly, the resulting function is not what we had hoped to obtain.

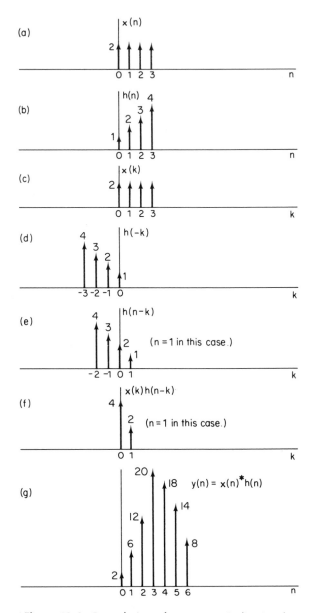

Figure 10-4 Convolution of two nonperiodic signals.

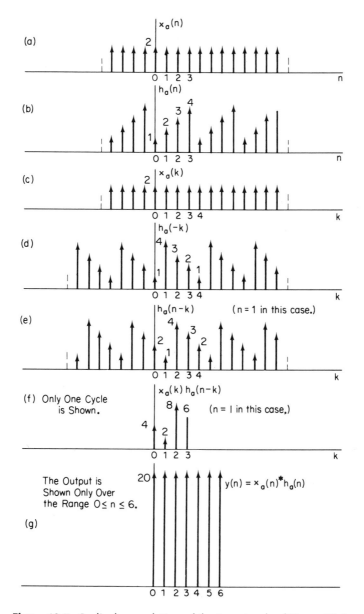

Figure 10-5 Cyclical convolution of the two signals of Figure 10-4.

The significant difference in the convolution process here as compared with Fig. 10-4 is that a portion of a different cycle of $h_a(n-k)$ moves into the summation interval as $h_a(n-k)$ is shifted to the right. This phenomenon is called *wrap-around error*, and this leads to the incorrect results.

A different way of explaining this process is related to the fact that the convolution of two nonperiodic signals yields a function whose width is approximately the sum of the widths of the two functions being convolved. If both signals are assumed to be periodic, with a period equal to the record length, there is no room to spread in this sense, so that the resulting convolution will not be able to have the required width.

While there are different ways of resolving this type of difficulty, we will concentrate on some simpler schemes. Assume that both $x(n)$ and $h(n)$ are of equal length and have N points each. The period of each function may be artificially doubled by adding N zeros at the end. Let $\hat{x}(n)$ and $\hat{h}(n)$ represent the two new functions defined by

$$\hat{x}(n) = x(n) \text{ for } 0 \leqslant n \leqslant N-1$$
$$= 0 \text{ for } N \leqslant n \leqslant 2N-1 \qquad (10\text{-}15)$$

$$\hat{h}(n) = h(n) \text{ for } 0 \leqslant n \leqslant N-1$$
$$= 0 \text{ for } N \leqslant n \leqslant 2N-1 \qquad (10\text{-}16)$$

The convolution of $\hat{x}(n)$ and $\hat{h}(n)$ is a function $\hat{y}(n)$ having a period 2N, but in which the function during one cycle is equivalent to the original nonperiodic convolution of $x(n)$ and $h(n)$. This process is illustrated in Fig. 10-6 for the functions considered earlier. Only one period of the quantities shown in (f) and (g) is shown. The result in (g) during this period is clearly seen to agree with the result of Fig. 10-4. Thus, if the DFT process were applied to the functions $\hat{x}(n)$ and $\hat{h}(n)$, the desired convolution would be obtained.

It should be recognized that in eliminating the wrap-around error, we have been forced to double the required capacity of the DFT or FFT algorithm. The quantity N should be replaced by 2N in the various DFT expressions. Placing N zero values at the end of each function provides an effective total period of 2N, which is sufficient for the convolution of two functions with N points each.

The discrete convolution of two nonperiodic functions with N points each yields a new function with $2N-1$ points. When N zeros are

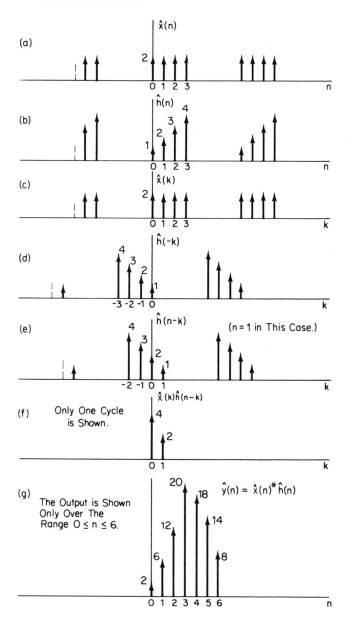

Figure 10-6 Cyclical convolution of the two signals of Figure 10-4 with extra zeros added.

added to the original functions, the resulting cyclical convolution has a period of 2N, which is one more point than is required for the original nonperiodic convolution. The one additional point in each cycle has a value of zero.

If the two functions are reasonably close, but not equal, in length, additional zeros may be first added to the shorter signal so that the resulting signals are equal in length before adding additional zeros. This means that more than N zeros would be added to the shorter signal overall.

To summarize the highlights discussed so far, the process of highspeed convolution can be achieved as follows:

(a) Modify $x(n)$ and $h(n)$ by adding zeros so that wrap-around error will not appear. The modified functions are $\hat{x}(n)$ and $\hat{h}(n)$.

(b) Compute $\hat{X}(m)$ and $\hat{H}(m)$, the DFT's of the two modified functions, using an FFT algorithm or processor.

(c) Determine $\hat{Y}(m) = \hat{X}(m)\,\hat{H}(m)$ by multiplying the values of $\hat{X}(m)$ and $\hat{H}(m)$ together at all frequency integers.

(d) Compute $\hat{y}(n) = D^{-1}[\hat{Y}(m)]$ using an FFT algorithm or processor. One cycle of this function is the desired convolution.

(e) Multiply the result by any additional constants required, such as the factor T in (10-11), when the convolution represents an approximation to a continuous-time process.

The method just described becomes rather inefficient when the two functions to be convolved differ appreciably in length. This method also breaks down when one or both of the functions are so long that they exceed the capacity of the FFT processor available. A method referred to as "selectsaving" can be employed for such cases.

Consider the functions $h(n)$ and $x(n)$ shown in Fig. 10-7. For the sake of clarity, these quantities are shown as continuous curves, but they are assumed to be discrete-time functions. The function $h(n)$ is assumed to be of relatively short length, with N points. The function $x(n)$ is assumed to be very long and could, in fact, represent a random signal of indefinite length.

The period of the function $h(n)$ is increased to 2N by adding N zeros according to the scheme previously discussed. Letting $\hat{h}(n)$ represent this function, we have

$$\hat{h}(n) = h(n) \text{ for } 0 \leqslant n \leqslant N-1$$
$$= 0 \text{ for } N \leqslant n \leqslant 2N-1$$

$$(10\text{-}17)$$

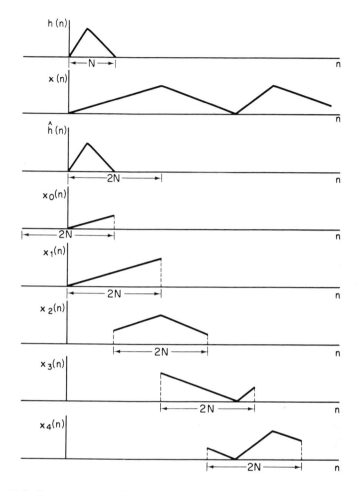

Figure 10-7 Representation of a long signal in terms of shorter signals in order to use the "select-saving" method.

Assume that $x(n) = 0$ for $n < 0$. This function is then sectioned into an arbitrary number of 2N point signals $x_i(n)$ in which the first N points are used to establish the proper "history" of the signal required in the convolution process, and the last N points actually determine the required output. The sections are defined by the relationships

$$x_0(n) = x(n - N) \text{ for } 0 \leq n \leq 2N - 1$$
$$= 0 \qquad \text{otherwise}$$

$$(10\text{-}18)$$

$$x_1(n) = x(n) \qquad \text{for } 0 \leq n \leq 2N-1$$
$$= 0 \qquad \text{otherwise}$$

(10-19)

.

.

.

$$x_i(n) = x(n+iN-N) \text{ for } 0 \leq n \leq 2N-1$$
$$= 0 \qquad \text{otherwise}$$

(10-20)

This process is illustrated in Fig. 10-7. The point $n = 0$ is assumed to be redefined at the beginning of each segment of $x_i(m)$.

The convolution of $h(n)$ with all of the sections $x_i(n)$ yields a set of 2N-point periodic signals. The verification of some of the properties will be left as an exercise (Prob. 10-3), but the results will be stated here. The major properties of each of the signals are as follows: (a) The first N points in the convolution, corresponding to $0 \leq n \leq N-1$, represent either incorrect data due to inadequate history or, in the case of the point $n = N-1$, a correct value which has already been computed in the preceding convolution. Thus, this data can be discarded. (b) The next N terms, corresponding to $N \leq n \leq 2N-1$, are the correct values of the convolution, corresponding to the second half of $x_i(n)$. Letting $y_i(n)$ represent the set of convolved functions, the desired function $y(n)$ can be expressed as

$$y(n) = y_0(n+N) \text{ for } 0 \leq n \leq N-1 \qquad (10-21)$$

$$y(n+N) = y_1(n+N) \text{ for } 0 \leq n \leq N-1 \qquad (10-22)$$

.

.

.

$$y(n+iN) = y_i(n+N) \text{ for } 0 \leq n \leq N-1 \qquad (10-23)$$

Note again that the beginning of each segment $y_i(n)$ is defined as $n = 0$ as far as the convolution is concerned.

Let us now turn our attention briefly to the possibility of using the DFT for digital filtering by operating directly on the spectrum. At first glance, it would seem that an ideal block filter characteristic could be readily applied to the spectrum, which would result in an infinitely sharp amplitude response. The difficulty arising with this concept is that the resulting impulse response in the time domain would have a $\sin x /x$ type of response, with infinitely long tails in both directions. Since the frequency function can be sampled only at a finite number of points, the time response would exhibit an aliasing effect analogous to frequency-domain aliasing when a time function is sampled at too low a rate. The solution to this problem is to choose a filter function whose impulse response can be truncated to a finite range without introducing intolerable errors in the frequency response.

10-4 POWER SPECTRUM

We have seen that when a time series $x(n)$ is transformed by an FFT algorithm, a complex transform $X(m)$ is obtained. For reasons that will be clear shortly, we will refer to $X(m)$ as a *linear* spectrum. Since the linear spectrum is complex, it has both real and imaginary parts. These individual parts are each dependent on the position of the signal, but the resulting magnitude is, of course, independent of the position.

While the linear spectrum is sufficient for many purposes, there are applications in which the square of the magnitude is of primary importance. Since the square of the magnitude is proportional to power, the term *power spectrum* is widely used in reference to this function. Let $S_{xx}(m)$ represent the power spectrum. (The significance of the double subscripts will be seen in the next section. At that point, the adjective "auto" will also be used in the definition.) The power spectrum can be expressed as

$$S_{xx}(m) = \frac{|X(m)|^2}{N} = \frac{X(m)\widetilde{X}(m)}{N} = \frac{X_r^2 + X_i^2}{N} \qquad (10\text{-}24)$$

From the last term on the right of (10-24), it can be seen that the power spectrum is readily calculated from $X(m)$ by squaring the real and imaginary parts and adding the results. Many FFT processors have a direct provision for determining some form of the power spectrum.

The function $S_{xx}(m)$ may or may not actually represent true power in watts, as this would depend on what physical variables are involved and in what manner the signal is used. However, it is conceptually useful to think of this quantity as representing the power in a general sense.

Additional insight into this concept can be gained by a modified form of Parseval's theorem as applied to discrete-time signals. This theorem, which will be derived at the end of the next section in Ex. 10-3, reads

$$\sum_{n=0}^{N-1} x^2(n) = \sum_{m=0}^{N-1} S_{xx}(m) \qquad (10\text{-}25)$$

The expression on the left of (10-25) is proportional to the energy represented by the signal in one time-domain cycle. According to this theorem, the same result may be obtain directly from the spectrum by summing the terms of the power spectrum over a frequency-domain cycle.

Example 10-2

(a) Determine a closed-form expression for the DFT of $x(n) = 1$, for $0 \leqslant n \leqslant N-1$. (b) Verify Parseval's theorem for this function.

Solution

(a) The DFT of $x(n)$ is given by

$$X(m) = \sum_{n=0}^{N-1} (1) W_N^{mn} \qquad (10\text{-}26)$$

The series of (10-26) constitutes a finite geometric series that can be expressed as

$$X(m) = \frac{1 - W_N^{Nm}}{1 - W_N^m} = \frac{1 - \epsilon^{-j2\pi m}}{1 - \epsilon^{-j(2\pi m/N)}} \qquad (10\text{-}27)$$

The expression of (10-27) is zero for all integer values in the range $0 \leqslant m \leqslant N-1$ except for $m = 0$, where the expression initially has an indeterminate form. Application of L'Hospital's Rule for $m = 0$ results in

$$X(0) = \lim_{m \to 0} \frac{Nj2\pi\epsilon^{-j2\pi m}}{j2\pi\epsilon^{-j(2\pi m/N)}} = N \qquad (10\text{-}28)$$

(b) The "energy" contained in the time signal is readily determined as

$$\sum_{n=0}^{N-1} x^2(n) = \sum_{n=0}^{N-1} (1) = N \qquad (10\text{-}29)$$

Since there is only one term in the power spectrum, we have

$$\sum_{m=0}^{N-1} S_{xx}(m) = \frac{|X(0)|^2}{N} = \frac{N^2}{N} = N \qquad (10\text{-}30)$$

Comparison of (10-29) and (10-30) verfies the theorem for this case.

10-5   CORRELATION AND STATISTICAL ANALYSIS _____

The concept of lagged products was introduced in Chapt. 9 in conjunction with transform pair DO-5. There are two primary operations in which this form is used: (a) *cross-correlation* and (b) *autocorrelation*. These functional operations are used extensively in signal and statistical analysis, both in continuous-time systems and in discrete-time systems. Many of the correlation applications previously performed with analog circuits for continuous-time signals can now be achieved with either a general-purpose computer or with a special-purpose digital processor using discrete-time techniques.

Treatment of the theory serving as a basis for correlation theory is covered extensively in books dealing with statistical communication theory. We will concentrate here on applying these concepts to possible applications using the FFT and related numerical techniques.

For the sake of simplicity, the basic correlation relationships will first be discussed in terms of their continuous-time forms. Let $x(t)$ and $y(t)$ represent two random continuous-time signals. The *cross-correlation* function $R_{xy}(\tau)$ of the two signals over an interval t_p can be defined as

$$R_{xy}(\tau) = \overline{x(t)y(t-\tau)} = \lim_{t_p \to \infty} \frac{1}{t_p} \int_0^{t_p} x(t)y(t-\tau)dt \qquad (10\text{-}31)$$

The quantity τ represents a *delay* or *lag* variable. The integral represents the area of the product of the two signals expressed as a function of the amount by which one signal is delayed. The line above the product $\overline{x(t)y(t-\tau)}$ is used to denote a time average of the quantity involved.

The relative value of $R_{xy}(\tau)$ indicates how well the two signals are correlated for that particular value of delay. If the correlation function peaks for a particular value of τ, this would indicate a very good correlation, which means that the two signals match each other very well. Conversely, a very small or zero value of the correlation function indicates little or no correlation.

The *autocorrelation* function $R_{xx}(\tau)$ can be considered as a special case of the cross-correlation function with $y(t) = x(t)$. The definition for continuous-time random signals reads

$$R_{xx}(\tau) = \overline{x(t)x(t-\tau)} = \lim_{t_p \to \infty} \frac{1}{t_p} \int_0^{t_p} x(t)x(t-\tau)dt \qquad (10\text{-}32)$$

This operation is simply the average of the product of the signal and a delayed version of the signal as a function of the delay.

The Fourier transforms of the cross-correlation and autocorrelation functions often provide useful interpretations of the nature of the signals. It can be shown that the Fourier transform of the autocorrelation function is the square of the magnitude of the Fourier transform $X(f)$ of the signal $x(t)$. This function is called the *auto power spectrum*, and it will be denoted by $S_{xx}(f)$. Hence,

$$S_{xx}(f) = F[R_{xx}(\tau)] = X(f)\widetilde{X}(f) = |X(f)|^2 \qquad (10\text{-}33)$$

In a similar fashion, the Fourier transform of the cross-correlation function can be calculated. This function is called the *cross power spectrum*, denoted by $S_{xy}(f)$. It can be shown that the cross power spectrum can be expressed as

$$S_{xy}(f) = F[R_{xy}(\tau)] = X(f)\widetilde{Y}(f) \qquad (10\text{-}34)$$

Note that while $S_{xx}(f)$ is a real function, $S_{xy}(f)$ is, in general, complex.

One of the primary applications of cross-correlation is in determining the delay of a signal that has been hidden in additive noise. For example, this operation arises in radar and sonar systems where a known signal is transmitted and reflected from a target at some later time. Measurement of the exact delay will provide information regarding the range of the target. Let $x(t)$ represent the transmitted signal and let $u(t)$ represent the additive noise. Although the transmitted signal will undergo some distortion, we shall neglect this effect in this discussion. The received signal $y(t)$ will then be of the form

$$y(t) = x(t - T_d) + u(t) \qquad (10\text{-}35)$$

where T_d represents the total two-way delay of the signal.

A cross-correlation can now be made at the receiver between a stored version of the transmitted signal $x(t)$ and the received signal $y(t)$. This operation yields

$$R_{xy}(\tau) = \overline{x(t)y(t)} = \overline{x(t)x(t - T_d)} + \overline{x(t)u(t)} \qquad (10\text{-}36)$$

The second term in (10-36) represents the correlation between the transmitted signal and the noise. In general, there is no correlation between these quantities, so the expected value of this function is zero. The first term in (10-36) is actually an autocorrelation if any distortion of the received signal is neglected. The function $R_{xy}(\tau)$ can be expected to show a peak for $\tau = T_d$, which would provide an accurate measure of the delay time. Using these methods, it is possible to measure the delay of a signal that has been virtually buried in noise.

The reader is invited to verify (Prob. 10-5) that the autocorrelation function of a periodic time signal is a periodic function of τ, and the resulting period is the same as that of the original time signal. This concept leads to a very useful application of autocorrelation. Consider the situation where an unknown periodic signal is buried in noise, but in which a measurement of the period is desired. If the signal is correlated with itself, the resulting autocorrelation function will display the desired period.

Certain statistical parameters can be related to the autocorrelation function. Let $p(x)$ represent the *probability density function* of the variable x. The function $p(x)$ is characterized by a number of useful statistical parameters, of which some of the most important are (a) the mean value $\overline{x}$, (b) the mean-squared value $\overline{x^2}$, and (c) the variance σ^2.

The mean (or DC) value is defined as

$$\overline{x} = \int_{-\infty}^{\infty} x p(x)\,dx \qquad (10\text{-}37)$$

The mean-squared value is defined as

$$\overline{x^2} = \int_{-\infty}^{\infty} x^2 p(x)\,dx \qquad (10\text{-}38)$$

Finally, the variance is defined as

$$\sigma^2 = \int_{-\infty}^{\infty} (x - \overline{x})^2 \, p(x) \, dx \qquad (10\text{-}39)$$

It can be readily shown from (10-39) that σ^2 can be expressed as

$$\sigma^2 = \overline{x^2} - \overline{x}^2 \qquad (10\text{-}40)$$

Assume that the process under consideration is an *ergodic* random process. This means that the *ensemble* averages given in the preceding few equations are equivalent to appropriate *time* averages taken from the same process.

The mean-square value is determined from

$$\overline{x^2} = \lim_{t_p \to \infty} \frac{1}{t_p} \int_0^{t_p} x^2(t) \, dt = R_{xx}(0) \qquad (10\text{-}41)$$

If the process contains a dc value, it would appear as a long-term constant in $R_{xx}(\tau)$. Assuming the absence of any periodic components, the square of the mean can be expressed as

$$\overline{x}^2 = \lim_{t_p \to \infty} \frac{1}{t_p} \int_0^{t_p} x(t) x(t - \tau) \, dt = R_{xx}(\infty) \qquad (10\text{-}42)$$

Finally, the variance is readily expressed as

$$\sigma^2 = R_{xx}(0) - R_{xx}(\infty) \qquad (10\text{-}43)$$

It can be seen, then, that for an ergodic process, some of the most important statistical properties may be determined from the autocorrelation function.

Having considered some of the basic definitions and properties of correlation and the associated statistical concepts, we will now investigate the possible digital implementation of these operations. In order to keep the notation as simple as possible, we shall continue to use the same basic symbols established in this section for continuous-time functions, but with the arguments replaced by integers for the discrete-time case.

Suppose that we are given two discrete-time signals $x(n)$ and $y(n)$. The discrete *cross-correlation function* will be denoted by $R_{xy}(k)$, and a suitable definition is

$$R_{xy}(k) = \overline{x(n)y(n-k)} = \frac{1}{N} \sum_{n=0}^{N-1} x(n)y(n-k) \qquad (10\text{-}44)$$

The *discrete autocorrelation function* will be denoted by $R_{xx}(k)$, and it can be expressed as

$$R_{xx}(k) = \overline{x(n)x(n-k)} = \frac{1}{N} \sum_{n=0}^{N-1} x(n)x(n-k) \qquad (10\text{-}45)$$

Using the DFT operation pair (DO-5) associated with lagged products, the DFT of (10-45) is readily determined as

$$D[R_{xx}(k)] = \frac{X(m)\widetilde{X}(m)}{N} = \frac{|X(m)|^2}{N} = S_{xx}(m) \qquad (10\text{-}46)$$

where $S_{xx}(m)$ is the *discrete auto power spectrum* of the signal as defined earlier in (10-24). The inverse DFT of the power spectrum is the autocorrelation function as expressed by

$$D^{-1}[S_{xx}(m)] = R_{xx}(k) \qquad (10\text{-}47)$$

The *discrete cross power spectrum* $S_{xx}(m)$ can be readily expressed as

$$D[R_{xy}(k)] = \frac{X(m)\widetilde{Y}(m)}{N} = S_{xy}(m) \qquad (10\text{-}48)$$

The inverse DFT of the cross power spectrum is the cross-correlation function

$$D^{-1}[S_{xy}(m)] = R_{xy}(k) \qquad (10\text{-}49)$$

The various relationships associated with the discrete cross-correlation function are illustrated in Fig. 10-8. The cross-correlation function of two signals $x(n)$ and $y(n)$ may be calculated directly, as shown on the left. However, an alternative procedure is to use an FFT algorithm to compute the spectra of the two signals and then multiply one spectrum by the conjugate of the other. The result of this operation

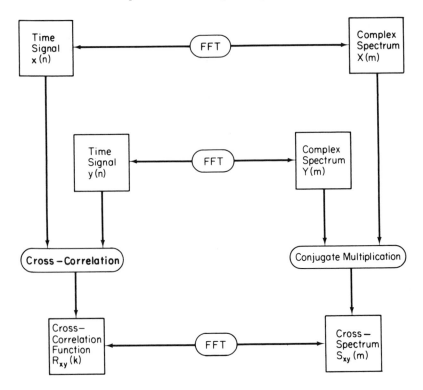

Figure 10-8 Various cross-correlation relationships.

is the cross-spectrum, which can then be inversely transformed with the FFT to yield the cross-correlation function. All of the operations apply to the autocorrelation function when the two signals are the same. Other computational combinations are possible depending on what functions are known in a given case.

When either of the correlation functions are computed by these DFT procedures, it is necessary to apply the same types of precautions discussed in Sec. 10-3 for convolution computation. In fact, inspection of operation pairs DO-4 and DO-5 reveals that the major difference between the two operations is that one of the functions is reversed in direction for one operation as compared with the other. Thus, the techniques discussed in Sec. 10-3 are generally applicable to correlation, as long as the basic differences are understood.

Use of the FFT and discrete-time techniques necessitates that the interval of analysis be restricted to a finite length having a finite number of sample points. When the composite signal is composed of a desired signal plus additive random noise, the effect of the noise is to reduce the certainty in both the time and spectrum measurements. The spectrum computation can be improved considerably by taking a number of different spectra and then performing an average of the corresponding frequency components on a point-by-point basis.

The basis for this concept is the fact that the components of the signal are correlated from one spectrum to the next, whereas the noise components are uncorrelated. The variance of the measurement is inversely proportional to the number of spectra averaged together, so that a considerable improvement in accuracy can be obtained by this process.

Example 10-3

Derive Parseval's theorem for discrete-time signals as given by equation (10-25).

Solution

The sum of $x^2(n)$ can be expressed as the discrete autocorrelation function evaluated at $k = 0$ from (10-45). Hence,

$$\frac{1}{N} \sum_{n=0}^{N-1} x^2(n) = R_{xx}(0) \qquad (10\text{-}50)$$

In general, $R_{xx}(k)$ can be expressed as

$$R_{xx}(k) = \frac{1}{N} \sum_{m=0}^{N-1} S_{xx}(m) W^{-km} \qquad (10\text{-}51)$$

The value of $R_{xx}(0)$ is readily expressed as

$$R_{xx}(0) = \frac{1}{N} \sum_{m=0}^{N-1} S_{xx}(m) \qquad (10\text{-}52)$$

Comparing (10-50) and (10-52), the desired result is readily obtained.

10-6   FREQUENCY SAMPLING FILTERS _____

In this section we will show how the DFT may be used to assist in the design of FIR filters. In particular, we will discuss a special class of FIR

functions called *frequency sampling filters* due to the manner in which
they are designed.

It will be recalled from Chapt. 8 that one of the major steps
required in the design of FIR filters is the determination of the coefficients of the time-domain impulse response. These coefficients are determined by evaluating the Fourier series associated with the periodic
frequency response, normally carried out by an integration process.

Instead of actually performing the integration, however, consider
the possibility of using the DFT (actually the *inverse* DFT, or IDFT) for
this purpose. In order to utilize the IDFT in this manner, the frequency
response can be specified at N equally spaced frequencies in the range
$0 \leqslant f < f_s$ or, equivalently, in the integer range $0 \leqslant m \leqslant N-1$. Let $H(m)$
represent the complex form of the desired frequency response function,
and let $A(m)$ and $\beta(m)$ represent the amplitude and phase functions,
respectively. The frequency response can then be expressed as

$$H(m) = A(m) \; \epsilon^{j \, \beta(m)} \text{ for } 0 \leqslant m \leqslant N-1 \qquad (10\text{-}53)$$

The guidelines for selecting the values of $A(m)$ and $\beta(m)$ are
somewhat involved, and they will not be given here. We shall concentrate on some interesting aspects of the realization and implementation properties. Thus, for our purposes, we assume that $H(m)$ as
expressed by (10-53) is given.

The desired transfer function $H(z)$ can be expressed as

$$H(z) = \sum_{n=0}^{N-1} a_n z^{-n} \qquad (10\text{-}54)$$

The coefficients a_n are determined from the IDFT as

$$a_n = \frac{1}{N} \sum_{m=0}^{N-1} H(m) \, W^{-nm} \qquad (10\text{-}55)$$

Substitution of (10-55) in (10-54) yields

$$H(z) = \sum_{n=0}^{N-1} \left[\frac{1}{N} \sum_{m=0}^{N-1} H(m) \, W^{-nm} \right] z^{-n} \qquad (10\text{-}56)$$

If the order of summation is reversed in (10-56), the function $H(z)$ can
be expressed as

$$H(z) = \frac{1}{N} \sum_{m=0}^{N-1} H(m) \sum_{n=0}^{N-1} W^{-nm} z^{-n} \qquad (10\text{-}57)$$

The summation on the right-hand side of (10-57) can be expressed in closed form as

$$\sum_{n=0}^{N-1} W^{-nm} z^{-n} = \frac{1 - W^{-Nm} z^{-N}}{1 - W^{-m} z^{-1}} = \frac{1 - z^{-N}}{1 - W^{-m} z^{-1}} \qquad (10\text{-}58)$$

Substitution of (10-58) in (10-57) yields

$$H(z) = \frac{1 - z^{-N}}{N} \sum_{m=0}^{N-1} \frac{H(m)}{1 - z^{-1} W^{-m}} \qquad (10\text{-}59)$$

$$= \frac{1 - z^{-N}}{N} \sum_{m=0}^{N-1} \frac{H(m)}{1 - z^{-1} \epsilon^{j(2\pi m/N)}} \qquad (10\text{-}60)$$

Each term in the series of (10-60) contains one of the poles of $H(z)$. The various poles p_m are located at

$$p_m = \epsilon^{j(2\pi m/N)} \qquad (10\text{-}61)$$

It is convenient at this point to use the normalized frequency $v = f/f_0$ that has been used extensively in earlier parts of the book. Let

$$v_m = \frac{mF}{f_0} = \frac{2m}{N} \qquad (10\text{-}62)$$

The values v_m represent a set of normalized frequencies occurring at integer multiples of the fundamental frequency F. The poles can be expressed as

$$p_m = \epsilon^{j\pi v_m} \qquad (10\text{-}63)$$

We shall now represent $H(z)$ as the product of two functions of the form

$$H(z) = H_1(z) H_2(z) \qquad (10\text{-}64)$$

where

$$H_1(z) = \frac{1 - z^{-N}}{N} \qquad (10\text{-}65)$$

and

$$H_2(z) = \sum_{m=0}^{N-1} \frac{H(m)}{1 - z^{-1} \epsilon^{j\pi v_m}} \qquad (10\text{-}66)$$

Observe that the notation of (10-62) has been used in (10-66).

The poles of H(z) corresponding to (10-62) are now associated with H$_2(z)$. It can be readily shown that the zeros of H$_1(z)$ are located at the same positions as the poles of H$_2(z)$. The reader is invited to show (Prob. 10-6) that the amplitude response A$_1(v)$ corresponding to H$_1(z)$ is given by

$$A_1(v) = \frac{2}{N} \sin \frac{\pi}{2} Nv \qquad (10\text{-}67)$$

This function is called a *comb filter*. There are N zeros of A$_1(v)$ in the range $0 \leqslant v < 2$. The form of $|A_1(v)|$ for a particular value of N (N = 16 in this case) is shown for the range $0 \leqslant v \leqslant 1$ in Fig. 10-9.

Each term in H$_2(z)$ can be considered as a complex resonator in which the amplitude response would be infinite at a particular frequency v_m. However, when H$_1(z)$ and H$_2(z)$ are connected in cascade, the various zeros of H$_1(z)$ can be shown to cancel the effects of the poles at the frequency values v_m. In fact, it can be shown (Prob. 10-7) that the overall amplitude response at $v = v_m$ is H(m), as originally specified.

This concept suggests a possible recursive realization in which a comb filter is connected in cascade with a bank of resonators as shown in Fig. 10-10. In practice, the various terms in H$_2(z)$ can be combined in pairs having complex conjugate poles plus single terms involving the real poles. Thus, a given resonator would be either a second-order or a first-order function with real coefficients. For the combination of any particular resonator with the comb filter, the frequency response will be zero at all discrete values of frequency satisfying (10-62), except the one or two corresponding to the pole (or poles) of the given resonator, at which the response will be as specified. The combination of all of the various resonators then produces the required overall response at the

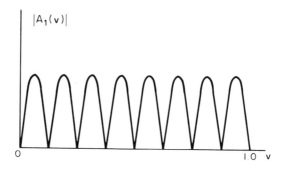

Figure 10-9 Form of the amplitude response of a comb filter (N=16).

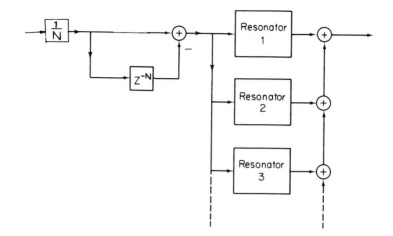

Figure 10-10 Form of the recursive realization of a frequency sampling FIR filter.

set of sampling frequencies specified. Hence, the term *frequency sampling filter* is quite appropriate.

It was stated in Chapt. 8 that recursive realizations of FIR filters were possible. The present approach achieves that result. Of course, frequency sampling filters can be realized nonrecursively by solving for the impulse response coefficients using the DFT.

The primary advantage of recursive realization for a frequency sampling filter is related to the fact that the majority of samples of $H(m)$ are either 1 or 0 for most filter functions. Furthermore, if the passband of the filter is relatively narrow, the majority of the values are zero, corresponding to the stopband. This means that only a relatively few nonzero values of $H(m)$, corresponding to the passband and transition band, are present. Consequently, only a limited number of resonators are required, so that a very efficient design may be achieved.

In theory, the zeros of the comb filter cancel the poles of the resonators. In practice, there may be slight differences that could result in instability problems. These can be avoided by moving the zeros and poles very slightly inside the unit circle without degrading the nature of the response.

Filters designed using the frequency sampling method will always achieve the response specified at the frequency values v_m. If the designer simply specifies the value one in the passband and zero in the stopband without providing any transition band, the response may display significant ripple between frequency sample points. This difficulty can be minimized by providing a sufficiently wide transition band. Unfortunately, it is not intuitively clear as to how much of a transition band should be used in a given case. This uncertainty has led to computer-aided methods for design using optimization criteria. Many future designs for finite impulse response filters will probably be obtained from these computer-aided optimization techniques.

_____ *PROBLEMS* _____

10-1 An FFT processor is to be used to estimate the spectrum of a real signal. Assume that the number of points must be an integer multiple of two, and assume that no special data modifications are used. The specifications are: (1) resolution between frequencies ≤ 0.5 Hz, (2) highest frequency in signal ≤ 250 Hz. Determine the following parameters: (a) minimum record length, (b) maximum time between samples, and (c) minimum number of points in a record.

10-2 A certain FFT processor has a maximum capacity of 2048 points, and the maximum time required to load and compute a complete spectrum is 200 ms. The unit is to be operated in real time, and sufficient auxiliary storage is used to permit one record to be stored while the previous one is transformed. Determine (a) the highest frequency that can be resolved, and (b) the frequency resolution. Assume that no special data modifications are used.

10-3 Using Fig. 10-7 and the definitions of the various segments indicated by equations (10-18), (10-19), and (10-20), verify the properties of the "select-saving" method leading to equations (10-21), (10-22), and (10-23).

10-4 Consider the signal defined over eight points as

$$x(n) = 1 \text{ for } 0 \leq n \leq 3$$

$$= 0 \text{ for } 4 \leq n \leq 7$$

(a) Determine a closed-form expression for the DFT of $x(n)$, i.e., $X(m)$.
(b) Verify Parseval's theorem for this function.

10-5 Prove that the autocorrelation function of a periodic time signal is a periodic function of τ.

10-6 Show that the amplitude response of the comb filter of equation (10-65) is of the form of equation (10-67).

10-7 Show that the amplitude response of $H(z)$ for the frequency sampling filter at $v = v_m$ is $H(m)$.

GENERAL
APPLICATIONS
OF
DIGITAL SIGNAL
PROCESSING

BY

GARY R. DOUGHERTY

AND

RAY DOUGHERTY

11

GENERAL APPLICATIONS OF DIGITAL SIGNAL PROCESSING — AN OVERVIEW

11-0 INTRODUCTION

Applications of digital signal processing include the following:

1. Voice synthesis and recognition.
2. Radar.
3. Spectral analysis.
4. Industrial control systems.
5. Digital communication.
6. Image processing including computer, axial tomography, ultrasound, lasers.
7. High-speed modems and digital filters for improving signal quality over telephones.
8. Audio reverberation systems.
9. Psychoacoustics.
10. Robotic vision systems.
11. Others.

The optical signal processing system represents the bandwidth products of current sophisticated waveforms, as well as the necessary operations performed on these data and require advanced processing techniques. Solid state semiconductor diode arrays and vidicon cameras are presently used in optical processing. The specific use of optical signal processing techniques in spread spectrum, radar, sonar, and electronic warfare is also of interest.

The field of digital image processing applications continues to generate considerable interest in the engineering community as well as in other scientific fields.

Some further applications of digital signal processing, in addition to the ones mentioned above, are:

1. Audio processing chips.
2. Analysis of sound and vibration signals generated by a fly shuttle loom.
3. Implementing speech recognition algorithms on microprocessors.
4. Newer digital signal processor (DSP) algorithms, which extract more information from monolithic processors with greater computational power.
5. Advanced fiber optics.
6. New directions in sensor usage of multiprocessor networks.
7. Very large scale integration (VLSI) applications.
8. Telecommunication networks.
9. Computer graphics.
10. Computer-aided drafting.
11. Microcomputer/microprocessor systems.
12. Neurosurgery.
13. Satellite communications.
14. Antenna patterns.
15. Telephony transmission.
16. Microprocessors with architecture chosen to perform digital signal processing algorithms.
17. Digital signal processor integrated circuits for adaptive differential pulse code modulations for encoding and decoding techniques.
18. Very high speed integrated circuits (VHSICs).
19. Aviation.
20. Astronomy.
21. Switched capacitor filters.
22. Industrial noise control.
23. Arrays of microcomputers for the implementation of general-purpose signal processing algorithms.
24. Cybernetics.
25. Transmission lines.

11-1 APPLICATION OF FILTERS TO ANALOG AND DIGITAL SIGNAL PROCESSING* _____

Since all analog signals can be digitized via an A/D converter, we start our discussion at this point. The information content of the signal may be analyzed by examining its Fourier transform. Signals encountered in real physical systems have finite, limited rates of change; hence, the Fourier spectrum of such a signal is limited to a finite frequency band and does not contain an infinite band of significant frequency components.

A useful definition is that of the upper limit of the frequency spectrum, f_N. This may be defined as:

$$f_N = \text{frequency of highest spectral component}$$
$$\text{(of significant amplitude)} \qquad (11\text{-}1)$$

If a unipolar signal remains constant for any appreciable length of time, its spectrum will extend from f_N down to dc (zero frequency). If the signal has an average value different from zero, it has a dc (zero-frequency) component, regardless of whether its spectrum is continuous down to dc. It can be shown that if the signal is sampled at a rate

$$f_s = 2f_N \qquad (11\text{-}2)$$

then it is theoretically possible to reconstruct it from the sampled data without loss of information. The intersample time interval T is then

$$T = \frac{1}{f_s} \le \frac{1}{2f_N} \qquad (11\text{-}3)$$

Unfortunately, given a set of sampled values, we cannot relate them specifically to one unique signal. As Fig. 11-1 shows, the same set of samples could have resulted from measurement of any one of the three waveforms shown and from an infinite number of higher-frequency waves (each an integral multiple of the lowest frequency wave) that could be drawn so as to pass through the sampled-data points. All such waveforms that fit the sample data are called *aliases*. The lowest frequency wave that fits the sample data has a frequency

$$f_L \le \frac{1}{2T} \qquad (11\text{-}4)$$

*Sections 11-1 through 11-4 material and figures, Courtesy of Wavetek Rockland Inc., Rockleigh, New Jersey.

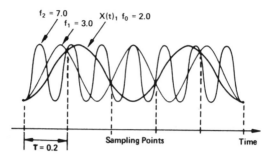

Figure 11-1 Many different signals may, when sampled, yield the same set of data. These are called "aliases" of each other. Courtesy of Wavetek Rockland, Inc.

It is important to observe that if we restrict the signal content to frequency components less than $f_0 = f_s/2$, then no errors due to aliasing are possible. Ideally, then, the input signal spectrum should not extend beyond f_0, i.e.,

$$f_N \leqslant f_0 \qquad (11\text{-}5)$$

or

$$f_N \leqslant \frac{1}{2T} \qquad (11\text{-}6)$$

or

$$f_N \leqslant \frac{f_s}{2} \qquad (11\text{-}7)$$

The folding frequency $f_0 = f_s/2$ describes graphically what happens if there are higher frequency components in the signal spectrum than are permitted for nonaliased sampling and interpretation. Fig. 11-2 shows that if we have been careful to make f_N no higher than f_0,

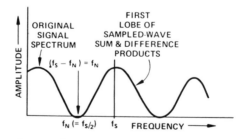

Figure 11-2 When the sampling rate is at least twice the highest frequency component in the signal spectrum, folding does not occur. Courtesy of Wavetek Rockland, Inc.

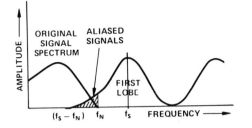

Figure 11-3 When the sampling rate is too low, the spectra overlap, and aliased (false) signals appear in the sampled data. Courtesy of Wavetek Rockland, Inc.

the signal and sampled wave spectra do *not* overlap, or "fold over" each other.

If however, there is any frequency component (f_N) present in the signal spectrum that is higher than f_0, the difference between it and the fundamental sampling frequency f_s will be ($f_s - f_N$), and that frequency component of the sampled-wave spectrum will fall within the signal spectrum and will constitute an alias, as shown in Fig. 11-3. This alias contributes energy to the measurement that is indistinguishable from energy contributed by the true signal, so that the sampling process has actually created a false signal (ergo, the name "alias," or "false name"). The sampled values that make up the measurement will not truly represent the signal, nor could we reconstruct the real signal from them.

Fig. 11-4 shows a practical example of what happens when a signal-plus-noise spectrum is sampled. Even though the spectrum of the signal contains no frequency component above f_0, the noise contribution does have frequency components above f_0, and these result in a broadening of the sample-wave spectrum, so that it folds over the signal spectrum, creating very significant errors.

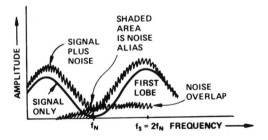

Figure 11-4 How noise components that extend beyond the folding frequency create aliases, increasing noise errors. Courtesy of Wavetek Rockland, Inc.

In actual practice, it is impossible to sample at $f_s = 2f_N$ unless one can guarantee that there is absolutely no signal or noise component above f_N. The only way to do this would be to filter the signal prior to sampling with a filter having infinite rolloff, a physical impossibility.

Instead, we use filters with finite rolloff where $f_s \geqslant 2f_N$, $2.5f_N$, $3f_N$, $4f_N$ are some common values. The higher the value of f_s, the lower the design stress on the filter, as we shall shortly see in a numerical example. No matter how high f_s is, a bandwidth limitation (and therefore, filtering requirement) must be imposed on the signal being sampled to avoid aliasing.

If $f_s \geqslant 2f_N$, the critical frequency at which the alias appears is $f_s - f_N$. It is at this particular frequency that we must meet the maximum acceptable aliasing error requirement.

The implications of aliasing should be clarified. Unless we can effectively cut off (reject) all frequencies above f_N, we incur either aliasing errors or the necessity to sample at a much higher rate, thus extending f_s. However, increasing the sampling rate could mean more expensive A/D conversion circuitry. In general, care must be exercised in designing faster systems, because there is a greater chance of error due to slew-rate or settling-time restrictions. In practice, the designer faced with the requirement to sample and digitize data from a fairly broadband signal (one with fast rates of change) is forced to seek the best compromise between the "rolloff rate" of the input filter (i.e., its sharpness of cutoff and the rate at which its attenuation increases with frequency) and the speed of sampling, and hence, of digitizing.

For example, if we have a signal that we know does not have significant frequency components in its spectrum above 8 kHz, then

$$f_N = 8 \text{ kHz} \qquad (11\text{-}8)$$

Figure 11-5 shows such a spectrum, with the effect of noise overlaid on the signal spectrum. If we establish the further criterion that the noise contribution due to aliasing (folding of the noise spectrum above f_N into the signal spectrum) shall not exceed 1% of the noise already present at f_N, then we know that we want a filter that attenuates noise by 100 to 1 at $f_s - f_N$.

Let us assume that the sampling can be done economically at $4f_N$, or 32 kHz. The filter response must be uniform to 8 kHz, and attenuate by at least 40 dB (100:1) at the folding frequency, which now is $f_s - f_N$ = 32 − 8 = 24 kHz. If we interpret the phrase "uniform to 8 kHz" to mean a 10 kHz cutoff frequency, then the rolloff, or increase in attenuation, per unit change in frequency is 40 dB from 10 kHz to 24 kHz, which may be expressed in dB per octave by calculating the corresponding attenuation from 10 kHz to 24 kHz, which is

$$40 \frac{\log 2}{\log \dfrac{24}{10}} = 7 \text{ dB/octave} \qquad (11\text{-}9)$$

Now, 31.7 dB per octave of rolloff is not attainable with simple filters. it requires at least a six-pole filter. (The maximum attainable rolloff rate of a filter is 6 dB per octave per pole.) Such filters are readily available, of course, but before accepting the rolloff rate requirements, we should investigate the possibility of relieving the design stress on the filter by increasing the sampling rate.

Converters are currently available that make as many as several million 8-bit conversions per second, but they are expensive, and such high sampling rates are unjustified except when the signal bandwidth (f_N) is very high. For our example, it would be reasonable (and economical) to select a converter with a conversion rate of 50,000 to 100,000 conversions/second. (Moderately priced converters with 10–12 bit resolutions are available at that speed.) At 50,000 conversions (samples) per second, the stress on the rolloff rate would be greatly relieved. For this sampling rate,

$$f_s - f_N = 50 \text{ kHz} - 8 \text{ kHz} = 42 \text{ kHz} \qquad (11\text{-}10)$$

and the required rolloff is reduced to 40 dB from 10 kHz to 42 kHz, or

$$40 \frac{\log 2}{\log \dfrac{42}{10}} = 19.3 \text{ dB/octave} \qquad (11\text{-}11)$$

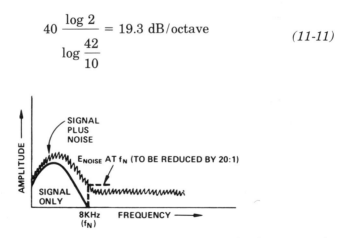

Figure 11-5 Signal-plus-noise spectrum is compared with signal-only spectrum (determined from analysis of waveform) and filter's noise rejection above f_N is established. Courtesy of Wavetek Rockland, Inc.

Supporting the sampling rate may be much more difficult than it appears to be from the A/D converter speeds just quoted. Clearly, in time analysis, the sample time must be short compared with the conversion time, and, as Fig. 11-6 shows, this demands a very fast sample-hold circuit. In particular, one with very fast slew rate and very short acquisition and aperture uncertainty times is required.

A simple experiment will serve to suggest how it is possible to determine the effect of a filter in suppressing an aliased component, both qualitatively and quantitatively. Fig. 11-7 shows a test setup in which two signal sources, one at 1.5 kHz (the signal) and the other at 8 kHz (the noise) are combined (by adding, not multiplying), and the combined signal-plus-noise, after filtering in a low-pass filter, is sampled at 10 kHz. The filter is set to a 4 kHz cutoff. For accuracy in measuring the aliased component, the level of the noise energy is set at +20 dB with respect to the signal energy, ten times higher in amplitude. The sampled signal is then examined on a spectrum analyzer with a logarithmic response (linear-dB vertical scale). The input to the filter is shown in Fig. 11-8.

The effect of the rolloff rate is immediately apparent. With 24 dB/octave rolloff, the output of the filter is that shown in Fig. 11-9. The 8 kHz component, one octave higher than the 4 kHz cutoff frequency, has been reduced by 24 dB, so that it is now −4 dB with respect to the 2 kHz signal. A large 8 kHz component will in fact produce an alias at (10 kHz − 8 kHz) = 2 kHz. Fig. 11-10, which shows the output of the

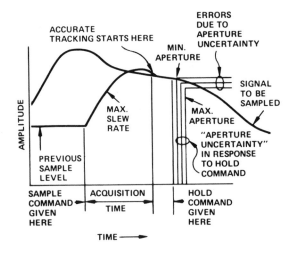

Figure 11-6 Sample-hold circuit dynamics, and the errors they may create. Time scale is greatly expanded. Courtesy of Wavetek Rockland, Inc.

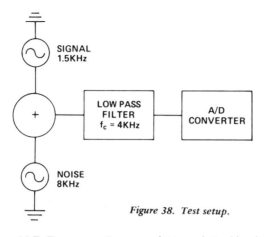

Figure 38. Test setup.

Figure 11-7 Test setup. Courtesy of Wavetek Rockland, Inc.

A/D converter, illustrates this clearly: the 1.5 kHz and 2 kHz components (on the left) have the same relative amplitudes as did the 1.5 kHz and 8 kHz components before sampling. Note also the sampled-data spectrum to the right, which contains an 11.5 kHz and a 12 kHz component ($f_s + f_N$ and $f_s + f_{\text{noise}}$). These do not affect accuracy, of course.

Clearly, we need to either increase the rolloff rate, lower f_{co}, or sample faster. But lowering f_{co} will cause appreciable error in the signal measurement, and sampling faster means changing the A/D converter design; therefore, increased rolloff rate is the only viable remedy.

Fig. 11-11 and 11-12 show the effect of going from a four-pole filter (24 dB/octave) to an eight-pole filter (48 dB/octave). Fig. 11-11 shows the 8 kHz component down to 28 dB below the signal (before sampling), and Fig. 11-12 shows that the alias (2 kHz) is also reduced by the same amount.

Finally, if we were to cascade two eight-pole 48 dB/octave filters for 96 dB/octave rolloff, the alias would disappear into the system noise floor as shown in Fig. 11-13. At this point, the noise, which is 10 times larger in amplitude than the signal, produces an alias that is only 0.016% of the signal!

Shifting f_{co} to a lower frequency may be very tempting, since it takes only a small shift downward to increase the effectiveness of a given filter with a given rolloff rate. The danger lies in the fact that it takes only a fraction of a dB of loss in the passband to create a measurement error larger than can be gained by a large reduction is aliasing. Recall that 1 dB down is about an 11% loss of amplitude!

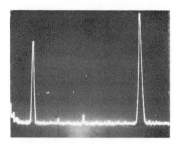

Figure 11-8

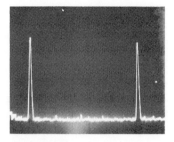

Figure 11-9

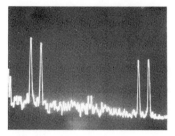

Figure 11-10

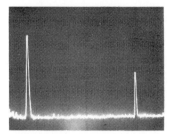

Figure 11-11

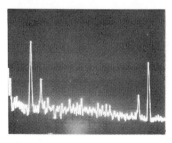

Figure 11-12

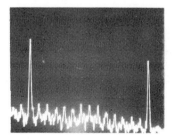

Figure 11-13

Figures 11-8–11-13 Filter spectrum analysis to show how the low-pass filter suppresses an aliased component. Courtesy of Wavetek Rockland, Inc.

The instances in which f_{co} can be moved down very near to f_N, the highest frequency in the signal spectrum, are those in which the signal spectrum shows very small higher frequency components, like that of Fig. 11-14. An 11% loss in amplitude of a component having only about 10% of the amplitude of most of the components in the spectrum cannot create more than about 1% error—probably less, since signal components do not necessarily add algebraically. In such cases, it pays to consider setting f_{co} very near f_N.

Automated data-acquisition systems frequently use multiple sets of digitally programmable filters preceding the multiplexer inputs, one

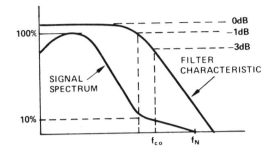

Figure 11-14 Signal spectra having relatively small higher-frequency components permit positioning f_{co} very near f_N without serious errors. Courtesy of Wavetek Rockland, Inc.

per channel. (See Fig. 11-15.) The cutoff frequency of each filter can be programmed manually or remotely (by a computer, for example) before each multiplexer pass. In some designs, this is implemented by providing a register in each filter's control logic that stores the f_{co} setting. The computer addresses each register in turn and sets it to the desired control code. Then, after allowing for settling time, the multiplexer can be scanned through the channels, each of which will have been signal-conditioned approximately, and the data can then be sampled rapidly without aliasing or direct noise errors.

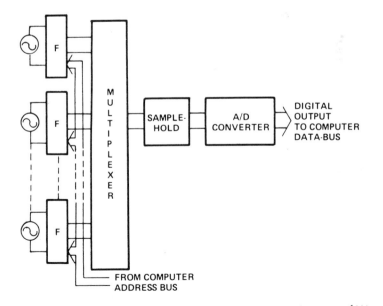

Figure 11-15 Filter-per-channel multiplexed data acquisition. Courtesy of Wavetek Rockland, Inc.

Data "skew" is inevitable when there is simultaneous sampling of many filtered channels, because of phase mismatch in the filters. For example, if the signals fed to the system of Fig. 11-16 were 400 Hz synchro and resolver waveforms, and if the filters were all four-pole, low-pass Butterworth designs set to f_{co} = 800 Hz, then the phase shift (at 400 Hz) in the filter would nominally be about 80°. However, if the phase match were, say 2% (a common rating), then the error due to random data skew would be of the order of sin (81.6°) − sin (80°) = 0.0045, or about 0.5%. In a precise system, phase trimming might be advisable, though quite expensive.

In signal-recovery systems, the specification of the recovery filter must be approached in the same way as that of the input filter in signal-sampling systems. The reason is that the application of digitized values to the filter results in the same "convolution" effect as does the taking samples: the spectrum of the resulting signal is the product of a stepfunction sin x/x spectrum (the output of the D/A converter) and a bandlimited analog spectrum (the transfer function of the filter). The analogous problem caused by the resultant aliasing is a loss of accuracy in reproducing the original signal. Additionally, there is attenuation due to the sin x/x spectrum shape.

For example, suppose that in the system of Fig. 11-17 we want to

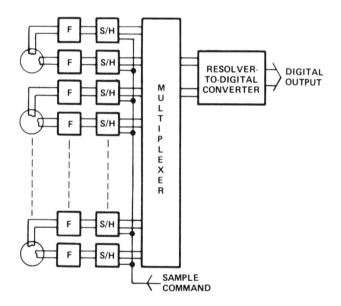

Figure 11-16 In simultaneously sampled systems, such as this multichannel resolver position digitizer, data "skew" due to delay tolerance in the filters may be a problem. Courtesy of Wavetek Rockland, Inc.

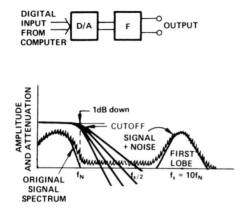

Figure 11-17 System and spectrum for single-channel recovery-filter example in text. Courtesy of Wavetek Rockland, Inc.

recover a waveform having a spectrum from dc to $f_N = 2$ kHz. Suppose that we have sampled this waveform at $f_s = 4f_N = 8$ kHz and that we wish to suppress all aliased components by at least 55 dB. Moreover, we want passband response from dc to 2 kHz to be within 1 dB. What low-pass filter do we need?

1. We must first calculate the attenuation produced by the $\frac{\sin x}{x}$ spectrum shape, where, $x = \pi \frac{f}{f_s} = \pi \frac{f}{8}$. At $f = f_N = 2$ kHz,

$$\frac{\sin x}{x} = \frac{\sin \pi/4}{\pi/4} = 0.9 \ (-0.91 \text{ dB}).$$ We immediately see that the filter can have no more than about 0.1 dB attenuation at f_N. Thus, we need a maximally flat (Butterworth) filter with a cutoff frequency somewhat beyond 2 kHz.

2. We next calculate the attenuation produced by $\frac{\sin x}{x}$ at the frequency $(f_s - f_N)$ (8 kHz − 2 kHz) = 6 kHz. At 6 kHz, $\frac{\sin x}{x} = \frac{\sin 3\pi/4}{3\pi/4}$

$= 0.300 \ (-10.5 \text{ dB})$.

3. Therefore, the filter has to produce an additional attenuation of at least $55 - 10.5 = 44.5$ dB at 6 kHz. We can now specify the cutoff frequency and rolloff rate of our filter.

4. Try a 6-pole (36 dB/octave) Butterworth filter. From response curves, we must set $f_{co} \geqslant \frac{1}{0.6} \times 2$ kHz to have flat response to 2 kHz. If we set $f_{co} = 3.5$ kHz, attenuation at 6 kHz will be $36 \times \frac{\log 6/3.5}{\log 2} = 28$ dB, which is not enough.

5. Try an 8-pole (48 dB/octave) filter. Now, $f_{co} > \dfrac{1}{0.7} \times 2$ kHz. If we set $f_{co} = 3$ kHz, attenuation at 6 kHz will be 48 dB, which satisfies the requirement.

6. To summarize, we need a 48 dB/octave low pass Butterworth filter with a cutoff frequency of 3 kHz.

11-2 THE ARCHITECTURE OF A MODERN FFT SPECTRUM ANALYZER

With the theoretical background described in Chapter 9 of this text, we are ready to examine the architecture (Fig. 11-18) of a modern fast-Fourier real-time spectrum analyzer.

First, we shall sample the time-domain signal N times, sampling once every T seconds, where T is the time-window duration τ divided by N, the number of samples. Thus, we would appear to need a signal-sampling rate of N/τ samples per second.

Next, we agree to be satisfied with the fact that this sampling rate will restrict the bandwidth of the computed spectrum to a frequency "analysis range," which is equal to the number of filters K, times the bandwidth of each filter β.

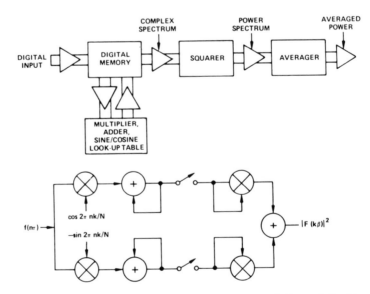

Figure 11-18 Architecture of an FFT analyzer. Courtesy of Wavetek Rockland, Inc.

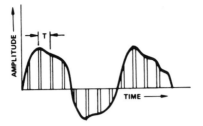

Figure 11-19 Sampling the time-domain signal is equivalent to multiplying it by the sampling function. Courtesy of Wavetek Rockland, Inc.

Finally, we agree to accept a representation of the computed spectrum that is equivalent to the output of a bank of filters, each having a bandwidth of β Hertz, where $\beta = 1/\tau$, so that N samples, taken in a time window τ at a sampling rate N/τ, would yield data for K filters, spaced $1/\tau_w$ Hertz apart, each with a bandwidth of $1/\tau_w$. (We note that K cannot exceed N, and we shall soon see that K must be less than one-half of N, for practical as well as theoretical reasons.)

In Fig. 11-18, the signal, after appropriate scaling, is fed to a sample-hold circuit through a low-pass filter (not shown). It is very important to understand both the reason for using this low-pass filter and its profound influence on the performance of the spectral analyzer.

When an analog signal is sampled, the mechanism of sampling (Fig. 11-19) may be defined as multiplying the time-domain waveform of the signal by another time-domain waveform: the test of the sampling function. The sampling function may be represented as a periodic rectangular pulse of unit amplitude and very short duty cycle (very small ratio of on to off times). This multiplication of two time-domain waveforms modifies the original Fourier spectrum (Fig. 11-20) so that

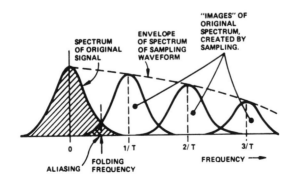

Figure 11-20 Spectrum of sampled signal, showing aliasing effect due to folding of first image over original spectrum. Courtesy of Wavetek Rockland, Inc.

it now corresponds to the spectrum of the unsampled analog signal plus an infinite number of sum and difference components, called aliases, that did not exist in the original signal, but which appear in the spectrum of the sampled signal. The lowest frequency at which such a false signal, or alias, can occur is one-half the sampling rate; hence, one frequently reads about the "Nyquist criterion" or the "Shannon limit," in which one is warned that the sampling rate must be *at least twice the highest frequency of interest* in the spectrum of the signal being sampled. Thus, if the lowest frequency at which an alias can appear is established to be 25 kHz by a 50 kHz sampling rate, then we must be sure to exclude from the input to the sampling circuit any signal component, or even any extraneous noise, that has a frequency higher than 25 kHz. Such exclusion is the function of the low-pass, or *antialiasing* filter.

Unfortunately, low-pass filters do not have ideal rectangular transfer functions. As Fig. 11-21 shows, even a very sophisticated low-pass filter with many poles has a transfer function with a finite rolloff rate, although it may, and should, be very steep; therefore, if we are to prevent aliasing at a given sampling rate, we must be content to limit the bandwidth of interest to *even less than the folding frequency,* i.e., even less than 50% of the sampling rate. How much less depends on how fast the filter rolls off and how effectively we wish to suppress aliased components. Suppression of aliases is one of the critical factors in determining the useful dynamic range and ultimate sensitivity of a spectrum analyzer; therefore, a high-performance FFT analyzer demands a superb low-pass filter. In the Wavetek Rockland Model 512

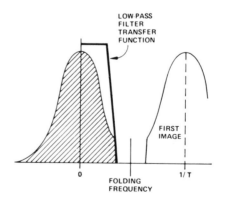

Figure 11-21   Positioning a very-steep-rolloff, low-pass filter so as to prevent aliasing. Courtesy of Wavetek Rockland, Inc.

spectrum analyzer, the input filter provides 120 dB/octave rolloff above its cutoff frequency. The passband ripple is only ± 0.5 dB.

Thus, as a result of aliasing problems, we find that the attainable spectrum bandwidth (the analysis range, AR) is somewhat less, in practice, than 50% of the sampling rate. As an example, a modern real-time analyzer, utilizing advanced design techniques, attains the following performance.

Sampling Rate = 256,000 per second at maximum analysis range

T = 4 microseconds (at maximum sampling rate)

N = 1024 samples (all ranges)

Maximum Analysis Range = AR (max.) = DC to 100 KHz (about 40% of sampling rate)

τ = (min.) = 4 milliseconds (at max. AR)

K = 400 filters (all ranges)

β (max.) = 250 Hz (at 100 KHz AR).

Making thousands of high-accuracy calculations in a few milliseconds requires digital computation, so the analyzer must digitize the analog samples it obtains as fast as it acquires them. A typical high-performance instrument uses a 12-bit high-speed A/D converter with a bit rate in excess of 3 MHz, producing a complete 12-bit conversion every 4 microseconds. Each of these data words is immediately stored in a digital memory in a predetermined location. One location is assigned to each of the N samples taken during the time window.

Most modern all-digital analyzers are designed to accommodate two popular types of general-purpose interfaces. (Custom variations of these are also possible, but are rarely needed.) One is the IEEE Standard 488/1975 "Instrumentation Interface," the protocols and formats of which are well suited to many Automatic Test Equipment (ATE) systems, as well as to several widely used calculator-based "smart terminals," or microcomputers.

The other popular general-purpose interface is one that is more likely to be compatible with the general-purpose I/O bus of a minicomputer. It is usually not restricted to the 8-bit byte of the IEEE interface, and it has protocols, flags, and control lines that permit higher-speed data flow, more variety in interactive behavior, and more efficient use of the processing time of the computer as well as the analyzer.

Each of these two types of interfaces is, clearly, designed to accommodate one particular class of applications, and the choice between them is usually made on the basis of the available external computing/programming equipment.

11-3 APPLICATIONS OF THE SPECTRAL ANALYZER

Perhaps the fastest way to check the amplitude response characteristic of a filter (or any other frequency-selective network, passive or active) is to apply a signal to it that has essentially uniform spectral response over the frequency band of interest and examine the Fourier spectrum of the resultant output signal.

Fig. 11-22 shows such a test setup. The excitation selected is a rectangular pulse of relatively low duty cycle, having a width T such that $1/2T > f_c$, where f_c is the nominal cutoff frequency of the filter. As shown in Fig. 11-23, the spectrum of a pulse with $T = \dfrac{1}{4f_c}$ is uniform within about 1 dB from dc to f_c, adequate flatness for most applications. (In fact, many production tests can be done with half-sine-wave excitation, the spectral distribution of which is surprisingly uniform up to about $1/3T$.)

The test is best performed using repetitive input impulses, so that averaging may be used to improve the signal-to-noise ratio. For a permanent record, an X–Y recording may be made of the final averaged spectrum.

Fig. 11-24 shows a typical test result on an eight-pole low-pass filter.

In the design of sonar circuits and transducers, as well as in related applications of ultrasound (e.g., medical B-scan imaging and ultrasonic soldering or cleaning), the real-time spectrum analyzer has much to offer, as both a development tool and a production-test instrument. Fig. 11-25 shows two test setups, one for detailed analysis of pulsed sinewave signals, and the other for impedance measurement, using the ratio-of-two-spectra facility.

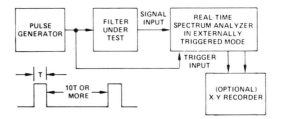

Figure 11-22 Impulse testing of filter characteristic. Courtesy of Wavetek Rockland, Inc.

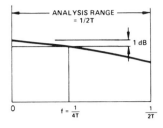

Figure 11-23 Spectrum of rectangular pulse of duration T is uniform within 1 dB from dc to 1/4T. Courtesy of Wavetek Rockland, Inc.

In analyzing the waveform of a pulsed sinewave, the real-time capabilities of the analyzer permit continuous monitoring of any point on the instantaneous spectrum (for example, to check side-lobe stability during self-heating of the transducer). The instantaneous spectrum also provides precise information on modulation envelope, harmonic content, and possible nonharmonic (jitter or phase-noise) components.

Figs. 11-26 and 11-27 show, respectively, the normal spectrum after averaging and a range-translated region near the carrier, "zoomed" to show nonharmonic sidebands.

Fig. 11-28 shows how a voltage and current spectrum may be used to implement an Ohm's-law measurement of the magnitude of the impedance of a loaded transducer by using the ratio-of-two-spectra mode. The impedance is, as might be suspected, very frequency-sensitive—almost a broad resonance near the carrier frequency. This measurement may be used dynamically to observe the effects of "tuning" the transducer matching network.

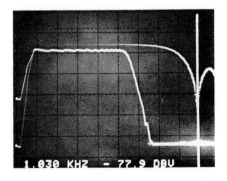

Figure 11-24 Typical test result. The log-frequency axis has been used for better resolution in the cutoff region. The analysis range is 2 kHz. The cursor is positioned at the first null of the input waveform. Courtesy of Wavetek Rockland, Inc.

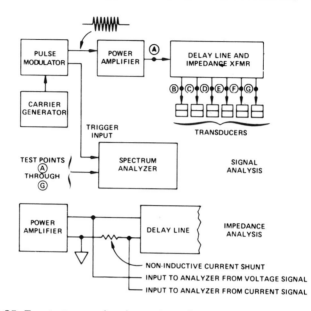

Figure 11-25 Two test setups for ultrasonic analysis. Courtesy of Wavetek Rockland, Inc.

In the narrowband power mode, the energy in the sidebands (essentially wasted) may be compared with the main-lobe and total energy.

Fig. 11-29 shows how a programmable frequency synthesizer of high spectral purity may be combined with an all-digital real-time spectral analyzer, under common control of a calculator-based CRT terminal, to perform accurate, wideband phase-noise testing of a signal source over a very wide range of frequencies. The signal under test is mixed with the output of the synthesizer, which is "jogged" in and out of the zero-beat condition until the phase relationship between the two signals is 90°, or close enough to 90° so that the average (DC) output of the mixer approaches zero. This can also be done automatically via a phase lock loop.

This technique is particularly well suited to analysis of structural weaknesses or anomalies in very large, heavy structures, e.g., multi-story buildings, bridges, and highway ramps, and it works effectively even in the presence of high levels of background noise, such as might be encountered on construction sites and highways. The simplest impulse source is (believe it or not!) a large sledgehammer with a force transducer pickup embedded in its head. Fig. 11-30 shows the setup and the impulse generator.

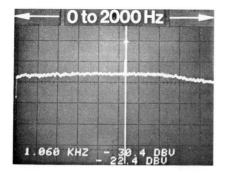

Figure 11-26 Normal spectrum, after averaging. Compare display and readouts with those of Figure 11-27. Courtesy of Wavetek Rockland, Inc.

At one end of the structure, the impulses are applied by repeatedly striking some important part of the main structure (a load-bearing beam is ideal) with the sledgehammer. The force-pickup output is cabled to the measurement point for use as an external trigger signal. Pickups at key points elsewhere in the structure are used to detect the time-domain signal that will be converted into spectra for immediate or later analysis.

There is usually a significant delay between the application of the impulse and the arrival of the response at the receiving pickups, but this propagation delay is generally within the range of the Time-Window Offset Control of the analyzer (if it has this useful feature).

By repeated averaging (usually, linear averaging is best in this application, but all three types have utility), the effects of ambient noise can be reduced to tolerable proportions. X–Y recording of the

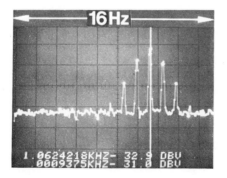

Figure 11-27 Magnified resolution reveals complex nature of spectrum in Figure 11-26, permitting more meaningful measurement. Courtesy of Wavetek Rockland, Inc.

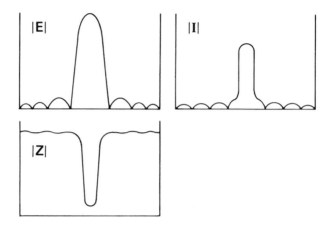

Figure 11-28 Impedance-vs-frequency of pulse-sine-wave sonar matching transformer, measured in ratio mode. Courtesy of Wavetek Rockland, Inc.

results, pickup point by pickup point, usually yields a quite complete picture of both primary resonances and higher order responses throughout the structure.

The real-time spectral analyzer is a proven, valuable tool for many types of biomedical research, as well as a clinical diagnostic instrument of great potential. As Fig. 11-31 shows, all of the traditional biomedically significant waveforms—electrocardiograms, electro-encephalograms, phonocardiograms, neurooptic and neuromuscular

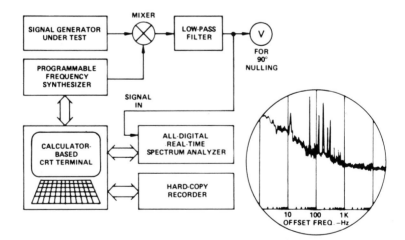

Figure 11-29 Automated phase-noise measurement. Inset is actual hard-copy recording from CRT screen. Courtesy of Wavetek Rockland, Inc.

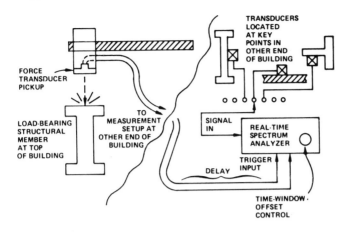

Figure 11-30 Impulse analysis of large-mass structural characteristics. Courtesy of Wavetek Rockland, Inc.

responses, etc.—lend themselves exceptionally well to study by the modern all-digital analyzer. In all of these applications, the built-in ensemble averaging capability of the modern analyzer obviates the need for signal processing before analysis, and the wide analysis range of the analyzer (compared with ordinary biomedical recorders) is a very significant advantage also, often revealing phenomena that are not evident or even suspected by other diagnostic means. Real-time analyzers have been used to differentiate between functional and essential anomalies in stress-response cardiology, to predict epileptic seizures well in advance of occurrence, and to detect premature fatigue degradation in neurooptic response time.

A more direct and unusual diagnostic procedure is depicted in Fig. 11-32, in which repetitive pressure pulsations are introduced into a large blood vessel, travel up the vessel (like radar or sonar propagations), and are detected at the same point (by Doppler effects due to normal counterflow in the bloodstream). Clots, strictures, stenosis, or other obstructive conditions may be sensitively detected, accurately located, and at least grossly categorized as to degree by examining the doppler spectrum of the echo.

The demodulated output of a Doppler radar is a low-frequency, relatively narrowband signal having characteristic spectral distribution for every significant operating state: fine-beam range with large, high-velocity up-doppler target; dispersed-beam range with small, slow, down-doppler target; multiple-target (high-noise) conditions with a wide range of target speeds in a single direction, etc. The development of this important kind of guidance and detection radar involves

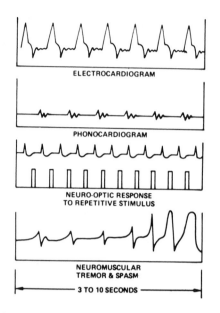

Figure 11-31 Typical physiological waveforms. Note similarity in time scales and relatively restricted bandwidth. Courtesy of Wavetek Rockland, Inc.

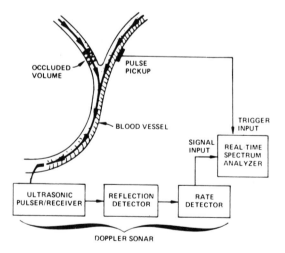

Figure 11-32 Doppler-sonar location and analysis of blood-vessel occlusions. Courtesy of Wavetek Rockland, Inc.

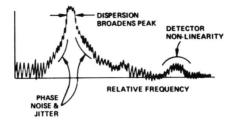

Figure 11-33 Typical doppler-radar outputs spectrum (voltage levels versus relative frequency). Courtesy of Wavetek Rockland, Inc.

many extremely difficult measurements, some of which can be done only by careful observation of the demodulated spectrum.

In Fig. 11-33, we see a simplified Doppler-radar output spectrum, with the following features evident: phase noise in the carrier; modulator jitter; detector nonlinearity; and "broadening" of the reflected-energy spectrum due to target irregularity, relative acceleration, and beam dispersion.

In Fig. 11-34, we see a simplified three-dimensional model of a subsurface shale stratum, overlaid by a sensor field used in explosive seismological testing. Multichannel analog tape recording is the preferred method of acquiring the data, and spectral analysis is the most productive method of processing the acquired complex of signals into useful data on subterranean discontinuities, profiles, and density gradients.

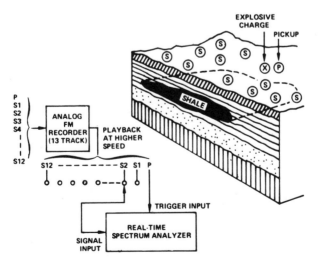

Figure 11-34 Seismic analysis data acquisition and processing. Courtesy of Wavetek Rockland, Inc.

The fact that the spectral analyzer is capable of high-speed real-time processing makes it possible to consider playing back the tapes at higher speeds than those at which they were recorded. The external trigger capability of the analyzer is very helpful in correlating the signals to relate propagation time to frequency (a critical measure of density).

Programming the spectral analyzer via a minicomputer (Fig. 11-35) makes it possible to use the analyzer in three different ways:

1. to condition, sample, and digitize the time-domain signal for simple digital storage on tape or disc, or in computer memory;

2. to generate the Fourier spectrum, and from it, the key features (peak locations, peak magnitudes, peak ratios, narrowband energy in selected peaks) of the seismic response at each sensing location; and

3. to accept reprocessed data from the computer as a substitute for its own processed samples, and compute the corresponding Fourier transform.

Fig. 11-36 shows the spectrum of a frequency-modulated RF signal after heterodyning has reduced the carrier frequency from 10 MHz to 50 MHz. Ignoring the effects of the frequency translation, we can write the following expressions relating the parameters of the first upper and lower sidebands to the carrier:

$m = \Delta f / f_m$ (index = peak deviation over modulating frequency)

$E_s / E_c = m/2$ (sideband volts over carrier volts = $m/2$)

$f_s = f_c \pm f_m$ (sideband frequencies = carrier frequency $\pm$ modulating frequency)

$E_s / E_c = $ (in dB) $= 20 \log \left(\dfrac{\Delta f}{2 f_m} \right) = 20 \log \left(\dfrac{m}{2} \right)$

Now, using the normal spectrum display, we can check the nominal parameters f_c, f_s, f_m, m, E_s, and E_c quite readily. But that is only the beginning: using the range translator, either near the carrier or at one or both sidebands, we can observe and measure sideband jitter and dispersion due to modulator noise, carrier dispersion due to low-level AM, and sideband asymmetry due to modulator dc drift and nonlinearity.

Figs. 11-37 and 11-38 show the use of the range translator in resolving sideband anomalies. The carrier in Fig. 11-37 looks normal, but magnified 128 times (Fig. 11-39), it is clearly badly dispersed.

In Fig. 11-39, we show a simple test circuit for checking the nonlinearity of a circuit or component. A sine-wave source is first checked for inherent purity. If the distortion in the signal source is considered

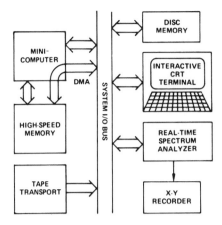

Figure 11-35 Typical automated seismic-analysis system. Courtesy of Wavetek Rockland, Inc.

negligible, the signal is applied to the circuit or component under test, and the spectrum of the output signal is checked for harmonics. Using a power calibration, the harmonic magnitudes may be directly added for the computation of total distortion. By having normalized $\sqrt{\text{power}}$ in the fundamental to unity, $\sqrt{\text{power}}$ of the harmonic magnitude will be read as a fraction relative to 1.

If the signal source has significant harmonic distortion, it can be accounted for by using the difference-spectrum mode, scaling the output spectrum so as to normalize it with respect to the signal spectrum, thereby eliminating the gain or loss (at the fundamental frequency) of the circuit under test.

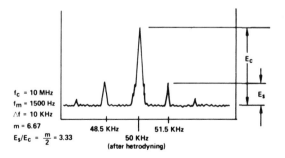

Figure 11-36 Typical FM spectrum. Range translation has been used to achieve good separation of sidebands from heterodyned carrier. Courtesy of Wavetek Rockland, Inc.

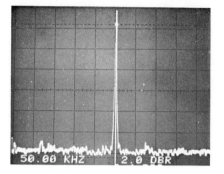

Figure 11-37 Unmagnified spectrum of modulated carrier, heterodyned down to 50 kHz on 100 kHz analysis range. Courtesy of Wavetek Rockland, Inc.

11-4 FREQUENCY SYNTHESIZERS

Direct frequency synthesizers use a sequence of arithmetic operations (either analog or digital) that are performed directly on the output of a harmonic generator driven by a standard to produce the desired output frequency.

The Wavetek Rockland model 5100 uses a patented* unique synthesis utilizing all digital techniques. The phase accumulator generates the linearity-increasing digital phase values of the sinusoid at a fixed output sample rate. This phase value advances for each output sample by an increment directly proportional to the frequency setting.

The read-only memory (ROM) is a sine function table that converts the phase information of the accumulator into digital samples of a sinusoidal waveform. The subsequent D/A converter and low-pass filter reduce the digital approximation to a pure sinusoid. Fig. 11-40 shows a direct digital frequency synthesizer block diagram.

Because of the digital nature of the synthesis, true phase and amplitude continuity are achieved when switching between two frequencies on the Model 5100 synthesizer.

All instruments having built-in standard TTL interfaces are remotely programmable for frequency and amplitude. GPIB interfaces are also available as separate stand-alone instruments.

The frequency synthesizer is used to generate the modulated carrier often discussed in regard to modems.

In indirect frequency synthesis systems, the output frequency is produced by a voltage-controlled oscillator (VCO) phase-locked to the reference standard.

*U.S. Patent No. 3, 725, 269.

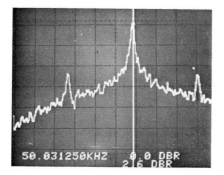

Figure 11-38 Magnifying resolution until total analysis range is only 800 Hz permits critical evaluation of sidebands. Courtesy of Wavetek Rockland, Inc.

As most digital system designers have discovered, the communication of data is almost as important as the computing of it. With the proliferation of microcomputers of lower and lower cost, the system designer if forced to keep this aspect of his design on the same declining cost curve.

11-5   MODEMS*

Modems have been used for transmitting data between computers over long distances for many years. They are used over the direct dial telephone network, conditioned and unconditioned leased telephone lines, TWX networks, dry unloaded cables, radio links, fiber optic links, and in acoustic couplers.

Better system integration is achieved through resident modem design. A modem can be incorporated into the basic product board. Elimination of formal interfaces, such as the RS–232, saves component space and cost and allows for a tighter package. Gone is the need for a "black box" modem next to the system and gone are the problems of cabling to this ancillary modem "box."

The properties of a modem include the following:

1. Baud rate.
2. ASCII Code.
3. Transmission modes.

*Section 11-5 from Application Note, CH 103F 300 Band Minimodem Application Notes, © 1981, DOC 42, CH 103F, Rev. 1-82. Courtesy of and reprinted with permission of Cermetek Microelectronics, Sunnyvale, Calif.

4. Synchronous versus asynchronous transmission techniques.

5. Network types.

6. Modulation systems.

In the narrowest sense, a *baud* is defined as a measure of the rate at which signals are transmitted through a communications channel, with one baud corresponding to a rate of one signal element per second.

With digital data, a signal element is often the same thing as a bit, so that 300 baud is the same thing as 300 bits per second. But that's not always the case when you're sending the same data over the telephone line. The modem, or modulator/demodulator, converts digital information into an analog format and back again into digital form. Depending on the type of modem, digital information is carried on the analog signal by varying either its amplitude, its frequency, or its phase.

The modem over the phone line acts like a 7-bit American Standard Code for Information Interchange (ASCII) character. A 300 baud or 300 bit per second modem sends about 30 ASCII characters per second down the line. But this can vary. In order to be able to pick the characters out at the receiving end, it is necessary to put on some extra bits to tell when the character begins and ends, among other things. So usually a 7-bit ASCII character is accompanied by one start bit, one stop bit, an optional parity bit for error checking, and an optional extra

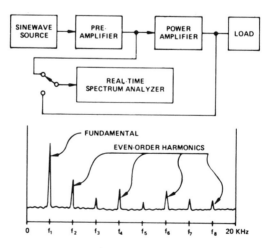

Figure 11-39 Test circuit and typical output spectrum of a broadband audio power amplifier, showing effect of asymmetric saturation. Courtesy of Wavetek Rockland, Inc.

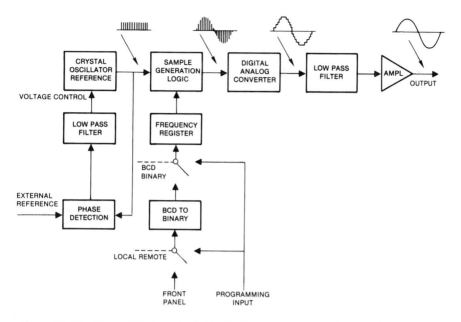

Figure 11-40 Direct digital synthesis block diagram. Courtesy of Wavetek Rockland, Inc.

stop bit. Thus, an ASCII character could get from 2 to 4 extra bits traveling along.

The most common usage is one each of start bits, stop bits, and parity bits. This works out well, because that means 10 bits per character, which makes the character rate at 300 baud easy to calculate as 30 characters per second.

The most commonly used forms of modems are those that are used to transmit data over voice-grade telephone lines with 2.7 kHz effective bandwidth (300 Hz to 4 kHz). Such voice-grade modems can operate in one of three transmission modes: simplex, half duplex, or full duplex.

A communications link that carries data from one point to another in only one direction is said to be a simplex link. The input unit can only receive, never transmit (i.e., originate), while the output unit can only transmit and never receive.

With a *half-duplex* channel, transmission is in both directions, but only one way at a time. It can transmit and receive, but not simultaneously. Usually, there is a turnaround time delay each time the direction of travel is reversed.

In a *full-duplex* system, transmission is in both directions at the same time. It can transmit or receive simultaneously and has no turnaround time delay, as in the half-duplex mode. The standard voice channel on the telephone network is the classic example of a full-duplex communications system: people speak back and forth, often at the same time.

Synchronous data transmission systems are used primarily to transmit data between machines. Once the originate and answer data sets are turned on, there is a continuous clock signal generated at each one, and the receive clock is synchronized by "Sync" pulses received from the transmit clock. The received data is faithfully reproduced (i.e., reproduced distortion free), because the synchronizing signal is generated continuously at the same code as the transmitted data.

There are two ways modems communicate with each other: over a switched line, or over a leased line.

The *switched line* network is used by the public. It's called switched because a call is automatically switched through to its destination after dialing has been completed.

A *leased line* is a permanent circuit for private use within a data communications network, the line being routed directly between the two locations or through central offices. The 103F is designed for use in just such a private leased-line system.

Three basic modulation schemes are used in modems: (1) frequency shift keying (FSK) (2) amplitude modulation (AM); and (3) phase modulation (PM).

FSK, the technique used in the 103F, is a form of frequency modulation. The 103F FSK system shifts the carrier frequency 100 Hz higher to represent a one and 100 Hz lower to represent a zero. Generally suitable for low-speed devices like teleprinters, FSK allows operation up to 1800 bits per second.

With AM, a modem can transmit and receive carrier amplitudes that represent binary one's and zero's. Several AM levels are possible, allowing more data to be sent in the same period. Although AM uses bandwidth more efficiently than FSK, FSK has a signal-to-noise advantage over AM.

PM modems transmit data by use of a complex phase-shifting procedure, an expensive technique to implement, and usually confined to high-speed communications channels, 1200 bps full duplex and above. PM shifts a transmitted signal's phase by a set number of degrees in response to the incoming bit pattern. For example, in a two-phase PM modem, a 180 degree shift indicates a change of state—to a one or zero, as the case may be. Thus, no shift represents a series of one's or zero's.

The essential parts of a communication system based on a modem of the 103F type are shown in Fig. 11-41. As illustrated, the data pulse train controls the frequency of an FM oscillator. A binary 1 causes the

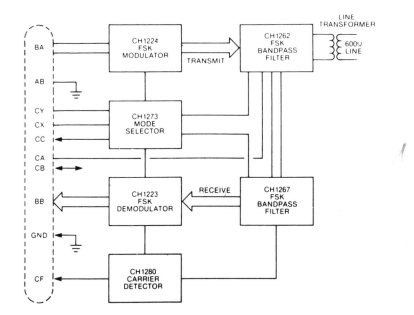

Figure 11-41 The essence of a functional 300 baud FSK modem. Courtesy of Cermetek Microelectronics.

"mark" frequency to be sent and a 0 causes the space frequency to be sent.

The band-pass filter associated with transmission limits the frequency spectrum to the bandwidth of the transmission facility. At the other end, a band-pass filter associated with reception removes noise and interference outside the band of interest. The filtered receiver signal is converted by a limiter into a rectangular wave so that residual AM is eliminated. The original signal is then recovered in a discriminator process of the demodulator block. The low-pass filter removes out-of-band modulation products and noise. The output of the low-pass filter is fed into a slicer, which performs a slicing function to produce a rectangular waveform again.

In the originate mode, the 103F sends a 1070 Hz sine wave for a *SPACE*, or 0, and a 1270 Hz sine wave for a *MARK*, or 1, usually at a phone line level of − 10 dBm, or around a quarter of a volt RMS. In the receiver mode, it transmits a 2025 Hz sine wave for a space and a 2025 Hz sine wave for a *MARK*. These frequencies have been chosen to allow two way conversions without interaction. In the handshaking procedure, the 103F always transmits a signal in dB with a certain periodicity on a high frequency, since a 2225 Hz tone is needed to automatically disable echo suppressors used on long-distance telephone lines and to provide a standard recognition signal for automatic dialing equipment.

There are several important factors to consider when designing a modem. The transmitted signal must be a low-distortion sine wave. In particular, its second harmonic must be extremely low to prevent the originate modem from polluting its own spectrum with its second harmonic. When acoustical coupling is used, the transmit level must be held low enough (approximately 20 dB) so that the second harmonic from the telephone speaker does not raise harmonics to an intolerable level.

Input signals must be filtered to get rid of other channel tones as well as interference from speech, noise, touch-tone coding, and other signals. In addition to getting rid of unwanted signals, there's a second severe restriction: both the 1's and 0's going through the input filter must be delayed by an equal amount. Otherwise, they will get out of step with each other and cause errors.

Fig. 11-42 shows the Cermetek 103F minimodem schematic diagram, and Fig. 11-43 shows a pictorial of the 103F. The Cermetek aids in digital signal processing by allowing remote programs. It can be used to download a new speech vocabulary in voice synthesis applications.

11-6 A MICROCOMPUTER FOR DIGITAL SIGNAL PROCESSING

The Intel 2920 was the first single microcomputer chip designed to implement real-time digital sampled data systems. As shown in Fig. 11-44 this device contains several operations per instruction, including on-board program memory, scratchpad memory, A/D circuitry, digital processor, I/O circuitry and D/A circuitry. The 2920 has the three operations required to implement a digital filter: storage, multiplication by a constant, and addition. Its own reprogrammable memory has sufficient space to store commands to implement a number of filters up to 44 total poles operating in real-time with signals having several kHz bandwidths. As shown in Fig. 11-44, with its on-chip multiplexed A/D converter and eight-channel D/A converters, the Intel 2920 can simultaneously process four analog input signals.

Once the z-transform of the digital filter that we would like to program is known, we can implement the design using the specialized instruction set of the Intel 2920. We shall also need hardware and

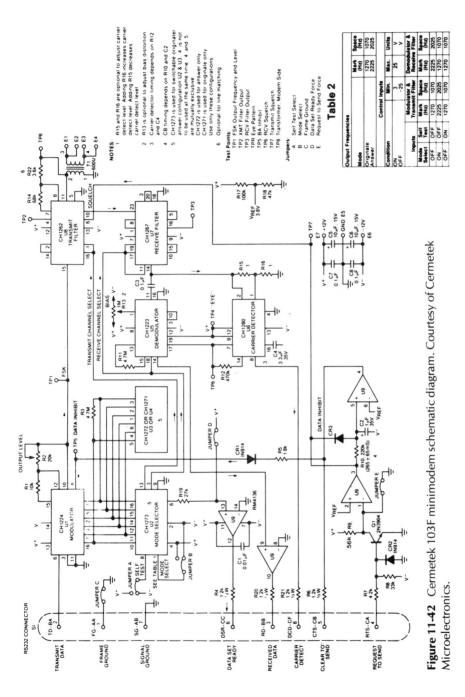

Figure 11-42 Cermetek 103F minimodem schematic diagram. Courtesy of Cermetek Microelectronics.

351

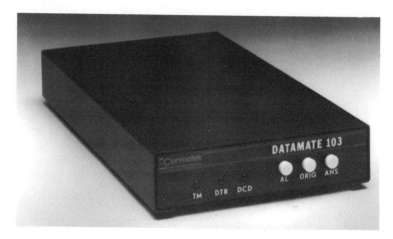

Figure 11-43 Cermetek 103 modem pictorial. Courtesy of Cermetek Microelectronics.

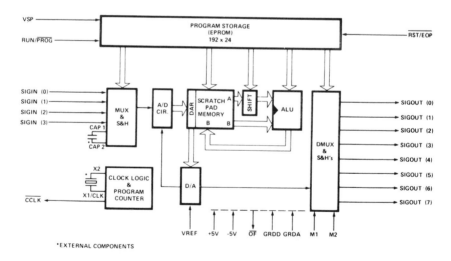

Figure 11-44 2920 block diagram. Courtesy of Intel Corporation. Reprinted from the 2920 Analog Signal Processor Design Handbook, p. 3–1, © August, 1980.

software developmental resources for the meaningful filtering tasks that this device is able to accomplish. In chapter 15 we will take up in detail the digital signal processing (DSP) chip.

_____ *PROBLEMS* _____

11-1 Discuss six applications of digital signal processing.

11-2 Assume in the system of Fig. 11-17 that we want to recover a waveform having a spectrum from dc to $f_N = 1$ kHz. Suppose that we have sampled this waveform at 4 kHz, that we wish to suppress all aliased components by at least 60 dB, and that we want the passband response from dc to 1 kHz to be within 1.0 dB. What low-pass filter do we need?

11-3 Using a block diagram, discuss the architecture of a modem spectrum analyzer.

11-4 Discuss the theory of a modem.

11-5 Discuss the microcomputer chip used for digital signal processing.

12

SELECTED TOPICS IN INDUSTRIAL SIGNAL PROCESSING

12-0 INTRODUCTION

In this chapter, selected topics in industrial signal processing are discussed. The discussion begins with discrete time analog signals, including sampled capacitor filters and transversal filters, which are also useful in digital signal processing application techniques. Correlation concepts are then discussed in Sect. 12-2. The digital correlator has many applications, found in Sect. 12-3. Time delay measurements (Sect. 12-7) are used in radar and are important in correlation theory. The microprocessor, discussed in Sect. 12-8, is responsible for creating a digital computing machine. Section 12-9 deals with digital filter configurations. A high-speed FFT processor and arithmetic architecture are discussed in detail in Sects. 12-12 to 12-14. The FFT has many applications. Some are discussed in Sect. 12-15, with an emphasis on correlation. It is the intent of this chapter to provide the reader with some important applications in industrial signal processing. Some of these also occur in the field of medicine, which is treated in the next chapter.

12-1   DISCRETE-TIME ANALOG
SIGNAL PROCESSING DEVICES* _____

The sampled analog signal processing devices in this section feature the following:

1. Sampled capacitor devices, including sampled capacitor filters and serial analog devices.

2. Bucket brigade devices, including delay lines, transversal filters, and analog-to-analog correlators.

Figure 12-1 shows the functional diagram of a typical sampled data system. Such a system quantizes the time, but not the amplitude, of the samples. These stored charge samples are then shifted through the device by multiphase clocks to produce the basic signal processing operations of delay, multiplication, and addition. By combining these operations appropriately, complex signal processing functions such as time compression and expansion, filtering, correlation, convolution, and the Fourier transform can be achieved. With the same technology, classical active filters are synthesized, utilizing the "switched capacitor (SCF) architecture."

Switched capacitor filters can implement the classical discrete functions of all-pass, band-pass, notch, high-pass, and low-pass filtering and the familiar responses of Chebyshev, Butterworth, Bessel, Cauer, etc. Resistors and inductors are replaced by sampled data integrators composed of a switched capacitor and an integration capacitor connected across an all-MOS op-amp. Figure 12-2 shows the switched capacitor network building block: an integrator that replaces an RC product with a capacitance ratio (C_2/C_1) and a toggle switch frequency (f_s).

The advantages of SCF devices are reduced circuit complexity, low sensitivity to coefficient variations, clock tunability of center/corner frequencies, and reduced silicon area. The stability of SCF's eliminates alignment problems, thus removing the need for tight-tolerance components and trimpots or laser trimming. Since multiple filters (up to 100 poles) can be designed for a single-chip package, a savings in circuit board manufacturing insertion, testing, and inventory costs will also be realized.

The quad chirped transversal filter Model R 5601, manufactured by EG&G Reticon, can be used in digital signal processing.

*Section 12-1 courtesy of EG&G RETICON, Sunnyvale, Calif. © 1982.

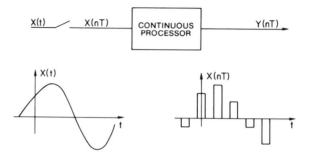

Figure 12-1 Sampled data system. Courtesy of EG&G Reticon, Sunnyvale, California.

The R5601 performs the convolution portion of the chirp Z algorithm to perform either a discrete Fourier transform (DFT) or the power spectral density of the input signal in real time. A block diagram of these functions is shown in Fig. 12-3.

Each R5601 contains four 512-tap split-electrode transversal filters, two sine, and two cosine chirps. The device takes in 512 time samples and outputs 512 coefficients. It is capable of sampling the input signal at rates up to 2 MHz.

Reticon also has a circuit board that performs the entire function. The RC5601 board can operate to 100 kHz and has an output accuracy of 7 bits. Applications are numerous, as the Fourier transform is a basic tool for signal processing. Some application areas are in voice analysis, bandwidth compression, vibration analysis, instrumentation, radar, and communications. Applications for these include modems, voice processing, sonar processing, DFT spectrum analysis, spread spectrum processing, and noise analysis.

The digital signal processing chips to be discussed in Chapt. 15 use transversal filters, also known as FIR, or nonrecursive filters, in accordance with the concepts of Chapt. 8.

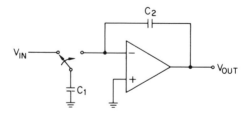

Figure 12-2 The switched capacitor integrator looks like an analog resistor only if f_s, the toggle frequency is rapid only. Courtesy of EG&G Reticon, Sunnyvale, California.

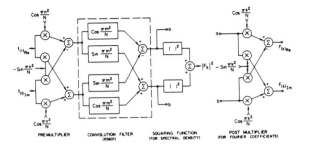

Figure 12-3 Block diagram for implementation of DFT or spectral density. Courtesy of EG&G Reticon, Sunnyvale, California.

Reticon has recently developed solid state image sensors for robotic pattern recognition. Vision for robotic movement and control; assembling, sorting, welding, painting, and other production-line operations are necessary when recognition of distinct patterns and shapes are required.

12-2   CORRELATION THEORY BACKGROUND* _____

Correlation techniques discussed in Chapt. 10 are used widely in communications, instrumentation, computers, telemetry, sonar, radar, medical, and other signal processing systems. Correlation has several desirable properties, including

1. The ability to detect a desired signal in the presence of noise or other signals.
2. The ability to recognize specific patterns within analog or digital signals.
3. The ability to measure time delays through various media, such as materials, the human body, RF paths, electronic circuits, etc.

As these properties indicate, correlation is essentially a comparison process. In fact, we use correlation daily when we compare sounds, images, or other sensations relative to other sounds, images, or sensations stored in our brain. The key function of the human comparison process is to measure mentally the degree of similarity between two or

*Section 12-2 to 12-7 from John Eldon "Correlation . . . A powerful technique for digital signal processing." Reprinted with courtesy of TRW LSI Products, La Jolla, Calif. © 1980.

more parameters. Generally, this sort of comparison is capable of discriminating extraneous forms of information and noise from a given sensum. The comparison can be made in real time, or we can mentally store the data until some later time.

The mental correlation process works well where the decision-making process is not limited by time constraints. However, in electronic systems we do not usually have the luxury of performing correlation at our leisure. Correlation must be performed in real time, requiring the use of electronic circuits that are compatible with the system in question.

Electronic systems that perform correlation have been around for years, but they have been bulky and inefficient. The development of VLSI has changed this; now correlation can be performed efficiently with a minimum number of components.

12-3 A DIGITAL CORRELATOR

A digital correlator circuit can perform both correlation and convolution in accordance with the discrete summation equations. The remainder of this chapter describes a monolithic digital correlator that can perform digital correlation and convolution at a 20 MHz rate. Correlation and convolution will be discussed further in the chapters that follow, which also discuss several applications of the monolithic correlator.

The major functions of an all-digital correlator are shown in Fig. 12-4. A reference shift register stores the reference word, and the input word is applied to the input shift register. Both shift registers are n bits long, where "n" is any whole number. The respective bits of the two shift registers are connected to individual exclusive-NOR gates, whose outputs are applied to a summing network.

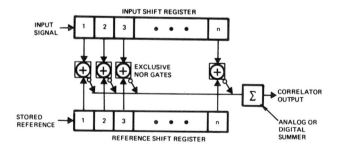

Figure 12-4 Basic correlator. Courtesy of TRW LSI Products, La Jolla, California.

In operation, the correlator output is obtained by aligning the input word (in the shift register) relative to the reference word. The respective bits in the two shift registers are compared by the exclusive-NOR gates, whose outputs are summed. The shift registers, the exclusive-NOR gates, and the summer fulfill the time delay, multiplication, and integration functions of correlation, respectively.

A new and first-of-its-kind monolithic digital correlator from TRW LSI Products is the 24-pin TDC1023J, which can perform 64-bit parallel correlation at 20 MHz. Its block diagram is shown in Fig. 12-5.

To perform correlation with the TDC1023J, the input signal is serially shifted into the independently clocked A-register, and the reference word is serially shifted into the independently clocked B register. A +1 logic value at "clock R" copies the reference word from the B register into the R latch. The user can then serially load a new reference word into the B register while correlation takes place between the A register and the R latch.

Data in the A register and R latch are continually compared bit for bit by the exclusive-NOR gates, whose outputs are applied to the digital summer via AND gates. The output of the digital summer is a 7-bit word representing, in binary, the number of bit positions in the A register and R latch that are in agreement at any instant of time.

The M register is a 64-bit, independently clocked mask register that permits the user to select bit positions where no comparisons are desired. This is accomplished by inserting a 64-bit serial word into it, with logical 0's in the "no comparison" bit positions. Since the outputs from the M register are applied to the AND gates that also contain the outputs from the exclusive-NOR gates, masked bits are prevented from reaching the digital summer.

Either true or inverted binary outputs can be obtained from the TDC1023J through use of the INV control line, which operates on the outputs of the digital summer. The inverters' exclusive-OR gate outputs feed seven three-state output buffers controlled by signal TS. (Logical 1 on the TS disables the buffered outputs by placing them in a high-impedance state.) When INV is a logical 1, the seven D_0–D_6 outputs are inverted; when INV is logical 0, they are true.

The TDC1023J also has a 7-bit, independently clocked T register, which is used to establish a correlation threshold. Exceeding the threshold causes a logical 1 on Flag T, the threshold flag. The threshold is set by first disabling the output buffers, using the TS control line, and then using outputs D_0–D_6 to parallel-load the desired threshold number into the T register. Flat T is activated when the binary number from the digital summer equals or exceeds the threshold stored in the T register.

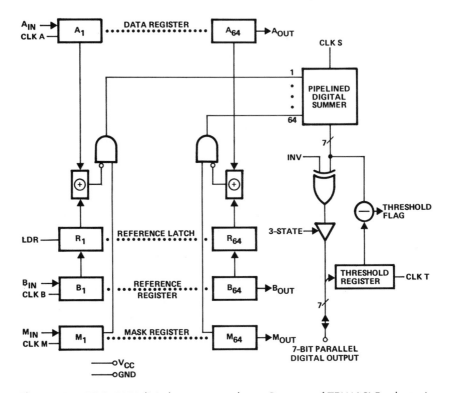

Figure 12-5 TDC1023J digital output correlator. Courtesy of TRW LSI Products, La Jolla, California.

12-4 BASIC CORRELATOR APPLICATIONS

A binary correlator compares, bit by bit, one sequence of binary digits against another. If the two binary sequences are derived from different sources, such as the phase patterns of a transmitted CW radar signal and its reflected return, the operation is cross-correlation. By contrast, autocorrelation is the comparison of a single binary sequence against a time-shifted copy of itself. Cross-correlation applications include

1. Detection of differences (e.g., errors) between two data sequences.
2. Determination of the time delay between two similar signals, such as a radar transmission and its returning reflection.
3. Correction of errors in expanded-code (redundant) data streams.
4. Multiplexing of data among several users.
5. Recognition of specified patterns within a data stream.

6. Synchronization of a decoding process or analyzer (such as a TV receiver's scanning circuits) with an incoming data stream.
7. Diagnosis of medical disorders (dysrhythmia monitors, etc.).

Autocorrelation is often employed to identify periodicities within a data stream as a time-domain alternative to spectral analysis and the associated time domain-frequency domain transformations. Similarly, it can "extract" a periodic signal from its random noise background, since the signal will yield high autocorrelation levels, while the random interface will not.

The TDC1023J fits three broad classes of correlator applications:

1. Direct autocorrelation or cross-correlation of nonredundant, nonexpanded data.
2. Comparisons of expanded-code data sequences in which extra bits have been added for error-rejecting redundancy or for other uses, such as multiplex addressing.
3. Synchronization of a receiver/analysis system with an incoming signal.

12-5 APPLICATIONS USING UNEXPANDED DATA

Many correlator applications involve comparing a given data sequence or pattern against a standard ("correct") sequence. As shown in Fig. 12-6, when presented with two sequences of up to 64 bits each, the correlator counts the number of bits in one sequence that match the corresponding bits in the other sequence. The difference E between the total number of bits under comparison N and the correlator's output R (the number of coincident bits) is the number of deviations (presumably errors) between the two sequences, i.e., $E = N - R$.

12-6 LOGIC ANALYZER

In principle, the TDC1023J correlator could be used in the automated testing of digital circuits. This trivial application is included as a tutorial example, to illustrate the correlator's function, rather than as a suggestion for a cost-effective, practical device. The other applications discussed in this paper use the correlator's unique capabilities far more efficiently. In this application the data values (logic levels) of a specified group of test points are entered serially into one of the correlator's registers. The remaining register is filled with the corresponding "correct" pattern for that device, test point(s), and test. The difference

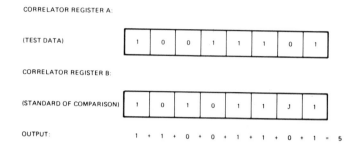

In this example, N = 8, R = 5, *and* E = 8 − 5 = 3. *The correlator's registers are filled serially with the two binary sequences shown; the correlator's output of "5" indicates that in 5 of the positions, the two sequences coincide.*

Figure 12-6   Correlation of a data sequence against a standard. Courtesy of TRW LSI Products, La Jolla, California.

between the number of bits under comparison and the number of agreements is the number of errors detected.

Although this type of operation does not identify the exact location of a given error, it flags and counts errors rapidly and automatically. In the automatic testing of a complex device, the correlator can count agreements as they arise during a long test cycle. The resulting total number of agreements (correlation score) can be regarded as a figure of merit for the device under test. A maximum possible score throughout the test procedure indicates error-free performance. This application is suitable for assembly line testing, where parts exhibiting no errors are passed, those exhibiting one or more errors are rejected, and there is generally no need to describe or locate each error precisely.

A complication in this application is that the correlator can be loaded only with serial streams of data, whereas most test situations involve the simultaneous examination of data values at several parallel test points. Therefore, parallel-to-serial conversion of the data is often required. This requirement is a constraint primarily in high-speed multipoint testing, where the correlator's input must be rapidly multiplexed among several inputs (test points). Where high speeds are required, two or more correlators may be employed in parallel, with each correlator monitoring a group of test points.

Since a typical TDC1023J correlator can accommodate a 20 MHz bit rate, the number of correlators required is at least $N \times R/20$, where N is the number of test points to be examined and R is the rate at which they must be checked (in MHz).

Figure 12-7 is a simplified block diagram of a multiple-correlator system designed to perform high-speed error analysis of several test points simultaneously. For simplicity, a separate correlator is wired to each test point in the circuit. During the test, the sequence of data values appearing at each test point is clocked serially into the corresponding correlator's A register. At the end of the test, each correlator's output score is read.

In this example, the test fixture includes a separate TDC1023J correlator for each test point. During testing, the values appearing at these test points are fed serially into the respective A register inputs. Each correlator's B register holds the "correct" pattern for its test point. When a full test sequence is stored in each A register, the correlator outputs are summed.

The TDC1023J 64-bit digital output correlator has three features that simplify actual implementation of the system in Fig. 12-7. First, if fewer than 64 bits are required in a test sequence, the masking register can be used to select only the desired A register contents, ignoring all others. Second, the digital summer outputs and the register input and output ports facilitate serial connection of n correlators, allowing test sequences longer than 64 bits. Third, when set to the appropriate "pass" level, the threshold register will automatically activate a flag to distinguish between parts passing and failing the test sequence.

The correlator's input registers must be appropriately clocked to ensure that they read the desired test data values without omissions or duplications. This is particularly critical where parallel-to-serial con-

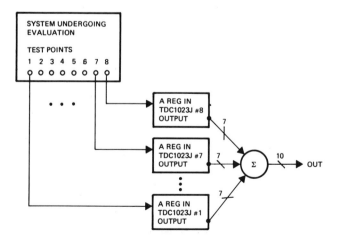

Figure 12-7 Multiple-correlator test fixture block diagram. Courtesy of TRW LSI Products, La Jolla, California.

version (multiplex switching) is employed to enable each correlator to evaluate several parts or test points. Furthermore, since its inputs feed directly to one-bit-wide serial shift registers, the correlator is limited to verifying high (logic "1") and low (logic "0") levels, rather than indeterminate, high-impedance, or rapidly oscillating levels. When properly timed, the correlator can process brief impulses, as long as its maximum shift rate of 20 MHz is not exceeded. Since the input register setup time is 25 ns, each input signal must remain valid for at least this long to ensure proper data handling. The minimum correlation clock time of 50 ns also limits the TDC1023J's real-time correlation rate to 20 MHz.

Two signals can be loaded into and across the A and B registers at a bit rate of 20 MHz for precorrelation alignment. They can also be clocked at 20 MHz during real-time correlation, in which a correlation score is computed for each new alignment. Although the data can be realigned and correlated continuously at 20 MHz, the three steps of internal pipelining in the digital summation network imply that the nth correlation score will be available while the $n + 3$rd alignment is being clocked into the A and B registers. The user's timing and control logic must allow for this pipelining latency period.

12-7   TIME-DELAY MEASUREMENT

A simple correlator-based system can determine the time delay between two similar patterns of bits, such as a transmitted radar or sonar signal and its reflected return. In this example, the two signals appear similar in shape or bit pattern, but will exhibit a relative time shift of 2 D/C, where D is the antenna-target separation and C is the speed of light (or the speed of sound in sonar and ultrasound systems). Theoretically, this time delay will cause a low correlation between the two signals, even though without the delay, the two signals would correlate well. As shown in Fig. 12-8, correlator-based time delay measurement entails gradually "eliminating" the time delay by shifting one signal with respect to the other. The highest correlation is obtained when the total shift just compensates for the original time delay between two signals. The transmitted signal can be a burst of energy that contains a particular phase or amplitude pattern, or it can be a continuous signal comprising periodic repetitions of a pattern.

For time delay measurements, the TDC1023J's B register is fed the "original" signal, such as a transmitted radar (or sonar) pattern, while the A register is simultaneously filled with the (delayed) "return" signal. The two registers are clocked together, so that the time

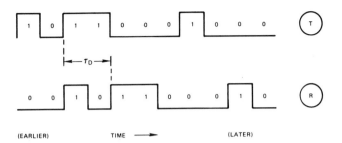

Signal "T" is the original transmission; "R" is the reflected return. In real time, R and T are separated by the time delay τ_D, which causes them to correlate poorly. Shifting R to eliminate the relative time delay will yield a high correlation. The time behaviors of both signals determine the correlation pattern. In this figure, earlier values are to the left of later ones.

Figure 12-8 Data shifting for time delay measurement. Courtesy of TRW LSI Products, La Jolla, California.

delay between the signals appears as a displacement in their relative register positions, as shown in Fig. 12-9. After loading both registers, the system monitors the correlator output while continuing to clock the A register only. This loads progressively later return signal bits, while shifting the delayed pattern across the original pattern as in Fig. 12-9. The number of bit shifts required for an acceptable correlation times the signal's bit time (inverse of frequency) is the total time delay between the two signals.

For time delay measurement, the transmitted code must be long and complex enough to avoid false or ambiguous alignments. For example, a code such as 101010101 would clearly be unsuitable for time delay measurement, since all shifts of 2N bits (where N = 1, 2, 3, . . .) would yield high correlations, causing ambiguous results. In contrast, a code which repeats only once every 500 characters is much more likely to provide an unambiguous measure of any time delay of less than 500 bit times, although even this code would be unsuitable in some applications involving longer time delays.

When a nonrecurring code, such as a single burst of information, is employed in time delay measurement, the length and pattern of the transmitted code are still constrained. Under ideal circumstances, where the only objective is to measure distance to a target, a simple isolated pulse, e.g., a single positive bit surrounded by negatives or zeros, can be transmitted, as shown in Fig. 12-10. The returning reflection of this signal contains a similar isolated pulse, delayed by the round-trip travel time between the antenna and the target. However, this is an insensitive alignment test, with a total correlation score of 62/64 when the transmitted and received pulses are misaligned versus 64/64 for perfect alignment.

In the presence of noise or interference, the return signal could contain one or more false positives, which could reduce the perfect-alignment correlation and generate other equally high correlations.

Longer codes are used to improve the accuracy and sensitivity of the time delay measurement, as shown in Fig. 12-11. Here, a seven-bit "Barker code" is chosen for its low correlation with random noise and with time-shifted versions of itself. Although the longer pulse code cannot improve the 64/64 correlation score for perfect time alignment, in the presence of noise it will greatly reduce the chance of a burst of random noise causing a high correlation. For a given level of interference and concomitant bit errors, increasing the Barker code length tends to reduce the frequency and magnitude of false correlations, thereby enhancing the accuracy of the range measurement system. The interested reader can refer to the literature on Barker codes, which

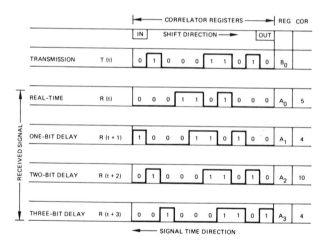

First, the original transmission and delayed reflection are loaded simultaneously into the B and A registers, respectively. Next, the B register clock is stopped, while the A register clock continues to read in the return signal and shift it across the register. The highest correlation occurs when the "A register only" clock cycles have just compensated for the original delay between the signals.

Figure 12-9 Time delay measurement with a correlator. Courtesy of TRW LSI Products, La Jolla, California.

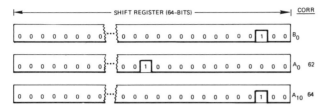

Figure 12-10 Single-pulse time-delay measurement. As in Fig. 12-9, the original signal is loaded into the B register. The return is clocked across the A register until a correlation of 64 is obtained. Note that the total correlation score is relatively insensitive to the imposed time delay, reaching 64 for perfect alignment, but 62 at all other times. Courtesy of TRW LSI Products, La Jolla, California.

offer the lowest achievable error rates and highest sensitivity for these applications.

A caveat in time delay measurement is that the bit rate of the code must be high enough to permit precise measurement of the time delay, since the correlator can measure time delay only to within ±1 bit time. A higher bit rate permits a more precise determination of delay time, but increases the amount of data to be handled.

12-8   A MICROPROCESSOR FOR CREATING A DIGITAL FILTER COMPUTING MACHINE*

The basic concepts of a general-purpose microprocessor can be expanded to create a high-speed digital filter computing machine (Fig. 12-12). Recursive and nonrecursive filters of any structure can be implemented.

The main emphasis here is on the arithmetic logic unit (ALU), which performs the necessary data arithmetic required to implement the desired digital filter. It is different from typical microprocessor ALU's in that its architecture is designed to perform operations that are sequence- rather than instruction-oriented. This implies a multi-data bus configuration with local storage and single-cycle multiple-add capability. As a result, a sequence of basic computer-type microinstructions (such as read, multiply, store) can be performed within a single microcycle, in contrast to the large number of instructions required in most small computing machines.

---

*Section 12-8 to 12-13 from R. J. Karwoski, "Hardware Development For a General Purpose Digital Filter Computing Machine." Reprints with courtesy of TRW LSI Products, La Jolla, Calif. © TRW, Inc., 1982.

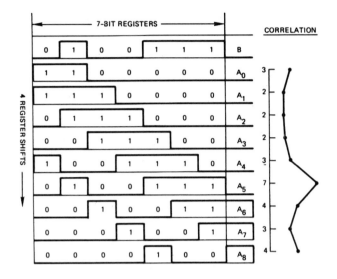

In this example, alignment within one bit time generates a significantly higher score than any other degree of relative timing between the two signals.

Figure 12-11 Time-delay measurement with a seven-bit barker code. Courtesy of TRW LSI Products, La Jolla, California.

The computer control unit is similar to that of most microprocessors, having a sequencer, microprogram ROM, and some assorted logic. It receives user-programmed instructions and directs the ALU to do the prescribed arithmetic. Control elements are the coefficient and memory offset generators, which are separate logic subsystems that provide multiplier coefficients and the correct data delays for the filter. They run in parallel with the general machine sequencer to ensure maximum computational speed. The reader will note that throughout testing, individual tasks are handled by separate dedicated elements rather than by a single processor. This fact, together with the enhanced ALU structure, provides a great improvement in speed and efficiency over other general-purpose machines.

Flexibility of speed, word size, and architecture are important considerations when designing a digital signal processor. As with the design of any computing machine, these items are closely interrelated, often making the initial conception of the machine confusing. Some design guidelines can help this situation. For instance, data and instruction memories should be kept separate. Also, the computer control section of the processor should be isolated from the main arithmetic logic unit (ALU) data ports. Thus, the controller does not borrow the ALU for computing effective addresses for instruction or data acquisition purposes. Speed requirements usually preclude this sort of inner computer activity, since controller functions usually waste so much time.

Little emphasis need be placed on elementary microoperations such as load accumulator, add, subtract, etc. These are typical instructions found in most microcomputer instruction sets. They provide the user with the utmost in program flexibility, but they are not efficient for implementating digital filters. The most complex filter configuration can be broken down into a manageable number of high-level mi-

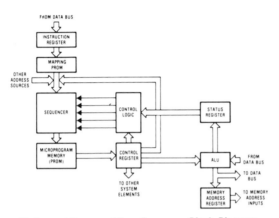

A) General Purpose Micro Processor Block Diagram

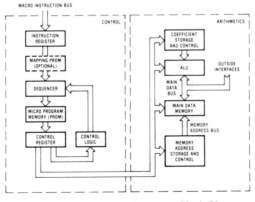

B) Simplified Fast Digital Processor Block Diagram

Figure 12-12 Microprogram machine block diagrams. Courtesy of TRW LSI Products, La Jolla, California.

croinstructions of which loading, adding, multiplying, etc., are all implied in a single statement. Normally, these instructions might be considered subroutines or branch routines in computer terms, since each involves the execution of a number of elementary computer operations; however, each instruction will take but one microcycle instead of the large number typical of most micros. For example, a common operation in digital filter synthesis involves reading data from memory, multiplying it by another number, adding it to a previous result stored in some working register, and re-storing the result in the same register.

Separation of data and control functions provides design simplification, allowing the creation of an efficient ALU with minimal regard for the effects on controller requirements. One finds that whether handling batch or real-time data, control and address functions are best handled by a small amount of specialized hardware. Figure 12-12 illustrates the difference between a simplified modern-day microprocessor and a microprogrammed fast digital sign processor. The obvious isolation of data, address, and instruction buses is in immediate contrast to the basic microstructure.

The fast processor can be a relatively noninteractive machine in that all the computational operations are performed under the unconditional direction of the controller. The controller needs little or no decision-making capability on the basis of ALU outcomes. Hence, no feedback is generally required from the ALU to the controller. A general microprocessor would lose much of its capability if this feature were omitted.

12-9 DIGITAL FILTER CONFIGURATIONS

As discussed in Chapts. 7 and 8, there are two classes of digital filters: recursive and nonrecursive. There are applications requiring a mixture of the two. Recursive filter outputs depend on present input samples and past output values and therefore employ feedback in their implementation. In nonrecursive filters, the filter output at any given time depends on the input at that time and on a finite number of past input values.

The data input to the digital filter is discrete in time (i.e., in the form of data samples rather than continuous data). For so-called batch processing, this data will probably reside in a buffer memory on the outskirts of the arithmetic section of the processor and will be updated and processed in chunks. For real-time data processing, where the output data rate is always the same as the input sampling rate, the data will most likely come from one or more A/D converters. The system development discussed in this section pertains to both situations. The reader may find more emphasis on the real-time case in some instances (e.g., the computer control unit).

12-10 NONRECURSIVE FILTERS

Nonrecursive (finite impulse response, or FIR) filters are generally implemented in one of two ways:

1. Via the summation of N-weighted outputs from a tapped delay line. The delay may be implemented using random access memory, or if the order of the filters is not too high, digital shift registers may be used. (See Fig. 12-13.) The z^{-1} terms represent data delays of one sample time.

2. A bank of second-order "elemental" filters preceded by a comb filter (Fig. 12-14). The resulting outputs from the elemental filters are summed to form the output y_n.

These implementations are the natural outgrowths of two mathematical criteria that lead to finite impulse response forms. The configuration of Fig. 12-13 stems from a mathematical development in which the coefficients $a_0, \ldots, a_{n-1}$ are the first N terms of the inverse DFT of the desired response. These terms may be modified to obtain the desired characteristics.

The frequency sampling technique leads to the configuration in Figure 12-14. The designer selects a sufficient number of frequency samples (amplitude and phase) to specify the desired spectrum. The frequency sampling filter provides the exact magnitude and phase at these points.

12-11 RECURSIVE FILTERS

Recursive (infinite impulse response, or IIR) filters have an infinite-length impulse response, and unless they are implemented with an infinitely long delay line, feedback must be used. Of the number of well-known equivalent configurations of this type of filter, probably the most common is the canonical form shown in Fig. 12-15. Although a filter of this type can be of any order, it is recommended that high-order filters be broken down into first- and second-order sections. Filter parameters are less susceptible to coefficient rounding effects for low-order filters.

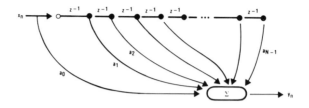

Figure 12-13 Basic FIR implementation. Courtesy of TRW LSI Products, La Jolla, California.

The signal flow graphs of Figs. 12-13, 12-14 and 12-15 give the impression that data is available at each signal node for immediate and simultaneous processing. In contrast to analog filters in which this is the case, digital implementations are done through a precise sequence of steps. The architectures developed for digital filtering are directed toward very efficient program execution, combining a number of basic computer operations to form higher-level microinstructions. Nonetheless, elimination of the sequential nature of the machine is unrealistic. For instance, those signal nodes that represent points on a tapped delay line may be stationary or precessing locations in memory, therefore having to be accessed at separate times (i.e., during different machine cycles). Figure 12-15 indicates data being extracted from memory (nodes 1 through $N-2$), added to input x_n, and stored back into memory at node $N-1$. A typical machine may take up to 2N machine cycles to complete the sequence.

For a real-time system, data samples may be received from an A/D converter at a given rate. Thus, the output sample rate must be effectively the same (ignoring resampling possibilities). Upon arrival

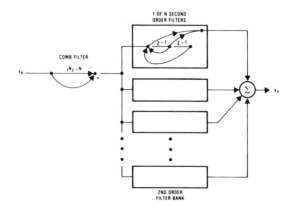

Figure 12-14 FIR implementation using the frequency sampling technique. Courtesy of TRW LSI Products, La Jolla, California.

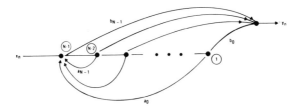

Figure 12-15 Nth order canonical IIR implementation. Courtesy of TRW LSI Products, La Jolla, California.

of a data sample x_n, the computation sequence commences. The sequence must be completed and ready to begin again before the arrival of the next sample x_{n+1}. Signals that contain relatively high frequency components must be sampled at high rates to avoid aliasing effects and therefore allow limited time for computation between samples.

12-12 ALU ARCHITECTURE

Confronted with the myriad of possible digital filter configurations, the designer's first impulse is to create a completely universal ALU bus structure as shown in Fig. 12-16. Each ALU element has direct and independent access to the output of any other ALU element. This allows data to run simultaneously on any number of paths, minimizing sequential steps and computer time, while allowing the synthesis of all filter forms.

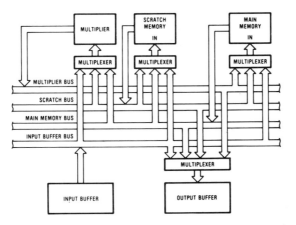

Figure 12-16 Type I–ALU architecture. Courtesy of TRW LSI Products, La Jolla, California.

The flexibility afforded in the configuration of Fig. 12-16 is not necessary, as efficient execution of even the most complicated algorithms involves variations of relatively few routines if the arithmetic unit is implemented with the TDC1010J multiplier-accumulator. These routines can be designed to require a maximum of two data buses running at any given execution time with little or no compromise in speed. Arriving at the exact structure for a given dedicated processor may require tracing out data paths on the architecture for some typical program executions. After a number of these, the design can eliminate unused paths, minimize the arithterure, and arrive at a suitable microinstruction set.

Figure 12-17 illustrates an ALU section that provides very efficient execution of all digital filters at modest hardware cost. Data is channeled in and out of the ALU via the input and output storage elements (X and OR). These may be A/D and D/A interfaces or additional memory. The heart of the ALU is the TCD1010J multiplier-accumulator, on which most of the data computations are done. Local rapid access storage is handled in the scratch pad memory (Sc), and the bulk data storage is done in the main memory, which provides the necessary data delays for digital filter implementation. The extra accumulator frees the 1010 from the responsibility of having to perform simple group addition tasks, which may be done automatically as

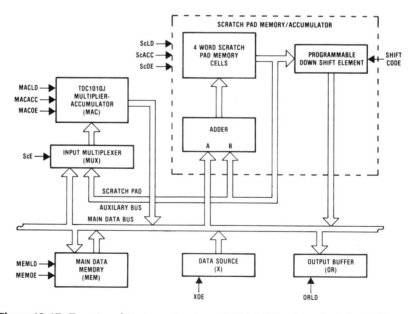

Figure 12-17 Type 2 architecture. Courtesy of TRW LSI Products, La Jolla, California.

multiplier products are shipped off for local storage. A combinatorial shifter is provided at its output, so that the accumulated data may be rendered instantaneously compatible with the main 16-bit bus. The shifter output is linked to the main bus, while the actual scratch pad memory output drives the auxillary bus into the multiplier input multiplexer (MUX).

As an introduction to the efficiency afforded by the auxilary bus, consider the following example. A second order canonical filter is to be implemented. The signal flow graph is shown in Fig. 12-18.

Input x_n is added to past (extracted from memory) data products $-b_0x_1$ and $-b_1x_2$. The result is written back into memory as indicated (node 3). During this write cycle, the MAC input section is free to do another multiply or multiply-accumulate. Unfortunately, during a write cycle, the memory I/O bus is tied up and cannot provide the necessary data (x_1, x_2, or x_3) for the multiplications to form output y_n. If during the recursive operation x_1 or x_2 is simultaneously stored in Sc while it is being transferred to the MAC, it can then be used during the write cycle when the MAC would otherwise be idle. Data will be running on both buses during this time, resulting in the elimination of one microcycle for the implementation of the filter. This constitutes a substantial savings in machine time since four to six cycles are necessary to perform the complete algorithm. (See instructions 3 and 5, Table 12-1, Sect. 12-14.)

12-13 CONTROLLING THE ALU

Directing the traffic in and out of each ALU element is a relatively straightforward task, performed by a controller.

The main control signals at each ALU element are as follows.

1. *Scratch Pad Memory/Accumulator (Sc) Controls*

   a. *Scratch Pad Load (ScLD)*. Clock enable used to load the memory.

   b. *Scratch Pad Read Address, Scratch Pad Write Address (SRA, SWA)*. Memory address directing data in and out of memory; addresses may be tied together or remain separate.

   c. *Scratch Accumulate (ScACC)*. Logic level activating scratch adder to perform accumulation. A logic 1 will allow data on the bus to be added to data in memory location specified by SRA and stored in memory location specified by SWA. When this signal is inactive, a simple data write or read can be performed.

   d. *Scratch Output Enable (ScOE)*. Logic level enabling shifted data onto the main bus.

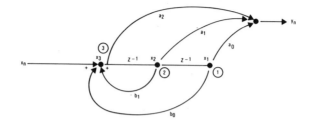

Figure 12-18 Signal flow graph. Courtesy of TRW LSI Products, La Jolla, California.

   e. *Shift Code (S)*. An n-bit code specifying the number of places the scratch pad word is to be shifted down; hence, division by 2^n is possible.

2. *Main Memory Controls*

   a. *Memory Output Enable (MEMOE)*. Logic level enabling memory data onto the main bus.

   b. *Memory Load (MEMLD)*. Clock enable for loading data into memory.

   c. *Memory Address (MEMA)*. An n-bit code specifying the location of the memory word that is accessed.

3. *TDC1010J Multiplier-Accumulator (MAC) Controls*

   a. *Multiplier-Accumulator Load (MACLD)*. Clock enable for loading data into X, Y, and accumulator registers.

   b. *Multiply/Accumulate (MACACC)*. Active logic level directing an accumulate operation within the TDC1010J after multiplication.

   c. *Multiplier Output Enable (MACOE)*. Active logic level enabling the multiplier product onto the main data bus.

4. *Multiplexer Input (MUX) Control*

   Scratch Pad Enable (ScE). Active logic level enabling data into the MAC from the scratch memory via the auxiliary bus.

5. *Input Source (X) Control*

   Source Output Enable (XOE). Active logic level enabling X data onto the main bus.

6. *Output Buffer (OR) Control*

   Output Load (ORLD). Clock enable for loading output (register on buffer memory).

Data may be sent on the bus connecting one ALU element to another by enabling the output (e.g., MACOE) of the sender and the input clock of the receiver (e.g., ScLD).

   All control lines are assumed to be a logic 1 for an enabling condition. This simplifies matters in the preliminary stages of the design. It is understood that each ALU element may have its particular requirements for loading and enabling. For example, the TDC1010J requires three input clocks and has five output enables. Also most logic will be tri-state, requiring logic zero for an output-enabling condition. These particulars may be taken care of with a small amount of random logic in the ALU control interface. During any given microcycle, the controller outputs report the state of the machine and may be used as enabling signals when necessary, as may the actual control signals.

Figure 12-19 is a simplified block diagram of the TDC1010J MAC, and Fig. 12-20 is a timing diagram illustrating a loading and output-enabling sequence of the 1010 during a typical computer cycle. Machine cycle T_1 contains an instruction requiring (1) a multiplication or multiply-accumulate and (2) transfer of the previous product, which is stored in the product register, to the main bus. The 1010 contains input registers for X and Y operands. It is not necessary to waste a complete clock cycle to load X and Y registers, since typical multiple-accumulate time for the MAC is under 150 ns and loading is not useful for anything other than multiplier operations. The clock interval may be subdivided such that loading, multiplying, adding, and final storage are carried out in various portions of a single microcycle (Fig. 12-21).

Due to the large number of inputs and outputs required for 16 × 16 double-precision multiplication, it is necessary for some functions to share common pins on the TDC1010J. This is a slight problem for implementations requiring multiplication by numbers greater than 1. For the synthesis of second-order filters, multiplication by 2 may be necessary. The required data shift by 1 bit (and subsequent multiplication by 2) is effected by connecting P_{30} (second-product MSB) to the MSB of the data bus (Fig. 12-12). Unfortunately Y_{15} (coefficient MSB) shares a pin with P_{15}, the new data bus LSB. These cannot be enabled simultaneously, so the microcycle is divided such that the output data from the P register is on the bus during the latter half of the cycle. X and Y are loaded during the first half.

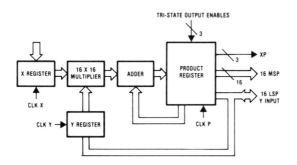

Figure 12-19 Simplified TDC 1010J multiplier-accumulator block diagram. Courtesy of TRW LSI Products, La Jolla, California.

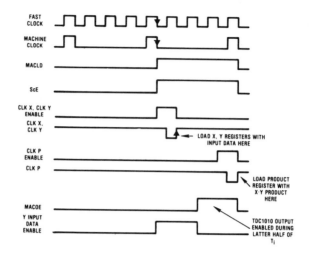

Figure 12-20 Typical TDC1010J loading sequence timing diagram. Courtesy of TRW LSI Products, La Jolla, California.

12-14 SIGNAL FLOW DIAGRAM FOR PRESCRIBED SECOND-ORDER FILTER*

The second-order filter is probably the hardest filter to implement since it involves many types of instructions and the use of all of the ALU's capabilities. In addition, "fencing" of data memory into many sections is required to form the second-order elemental filters.

The configuration calls for the implementation of many second-order recursive filters with transfer functions of the form

$$H(Z) = \frac{H(\theta_2)(\cos\theta - \cos(\theta_p - \theta)z^{-1})}{1 - 2r_p\cos\theta_p z^{-1} + r_p^2 z^{-2}} \qquad (12\text{-}1)$$

The z^{-1} and z^{-2} terms denote delay operations of one and two sample times (T and 2T). These delays are usually implemented with RAM, but may be envisioned as taps at T seconds and 2T seconds on a delay line.

The output of each filter is summed to form the composite filter output y_n. (See Fig. 12-14.) Filter parameters $H(\theta_p)$, $\cos\theta$, $\cos(\theta_p - \theta)$, and $2r_p\cos\theta_p$ can be combined, and the signal flow graph for the transfer function $H(Z)$ is shown in Fig. 12-21.

*Section 12-14 thru 12-19 appears in R. J. Karwoski, "An Introduction to Digital Spectrum Analysis Including a High Speed FFT Processor Design." Reprinted with courtesy of TRW LSI Products, La Jolla, Calif. © 1980.

The hardware operations indicated by the flow diagram proceed as follows. Input signal u_n, a digital word residing in a register (scratch pad, A/D register, etc.) at a time nT. It is summed with words $C_3 e_{n-1}$ and $C_4 e_{n-2}$ to form $e_n = C_0 U_n + C_3 e_{n-1} + C_4 e_{n-2}$. e_n is then written into memory at effective address A_i (node 3, the input of the delay line). e_{n-1} and e_{n-2} are the results of identical operations that occurred one and two data sample times before. They reside in memory at locations A_{i-1} and A_{i-2} during sample time period nT. During the next sample time $(n + 1)T$, when x_{n+1} is to be processed, e_n will advance to node 2 (address A_{i-1}), e_{n-1} will go to node 1 (A_{i-2}), and e_{n+1} will be generated and written into memory at node 2 (A_i). The filter output is formed in a fashion similar to that just described for the feedback operation. C_1 and C_2 are the multiplying coefficients, and $y_n = C_1 e_n + C_2 e_{n-1}$.

Including the input scaling multiplication ($C_0 U_n$), five multiplications and four additions are necessary to implement this filter. If we assume a 150 ns machine cycle time and can achieve one cycle per multiply/accumulate (multiply/add), the elemental filter computation will take 750 ns. The usefulness of the scratch accumulation capability is realized for this computation sequence. The filter outputs can be accumulated as each is piped from the 1010 output register through the adder into a scratch pad location. Two machine cycles per filter are eliminated. Ignoring initial setup and the small amount of overhead time that is likely to occur, a 100 frequency sample filter (i.e., a 200th-order filter), will take 75 ns to implement.

Table 12-1 lists a feasible instruction sequence for the frequency sampling filter.

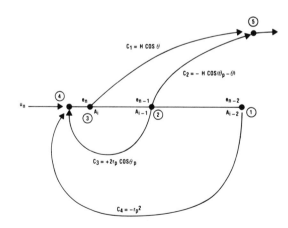

Figure 12-21 Signal flow diagram for prescribed second-order filter. Courtesy of TRW LSI Products, La Jolla, California.

The comb filter that precedes the filter bank is implemented in instructions 2, 3, and 4. Instruction 1 contains a NOP, but may be needed for program initialization. Instructions 6 through 11 implement the first second-order section. Twelve through 17, 18 through 23, etc., are repeats of 6 through 11, except that coefficients differ for all the filters. All the filter outputs are automatically accumulated (added) in ScO.

12-15   HIGH-SPEED FFT PROCESSOR DESIGN

High-speed digital signal processing computers generally differ from ordinary computers in a number of fundamental areas. For one, general-purpose machines usually perform arithmetic and control operations through a central processing unit (CPU). The CPU generates instructions, supervises indexing and other control functions, and directs arithmetic operations as well. Such a machine can be very flexible, but is not usually very fast, and therefore is inappropriate for most real-time DSP work. In a real-time processor, arithmetic and control functions are isolated. A sequence of arithmetic operations can

Table 12-1

Macro instruction sequence for the frequency sampling filter.*

Instruction Description	Instruction	Data Notation	Multiplier, C
1. Nothing (or program initialization)	NOP	—	—
2. Multiply MEM data by $_rN$; store in MAC register	MemMult	$C \cdot MEM \rightarrow MAC$	$_{-r}N$
3. Multiply input x data by C_i, add result to value residing in MAC register, restore in MAC register, write input x into memory	XWM/XMAC	$X + MAC \rightarrow MAC$ $X \rightarrow MEM$	C_i(Comb input scaler)
4. Store MAC output register value in Sc address 1	MACSTO1	$MAC \rightarrow Sc1$	
END OF COMB COMPUTATIONS			
5. Clear scratch pad location zero	C1Sc	$0 \rightarrow Sc0$	—
6. Multiply data in Sc address 1 by C_O, place product in MAC output register	Sc1Mult	$C \cdot Sc1 \rightarrow MAC$	C_0(canonical input scaler)
7. Multiply e_{n-1} by C_3, add result to value residing in MAC output register, place this sum in MAC output register; store e_{n-1} in Sc address 2	MemMAC/STO2	$C \cdot MEM + MAC \rightarrow MAC$ $MEM \rightarrow Sc2$	$C_3 \cdot 2r_p \cos \theta_p$
8. Multiply e_{n-2} by C_4, add this product to value residing in the MAC output register, place this sum in the MAC output register	MemMAC	$C \cdot MEM + MAC \rightarrow MAC$	$C_4 = -r_p^2$

Table 12-1 (continued)

Instruction Description	Instruction	Data Notation	Multiplier, C
9. Load MAC data into MEM; multiply present data in Sc address 2 by C_2, store in MAC output register	MWM/Sc2Mult	$MAC \rightarrow MEM$ $C \cdot Sc2 \rightarrow MAC$	$C_2 = -|H|\cos(\theta_p - \theta)$
10. Multiply e_n by C_1, add it to data residing in MAC register, restore result in MAC register	MemMAC	$C \cdot Sc2 + MAC \rightarrow MAC$	$C_1 = |H|\cos\theta$
11. Add data in MAC register to data in Sc address 0 and restore the result in Sc address 0	MACACC0	$MAC + Sc0 \rightarrow Sc0$	—
		FILTER NO. 1 COMPLETE	
12. Multiply data in Sc address 1 by C_0, place product in MAC output register	Sc1Mult	$C \cdot Sc1 \rightarrow MAC$	C_0 = input scaler
13. Multiply e_{n-1} by C_3, add result to value residing in MAC output register, place this sum in MAC output register; store a_{n-1} in Sc address 2	MemMAC/STO2	$C \cdot MEM + MAC$ $MEM \rightarrow Sc2$	$C_3 = 2r_p\cos\theta_p$
14. Multiply e_{n-2} by C_4, add this product to value residing in the MAC output register, place this sum in the MAC output register	MemMAC	$C \cdot Mem + MAC \rightarrow MAC$	$C_4 = -r_p^2$
15. Load MAC data into MEM; multiply present data in Sc address 2 by C_2, store in MAC output register	MWM/Sc2Mult	$MAC \rightarrow MEM$ $C \cdot Sc2 + MAC$	$C_2 = -|H|\cos(\theta_p - \theta)$
16. Multiply e_n by C_1, add it to data residing in MAC register, restore result in MAC register	MemMAC	$C \cdot Sc2 + MAC \rightarrow MAC$	$C_1 = |H|\cos\theta$
17. Add data in MAC register to data in Sc address 0 and restore the result in Sc address 0	MACACC0	$MAC + Sc0 \rightarrow Sc0$	—
		FILTER NO. 2 COMPLETE	

*Courtesy of TRW LSI Products, La Jolla, California.

be performed while the supporting control functions are done simultaneously (in parallel) by other sections.

The arithmetic unit performs computations strictly on input data and is not summoned to compute effective addresses, do indexing, or perform other control-oriented tasks. Instead, these are done with one or more individual control elements, depending on the requirements of the algorithm to be executed and the desired speed of the machine.

In this section, a parallel-control real-time machine is introduced. The machine is intended for frequency-domain work in particular FFT computations. It is characterized by an extremely efficient data arithmetic unit (DAU) which, with the proper control support, can also do time-domain jobs like correlation and digital filtering as well as spectral analysis. The DAU that is introduced in Section 12-17 contains a single, TRW multiplier-accumulator (MAC) and performs a butterfly in just six computer cycles. This is an improvement over many other arithmetic architectures, which may require up to 16 cycles. As indicated, four multiplications per butterfly, occurring at some time during the six cycles, are necessary.

The DAU is supported by the controller, which is broken into three areas:

1. DAU sequencing (Sequencer)
2. FFT address generation (Address generator)
3. Coefficient indexing (Coefficient generator)

Figure 12-22 is a block diagram of the system. The sequencer controls data routing in the DAU and provides indexing markers for the address and coefficient generators. Address and coefficient information is generated independently by these controllers, but the timing is provided by the sequencer via the indexing markers. The address controller generates signals that mark strategic points during the FFT sequence. These signals are fed back to the sequencer and to the coefficient generator. The details are discussed in Section 12-13.

The total number of cycles is an accurate criterion for the effi-

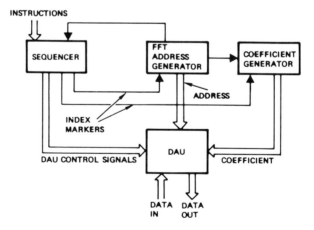

Figure 12-22 Simplified block diagram of the high-speed FFT processor. The sequencer directs data for in the DAU via the DAU control signals. FFT addresses coefficients generated by controllers prompted by the sequencer. Courtesy of TRW LSI Products, La Jolla, California.

ciency of a high-speed processor. With $N/2 \times \log_2 N$ butterflies per FFT and C operations per butterfly, (C) $(N/2) \log_2 N$ cycles are required to perform the complete FFT. In the proposed machine, $C = 6$ and $3N \log_2 N$ cycles are needed. For $N = 1024$, $3\ (1024)\ \log_2 (1024) = 30{,}720$ operations must be performed.

In a DFT computation, the number of multiplications may be considered equal to the number of operations. Thus, for $N = 1024$ and $C = 6$, the FFT savings factor is

$$\frac{\text{DFT operation}}{\text{FFT operations}} = \frac{4 \times (1 - 24)^2}{30720} = 133 \qquad (12\text{-}2)$$

12-16 COMPUTATIONAL CONSIDERATIONS FOR IN-PLACE ALGORITHMS

Discrete Fourier transforms are done on blocks of data that may be derived from an outside source such as an A/D interface or an external computer. A block of data can be loaded into the FFT processor data memory via an external bus or the DMA channel of a host computer. The transformed data may be returned to the same memory or to an output memory for further processing.

An FFT process is described here whereby the FFT is done in stages. During each stage (or pass), data is extracted from memory in sets of two, "butterflied," and returned to the same memory locations. Each stage is completed when each memory cell has undergone this process once. The process continues until the required number of passes is completed. The results of the final pass are the actual transform values. This technique is referred to as computation "in place." The main memory both acts as a working storage area and provides initial storage for $x(n)$ and final storage for $X(k)$.

Figure 12-23 shows the upper left section of the 32-point DLT. Groups 0 through 3 of pass 0, and groups 0 and 1 of pass 1 are shown, emphasizing memory locations for the operations just described.

Single-memory configurations are very efficient from a hardware standpoint, but have reduced speed compared to other variations. This is so because the FFT processor must remain idle while the input data are loaded and the output data are unloaded. Assuming that it takes N computer cycles to load and another N to unload, the total number of cycles required to do the FFT is actually (C) $(N/2) \log_2 N + N + N$, where C is the number of cycles per butterfly. With $N = 1024$ and $C = 6$, an additional 2048 cycles are required over the $3N\log N = 30{,}720$ actual computation cycles. The resulting reduction in speed may be a

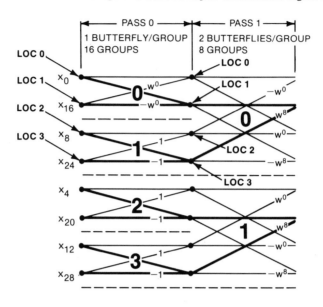

Figure 12-23 Northwest section of the 32-point FFT. Data initially resides in memory locations 0 through 31. The in-place algorithm extracts a pair of data points (e.g., X_0 and X_{16}), performs a butterfly, and returns the results to the original memory locations. Courtesy of TRW LSI Products, La Jolla, California.

small price to pay for the hardware simplicity provided by a single-memory scheme.

When the data are derived from an A/D, there may not be a choice in the matter. Space must be provided for the storage of the $(r + 1)$th block of data while the rth block is being transformed. Designers often use a scheme called double buffering, in which two N-word memories are provided at the processor input. An in-place FFT is performed on the data residing in the first memory while the second is being filled with data. Presumably, the first in-place FFT is done and the frequency data $X_1(k)$ are dumped by the time the second memory is filled with the next batch of data $x_2(n)$. An in-place algorithm is performed on $x_2(n)$ residing in the second memory while the first memory is filled with a new block of data $x_3(n)$.

More speed can be attained if a third memory is included at the FFT output. The frequency samples $X(k)$ computed during the last FFT pass are dumped directly into the third memory. The next FFT process is free to start without having to unload the last set of frequency samples. These samples may be unloaded at a reduced rate, since this memory space is not required until the last pass of the new FFT.

Consider a machine which has a 150 ns instruction time (cycle time). A 6-cycle butterfly takes 900 ns. Now assume that a processor is to perform continuous FFT's on data coming from an A/D converter. If the machine has three memories, the FFT throughput rate would be

$$\left[((C)(N/2) \log_2 N)(150 \times 10^{-9}) \right]^{-1} \text{ FFT's/sec} = R \qquad (12\text{-}3)$$

As a practical example, let $N = 1024$.* The machine will produce a new FFT batch every 5.12 ms, so that $R \simeq 200$ FFTs/sec. Because there are 1024 points, the effective real-time sampling rate is $(5.12 \times 10^{-3}/1024)^{-1} = 200$ kHz. A real-time bandwidth of 100 kHz could be accommodated.

12-17 ARITHMETIC ARCHITECTURE FOR A HIGH-SPEED FFT

The Data Arithmetic Unit (DAU) described in this section is configured to perform an in-place computational sequence for a decimation in time FFT. Addition, multiplication, data reading, and writing, the four basic FFT operations, are performed as indicated by the butterfly computational diagram shown in Fig. 12-24. For the present, our attention is directed toward the rapid execution of the required number of contiguous butterflies. We shall assume that correct memory address and multiplier data are always present when needed.

Two complex data points $X(n)$ and $X(m)$ are extracted from different locations in memory. $X(m)$ is multiplied by a complex exponential phase, or "twiddle" factor. The resulting real and imaginary parts are separated, combined with the respective parts of $X(n)$, and rewritten into the same memory slots in the manner indicated in Fig. 12-14. After the transformed data pair is returned to memory, the process begins again on a different pair of memory locations, using an updated phase factor value. The process continues until the required number of butterflies has been computed.

The complex multiplication of $X(m)$ by $e^{-j\theta}$ requires four individual real multiplications and two real additions and yields a complex result:

$$(X_R + jX_1)(\cos \theta - j \sin \theta) = (X_R \cos \theta + X_1 \sin \theta) \\ + j(X_1 \cos \theta - X_R \sin \theta) \qquad (12\text{-}4)$$

---

*An algorithm exists which reduces the FFT time by half when the input data is real.

Once the complex result is obtained, the respective real and imaginary parts are added to $X_R(n)$ and $X_1(n)$ to form $Y_R(n)$, $Y_R(m)$, $Y_1(n)$, and $Y_1(m)$.

A simple computing machine may be set up so that one machine cycle is allotted for each basic arithmetic operation. When real and imaginary data are contained in the same memory, they must be addressed separately. Four memory-read cycles are needed to extract $X_R(n)$, $X_1(n)$, $X_R(m)$, $X_1(m)$.

The arithmetic unit for performing this sequence is shown in Fig. 12-25. All of the multiplications and additions are done in the multiplier-accumulator (MAC), and the results are written back into the main data memory. The scratch pad memory, which is included for interim storage, is useful when intermediate computations are to be used again at a later time in a computation sequence.

The memory pipeline register situated between the memory output and the data bus is included to increase processor speed. DSP algorithms are characterized by memory multiply or memory multiply-add operations. The main memory continually sends data to the multiplier, which generates products or sums of products. Without the register, the total time to multiply a word from memory and generate the product is

$$t_{MM} = T_{MEM} + T_{MULT} \qquad (12\text{-}5)$$

Memory access time is T_{MEM}, and T_{MULT} is the multplier time. The maximum clock speed is $(t_{MEMMULT})^{-1}$. If the two times are relatively close in value, the data throughput rate can be significantly increased when the pipeline register is added. As the number of memory-multiply operations gets large, the improvement reaches 50% (half the original rate) when $T_{MEM} = T_{MULT}$. The effect is illustrated in Fig. 12-26. Fig. 12-26a (top) shows a data clock with a period of T seconds. During the T_0 interval, address A_0 is present at the memory. Data D_0 appears from the memory T_{MEM} seconds after A_0 has settled. Address A_0 remains fixed while D_0 goes into the multiplier. The product P_0 is formed T_{MULT} seconds later and is loaded into a holding register on the next clock, which marks the beginning of the T_1 interval.

The data transfer inefficiency in this case stems from the face that the multiplier waits from the time the address has settled until the data comes out before it can start multiplying. Similarly, the memory waits for the multiply process to end before its address is changed. Both elements are interactive about one-half of the time. However, if the pipeline register is added, then multiplication of D_0 can take place while the address on the memory is being changed to A_1. New data D_1

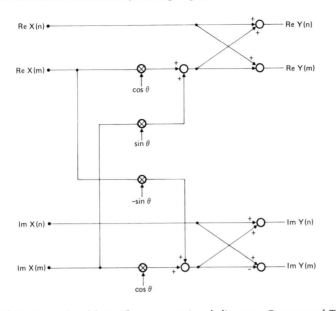

Figure 12-24 Generalized butterfly computational diagram. Courtesy of TRW LSI Products, La Jolla, California.

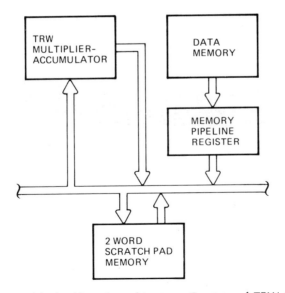

Figure 12-25 Simplified arithmetic architecture. Courtesy of TRW LSI Products, La Jolla, California.

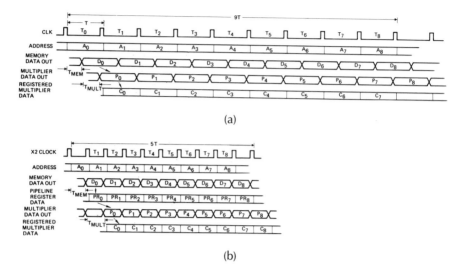

(a)

(b)

Figure 12-26 Increasing memory-multiply rate through data pipelining—T_{MULT} and T_{MEM} are multiply and memory access times. Courtesy of TRW LSI Products, La Jolla, California.

can be ready for the multiplier by the time it has produced P_0. The pipeline register holds the memory data for the length of time necessary to do a multiplication (i.e., T_{MULT}). As soon as the present data is locked onto the register from memory, the address is changed. Multiplication is performed on present data while future data is being accessed from the memory. This process is shown in Fig. 12-26b (bottom) for equal memory and multiplier times. Eight memory-multiply operations take 9T seconds without the pipeline, and 5T seconds with it.

Pipelining techniques are effective for improving speed of arithmetic and control elements alike. The disadvantages that accompany the improvement in speed are an increase in programming and circuit complexity and the initial time delay in "filling up the pipe." In Fig. 12-26b, reclocked data (C_0) do not appear until two cycles beyond T_0, the beginning of the sequence. Once they appear, however, data flow continuously.

DSP operations are not limited to memory-multiply-add type operations. Pipeline techniques can be effective in more general-purpose architectures, performing many types of high-level operations, not necessarily including memory. Nonmemory and memory instructions alike can come equipped with a "load memory register" command so that data can be loaded from memory during another operation. As an example, a data sample from an A/D converter may be brought in, multiplied by an input scaler, and stored in the MAC register during one machine clock cycle (A/D MULT instruction). During the next cycle, it may be desirable to extract a data sample from memory, scale it, add it to the scaled A/D sample, and store the result in the MAC output register (MEMMAC instruction). In anticipation of the memory-multiply-add operations, the memory data may be loaded into the memory pipeline register during the A/D MULT operation, thus saving a machine cycle.

12-18 DEVELOPMENT OF ARCHITECTURE

In designing a high-speed processor, it is usually easiest to start with an arithmetic structure that supports the basic needs of the algorithms to be performed. (See Fig. 12-25.) The efficiency can be improved by providing instructions that execute simultaneous operations. For the architecture of Fig. 12-25, the number of cycles can be reduced by taking advantage of the fact that memory register loading can occur at the same time as some multiplications.

The identification of simultaneous operations usually leads to additional data buses and the extension of the capabilities of individual arithmetic elements. The multiplier-accumulator shown in Fig. 12-27 has evolved from the simple multiplier. This evolution is quite natural, because in digital signal processing applications most multiplies are followed by addition to the previous product. A typical multiplier loading sequence is shown in Fig. 12-28.

For the butterfly, the four output data points $Y_R(n)$, $Y_R(m)$, etc., are formed through four additions (actually two adds and two subtractions) before being rewritten into memory. A single operation could accommodate the addition and memory write if an adder-subtractor were associated with the memory. The relatively large number of

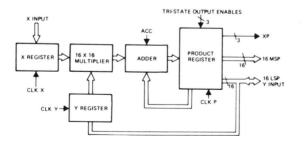

Figure 12-27 Simplified TRW series multiplier-accumulator. Courtesy of TRW LSI Products, La Jolla, California.

memory-add cycles in an FFT justifies extending the capabilities of the memories.

Figure 12-29 illustrates a memory-accumulator (MEAC), which has the capability of performing simple read/write functions. It can also add (or subtract) data on the main bus to memory data stored in the memory register (MR) by enabling the accumulate line and affixing the correct logic state to the add-subtract input. Because the addition of two digital numbers can result in word growth, a shifter may be included at the adder-subtractor output. A combinatorial downshift of one bit will render the output of the adder compatible with the memory I/O port if the addition is effected.

12-19 A SIX-CYCLE BUTTERFLY ARCHITECTURE STRUCTURE

Figure 12-30 shows a data arithmetic unit particularly well-suited for performing FFT and related computations. The data memory is divided into real (RMEM) and imaginary (IMEM) sections. Each has its own accumulator, so that independent operations can be done on real and imaginary components of the data. This memory configuration provides much of the efficiency afforded by the DAU.

The scratch pad memory (Sc) requires only two words for FFT computations, but the designer may want to use four or eight locations for other purposes. The scratch pad may receive data from the main bus and transmit into the MAC or into the RMEM adder. Data may be

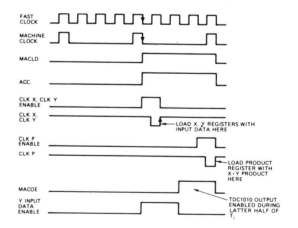

Figure 12-28 Typical TDC1010J loading sequence timing diagram. Courtesy of TRW LSI Products, La Jolla, California.

written to and read from separate scratch locations simultaneously. Hence, data may run on the two data buses concurrently.

The designer may wish to be more general and allow data to be read from Sc onto the main bus. However, the instruction set would be unnecessarily complicated for FFT work, and for our purposes, the configuration in Fig. 12-30 is sufficient.

Directing traffic into and out of each DAU element is the task performed by the sequencer in the main controller. The control signals listed in Table 1 originate from the sequencer microinstruction register. All control lines are assumed to be logic 1 for an enabling condition. Although much of the logic is tri-state (requiring logic zero output enabling), logic 1 enabling simplifies things in the preliminary design stage. The logic sense may be inverted in the microprogram PROM (sequencer) when convenient. Data may be sent on the bus connecting one DAU element to another by enabling the output (e.g., MACOE) of the sender and the input clock enable (e.g., ScLD) of the receiver.

12-20 CAPTURING INFORMATION
FOR THE FFT* _____

Time-varying voltages are the most convenient form of information to capture. The TEKTRONIX Digital Processing Oscilloscope (DPO) and the TEKTRONIX R7912 Transient Digitizer are two good examples of instruments designed to capture voltage waveforms and sample and digitize them for processing. The actual processing, which may include a variety of operations in addition to the FFT, is done by either DPO TEK BASIC or WDI TEK BASIC software.

Of course, not everything is a voltage waveform. For example, what about the call of a killer whale?

For any physical phenomenon, killer whale conversations included, all that is needed is the proper transducer. In the case of Namu, the killer whale, Singleton and Poulter simply used a hydrophone to pick up Namu's calls. The output of the hydrophone could have been fed directly into an analog-to-digital converter, but the researchers chose to record the output on magnetic tape instead. Later, at a more convenient time and place, the tapes were played back. The output of the tape player—the voltage equivalent of Namu's calls—was fed into an analog-to-digital converter, which was interfaced to a computer.

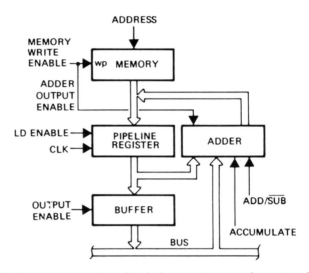

Figure 12-29 Memory accumulator block diagram. Data may be written directly into memory from the main bus through the adder when the accumulator signal is inactive, or bus data may be added with data residing in the pipeline register and written into memory when acc is active. Courtesy of TRW LSI Products, La Jolla, California.

Besides convenience, recording on magnetic tape offered another advantage. By playing the tape back at half speed, Singleton and Poulter effectively doubled the available sample rate of their analog-to-digital converter.

Other types of microphones can be used for transducing other types of sound and vibration energy to electrical energy. For example, speech can be transduced by a standard audio microphone. Similarly, seismic and geological information can be transduced by geophones.

12-21   THINGS THE FFT CAN DO

Once the waveform is acquired and digitized, it can be fast-Fourier-transformed to the frequency domain. The FFT results can be either real and imaginary, or magnitude and phase, functions of frequency. The choice of output format belongs to the user in DPO TEK BASIC or WDI TEK BASIC.

Since the FFT generates the frequency spectrum for a time-domain waveform, some fairly simple applications, e.g., harmonic analysis, distortion analysis, vibration analysis, and modulation measurements, suggest themselves immediately.

Another important application area is that of frequency response estimation. A linear, time-invariant system can be stimulated with an impulse function. Its output, the impulse response, can then be acquired and fast-Fourier-transformed to the frequency domain. The FFT of the impulse response, referred to as the frequency response function, completely characterizes the system.

Once a system's frequency response function is known, one can predict how that system will react to any waveform. Convolution is the mathematical tool for doing this.

An important aspect of the FFT is that convolution can easily be performed through frequency-domain multiplication. Let's say you know a system's impulse response, given by $h(t)$, and an input waveform, given by $x(t)$. The output, say $y(t)$, caused by $x(t)$, can be computed in the classical manner by the convolution integral. But this is tedious and slow. An easier and faster approach is to FFT $x(t)$ and $h(t)$ to the frequency domain. Then the product of their frequency-domain functions can be formed, giving $Y(f) = X(f) H(f)$. Forming this product corresponds to time-domain convolution, and the convolution result can be obtained by inverse-Fourier-transforming (IFT) the $Y(f)$ func-

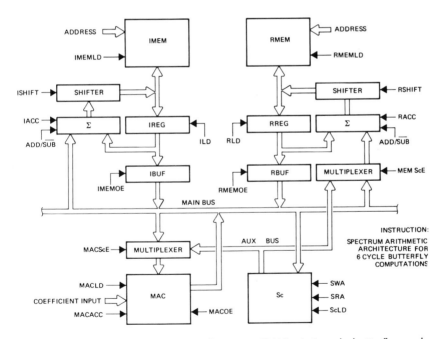

Figure 12-30 Fast FFT artithmetic architecture (DAU). A 6-cycle butterfly can be performed on this DAU. A data word may be transferred from one element to the next by enabling the desired source output control (e.g., IMEMOE) and the destination input control (e.g., MACLD). Courtesy of TRW LSI Products, La Jolla, California.

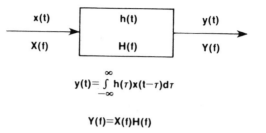

$$y(t) = \int_{-\infty}^{\infty} h(\tau)x(t-\tau)d\tau$$

$$Y(f) = X(f)H(f)$$

Figure 12-31 The characterizing parameters of a linear, time-invariant system. Courtesy of Tektronix, Inc.

tion back to the time domain. Fig. 12-31 shows the characterizing parameters of a linear time-variant system.

Correlation, discussed in Section 12-2, is another useful operation that the FFT makes easier. Mathematically, correlation looks and is performed in a manner similar to convolution. The difference is that one of the frequency-domain functions is conjugated before the frequency-domain product is formed. In the general form used, the equations describing correlation are defined by:

$$r(\tau) = \lim_{T \to \alpha} \frac{1}{2T} \int_{-T}^{T} x(t)y(t-\tau)dt$$

and

$$\begin{aligned} R(f) &= X(f)\, Y^*(f) \\ &= (X^*(f)\, Y(f)) \end{aligned} \tag{12-5}$$

where "*" denotes conjugation. Fig. 12-31 shows the characterizing parameters of a linear, time-variant system.

Although the operations of convolution and correlation may look similar, their applications are not. Correlation is a sort of searching or looking for similarities between two waveforms. When two waveforms have absolutely no similarity, like uncorrelated noise, their correlation function is zero. On the other hand, correlating two waveforms that are exactly alike produces a perfect correlation function.

This property of finding similarities makes correlation a useful tool for detecting signals that are hidden or masked by other signals. this is further demonstrated in Fig. 12-32.

Another useful property of correlation is its ability to indicate delay. This is illustrated in Fig. 12-33 and is particularly useful in measuring things like path delay, path diversity, and echo return times.

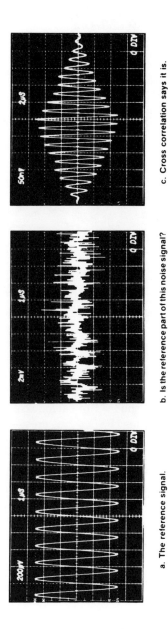
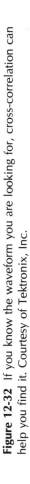

a. The reference signal.

b. Is the reference part of this noise signal?

c. Cross correlation says it is.

Figure 12-32 If you know the waveform you are looking for, cross-correlation can help you find it. Courtesy of Tektronix, Inc.

395

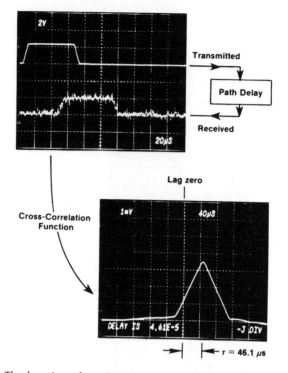

Figure 12-33 The location of maximum cross-correlation indicates the time delay between waveforms. Courtesy of Tektronix, Inc.

For still further analysis, the FFT of various correlation functions provides power spectral densities (PSDs) and cross-spectra functions.

Even from this brief list of properties, it becomes apparent that the FFT is indeed a very powerful tool. In fact, with the proper transducers and with judicious application and interpretation, the FFT can be used to analyze just about anything from killer whales to Q-switched lasers.

_____ *PROBLEMS* _____

12-1 Review the fast Fourier transforms or digital filter applications. Go to the library and create a computerized system project to make transducer measurements using the FFT.

12-2 Draw a block diagram of a microprocessor used in digital signal processing.

12-3 Draw a block diagram of a digital storage oscilloscope.

13

SELECTED TOPICS IN IMAGE PROCESSING APPLICATIONS

13-0 INTRODUCTION*

Modern technology utilizes all types of pictures, or images, as sources of information for interpretation and analysis. These may be portions of the earth's surface viewed from an orbiting satellite, the internal composition of a complex metallic or organic structure seen with the aid of x-rays, chromosomes viewed through a microscope, or schematic line drawings of electronic circuitry. The proliferation of these bases of pictorial data has created the need for a vision-based automation that can rapidly, accurately, and cost-effectively extract the useful information contained in images. These requirements are being met through the new technology of image processing.

Image processing combines computer applications with modern image scanning techniques to perform various forms of image enhancement, distortion correction, pattern recognition, and objective measurements. The technology thus overcomes many of the inherent difficulties associated with the human analysis of images or objects, as the following examples will demonstrate.

1. In production testing and quality control, the visual inspection process requires interpretations and assessments that often can mean the differ-

---

*Sections 13-0 and 13.1 from EyeCom Handbook of Image Processing, © 1980 by Spatial Data Systems, Inc., Goleta, California. Reprinted courtesy of Spatial Data Systems, Inc.

ence between a successful or a wasted production run. By adapting image processing to this important manufacturing function, it has been possible not only to eliminate human error from the inspection process, but also to increase production due to the rapid and accurate analyses that are now possible.

2. Image processing technology has been instrumental in the development of robots, wherein machines are used to simulate various activities by remote control. Robots permit the safe performance of many activities that would otherwise be hazardous to human life, for example, the handling of radioactive materials, and deep space and underwater exploration.

3. Through various aircraft and satellite programs, a profusion of remotely sensed images are constantly being acquired for use in solving Earth's resources management problems, such as geological exploration, land use planning, taking agricultural inventories, pollution monitoring, and oceanography and meteorology. Image processing technology is providing the ability to rapidly and cost-effectively extract the abundance of useful information embodied in this remotely sensed data.

The technology of image processing is based upon the same fundamental principles as visual recognition in human beings. Although the actual visual process is physiologically complex, the basic mechanism of vision utilizes the eyes and the brain as an automatic information interpreting system. The eyes receive stimuli in the form of visual light, and the brain processes and interprets this input for the observer of the image. The human visual system can be simulated using an electronic scanner, similar to a television camera, as the eyes, and a high-speed digital computer as the brain. This type of system can "see" images through the scanner and, by means of the programmed capabilities of the computer, can manipulate the images in various ways that are contributory to the extraction of desired information. Image processing activities may, then, be categorized by the two primary end-products of the system's programmed activities: an enhanced reconstruction of the original image, and a numeric or graphic report that relates specific information contained in the image. Simply stated, *enhancement* involves the sequence of:

IMAGE IN . . . PROCESS . . . (NEW) IMAGE OUT

Alternatively, *reporting* involves the sequence of:

IMAGE IN . . . PROCESS . . . NUMBERS (GRAPHS) OUT

In either case, the objective is to enable the extraction of information from raw image data in a more expeditious and efficient manner.

Spatial Data's EyeCom (Fig. 13-1) is a new type of computer terminal for processing images through a digital computer. All the tools required for efficient image processing are provided within the EyeCom. Combining the EyeCom with a digital computer such as the Digital Equipment PDP–11 minicomputer and image processing creates a stand-alone image processing system. The digital computer can be either a microprocessor contained within the EyeCom or a separate minicomputer, depending on the amount of image processing required.

The EyeCom II Model 109 PTS (Fig. 13-2) provides both the input and output functions for the processing of pictures. The Model 810 EyeCom II is the complete image processing system, providing the computer processor, image input digitizer and display, and image storage necessary to do basic image processing on gray scale images from film, microscopes, or real images.

Applications of the 810 include biomedical and industrial research. The complete software package measures brightness or density, distances, profiles, areas, and density distributions. The software also includes routines to enhance contrast and edges, filter noise, smooth background shading, contour isodensity areas, and edit picture content.

The Model 810 includes the EyeCom II Model 109 PTS, LSI–11/2 microprocessor with 64K bytes RAM, 1 megabyte dual floppy disk

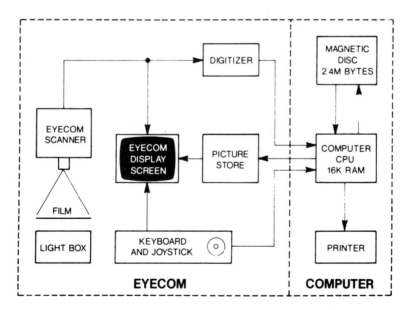

Figure 13-1 EyeCom system block diagram. Courtesy of Spatial Data Systems, Inc.

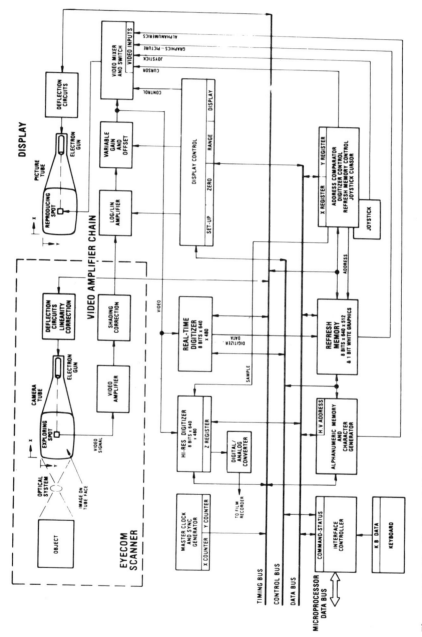

Figure 13-2 The EyeCom II Model 109PTS picture diagram and display. Courtesy of Spatial Data Systems, Inc.

drive, and LA 34 printing terminal. Software includes the RT–11 operating system, FORTRAN IV, and Log E/Spatial Data System's image processing software library. The Model 810 system can be expanded by adding real-time processing capability, additional refresh memory for multiple images, color mapping tables and color display monitor, and additional disk memory using the Winchester or hard disk storage.

The EyeCom III is a true pipeline processor that features individual processing modules that can be linked together under software control to provide the desired processing path. Each module has a source and destination address that are used to link the various modules through the IDEX Data Exchange. The processing path is defined by software, and the linking occurs during the vertical retrace interval of the television. Processing modules include analog-to-digital converters, digital-to-analog converters, mapping tables, shifter/bit masks, statistics tables, refresh memories, arithmetic logic units, image warp mapper, and image multiply module.

Primary application for the EyeCom III is in processing images for digital fluoroscopy in clinical medicine. The EyeCom III can provide 10-bit digitization, real-time subtraction, contrast enhancement, near real-time filtering, movie replay of stored images, and mask reregistration.

Other applications include on-line industrial inspection and real-time processing for research. Memories may be joined together under software control to form larger arrays for storage with a 640 × 480 roaming window display.

13-1 IMAGE RESOLUTION

Typical black-and-white photographs are called continuous-tone images because the shades of gray blend continuously both in intensity (level) and spatiality (area). However, the quantized EyeCom picture is not continuous, but is composed of a number of discrete picture elements with each having a discrete gray level assigned to it. System resolution may therefore be defined as the ability to reproduce images with a visual quality that is comparable to the continuous-tone originals. This requires a sufficient number of picture elements or "pixels" to give the appearance of spatial continuity and a sufficient number of gray levels to give the appearance of continuous depth and contrast.

The pixel is the basic element of picture resolution in the EyeCom system. The EyeCom picture is divided into an array of 640 horizontal columns and 480 vertical rows, thus producing 307,200 equal and discrete pixels. Each pixel is then assigned a value based on the average level of gray contained on that minute portion of picture that it encompasses. The gray scale, or Z-value of the pixels, ranges from 0 to 255, where 0 is black and 255 is white. All Z-values are available to the computer along with X and Y coordinate ˙data on the position of the corresponding pixels.

13-2 REAL-TIME DIGITAL IMAGE PROCESSING CONCEPTS* _____

A profound transformation has occurred in recent years in real-time digital image processing to meet the needs of such fields as medical imaging, nondestructive testing (NDT), product inspection, and scientific research.

"Real time" means that all incoming video signals are digitized, processed, and displayed at standard video rates of thirty frames per second with no perceptible delay. Many systems that are called real-time systems offer TV-rate frame-digitizing capability, but most are designed to store a single frame in one or more memories and then perform operations that may take one or more frame times. These are not real-time systems in the strict sense stated above. Using an architecture in which one of the operands into the arithmetic unit is received from the A/D converter while the other is received from memory makes it possible to perform many processing operations in real time.

As digital devices and circuitry have increased in speed and decreased in cost, it has become practical to perform a greater variety of image enhancement procedures in real time. The trend in this field is to combine hardware-based pipeline processing with control of alternate signal paths exercised by a micro- or minicomputer.

13-3 TYPES OF IMAGE PROCESSING OPERATIONS _____

The general field of image processing covers a broad spectrum that includes such areas as image data coding and scene analysis, image synthesis, pattern classification, feature extraction, image restoration, and image enhancement. Three operations are associated with image processing: geometric or address operations, point or pixel operations, and neighborhood operations.

---

*Sections 13-2 and 13-3 quoted from "Real-Time Digital Signal Processing: Its Advantages and Applications," by Paul E. Mengers, Optical Spectra, December 1981, pp. 54-58. Copyright 1981 by the Optical Publishing Company, Inc. All rights reserved.

Examples of geometric operations are image translation, rotation, and magnification. When these are caused to vary from region to region within the image, the term "warping" is sometimes used. Such processing may serve to correct for distortion. With current hardware, translation and magnification can be done in real time, but rotation and more complex operations usually require from a few to many frame times.

Point operations are carried out in the same way for each picture element in the image, independently of its position or the value of its neighboring elements. Examples of point operations are the single-pixel operations of contrast modification (e.g., windowing), function processing (e.g., extraction of logarithms), and histogram equalization; arithmetic combinations of two or more images (e.g., addition, subtraction, multiplication and division); and Boolean combinations of two or more images.

Neighborhood operations, as the name implies, are operations that modify the value of a picture element in a way that depends on the value of neighboring picture elements. The most important and general neighborhood operation is convolution. For sampled data images encountered in digital image processing, convolution is given by

$$P(x, y) = \sum_{\epsilon = -J}^{J} \sum_{\eta = -K}^{K} I(\epsilon,\eta)\, S\,(x-\epsilon, y-\eta) \qquad (13\text{-}1)$$

where I is the image function, S is the convolution function, P is the convolved image, ϵ and η are dummy variables, and K and J are the horizontal and vertical spatial dimensions, respectively. This simply says that the new function P is obtained by (1) reflecting the sample function successively about each axis (i.e., rotating it 180°); (2) superimposing the sample function over the image function at location x, y; (3) multiplying corresponding elements of the superimposed fields; and (4) summing all the products.

The procedure gives the value of the new image at one particular location x, y. By repeating it for all the possible combinations of x and y, the new image is completely defined. For the specific case of a convolution function having zeros everywhere over a 3×3 array convolved with a 512×512 sampled image, a total of 2,359,296 multiplications and 2,097,152 summations are required. Remarkably, it is possible to accomplish this in one frame time (1/30th second) with pipeline processing.

The importance of convolution is that it offers a method of performing spatial filtering of images in real time or nearly real time. It can be shown that convolution is equivalent to multiplying the frequency transform of the kernel function by the spatial frequency spectrum of the image. For example, a 3 × 3 unity coefficient filter array, or convolution kernel, has a transform that is given by

$$\frac{\sin(3\omega_x/2)}{\sin(\omega_x/2)} \cdot \frac{\sin(3\omega_y/2)}{\sin(\omega_y/2)} \qquad (13\text{-}2)$$

This is a low-pass filter response, as might be intuitively expected. By subtracting the low-passed image from the original image after multiplying by a constant, a high-passed image is obtained. Alternatively, the same result is obtained by directly using the kernel

$$
\begin{array}{ccc}
-1 & -1 & -1 \\
-1 & +8 & -1 \\
-1 & -8 & -1
\end{array}
$$

A closely related type of neighborhood processing is the use of edge operators to extract edge location from general gray-scale images. Edge operators are normally 2 × 2 or 3 × 3 sampling arrays convolved with an image, with the result passed through a threshold circuit.

13-4 REAL-TIME DIGITAL IMAGE FILTERING*

The need for more real-time image processing capability has become evident with the increasing application of television imaging to industrial, medical, and government/military problems. Many of these problems demand complete acquisition, processing, and decision in a few seconds. A common dynamic range problem in viewing television images is the loss of contrast-generated detail in dark areas, related to the tendency of the human visual system to lose sensitivity to this kind of detail when viewing scenes having high-contrast background. Since contrast-generated detail provides most of the image's intelligence, a filter that alters the normal image power spectrum to emphasize high spatial frequencies and attenuate low spatial frequencies with little or no delay is a useful tool. The output of such a filter can be adjusted to pass only edge information, or else a natural-looking image with illumination shading removed.

The low spatial frequencies found in images can be either derived from natural image content in terms of illumination and reflectance, or

*Sections 13-4 and 13-5 from Roger C. Dahlberg, "Real-Time Image Filtering and Shading Correction," Vol. 207, © 1979. Reprinted courtesy of the Society of Photo-Optical Instrumentation Engineers. All rights reserved.

induced by the sensor optics and sensor electro-optical properties. A simple model for the low spatial frequency modulation of an image defined on (x, y) could be given by

$$I'(x, y) = A(x, y) + (x, y) I(x, y) \qquad (13\text{-}3)$$

where $A(x, y)$ is an additive low-frequency image, $B(x, y)$ is a multiplicative low-frequency image, and $I(x, y)$ is the original or desired image for viewing. $I'(x, y)$ is the image presented to a filter given the task of removing $A(x, y)$ and $B(x, y)$.

A two-dimensional linear filter can remove $A(x, y)$ from the signal, but cannot separate $B(x, y)$ without additional processing steps. One way of separating $B(x, y)$ with a linear filter is to incorporate the linear filter in a homomorphic filter. A log table in front of the linear filter converts products into sums, thus allowing the linear filter to separate $B(x, y)$ from $I(x, y)$. An antilog table behind the linear filter restores the filtered signal to its input amplitude distribution. This was not the method chosen for the real-time digital image filter described above because of both the expense of building high-speed log tables with sufficient dynamic range and the existence of a more tractable method.

An example of $A(x, y)$ type low spatial (additive) frequencies is the dark current present in most television camera tubes and intensifiers. Another might be the enormous pedestal (relative to signal) present in pyroelectric vidicons. Multiplicative $B(x, y)$ type frequencies can be functions of the beam landing on the vidicon target, electron optics, optical vignetting, or scene illumination and reflectance. In a radiograph, the transparency of various materials within the field of view to x-rays or neutrons contributes low multiplicative spatial frequencies.

13-5 HARDWARE SYSTEM DESIGN

The objective in the design of the real-time digital image filter of the previous section was to provide a unit that was analog-video-compatible and that would solve the previously described image filtering problems. The image sample matrix is 512×512 pixels, which leads to 10 MHz sampling rates for standard television. At the input, the sync is stripped from the composite video and used to synchronize filter operations; it is regenerated and reinserted at the analog video output. A 10 MHz A/D converter injects the video into the filter processing pipeline. After processing, the signal passes via a D/A converter to a standard television monitor for viewing.

The central system element is the linear two-dimensional filter, implemented as a convolver having a kernel of N × N pixels, where N can be 3, 5, 7, 9, 11, 13, or 15. The kernel weights are chosen so that the impulse response of the kernel is appropriate and so that the convolution can be implemented with a minimum number of delay and arithmetic elements. The impulse response of the kernel in terms of its two-dimensional Fourier transform is a sum of complex cosines and sines. In one dimension the impulse response can be depicted as an inverted damped cosine function, as in Fig. 13-3. Fig. 13-4 depicts the coefficients for a 7 × 7 high-pass kernel.

The uniformity of the kernel allows the linear filter to be implemented with five adders and one multiplier (for the center weight). The multiplier proves to be both useful, as a means of mixing varied amounts of the original image with complementary amounts of the filtered image, and necessary, for preventing undershoot in the impulse response in the low-pass configuration.

The kernel is made low pass by changing all the -1 coefficients to $+1$. The impulse response is then the complement of the curves in Fig. 13-3. The distribution for a one-frequency image F_I modulated by a one-frequency function F_B, where the two frequencies are well separated is shown in Fig. 13-5.

Having extracted the low frequencies from the image, the filter system can then divide the original image by the low-pass image (in image space, not frequency space) and thereby demodulate the desired image frequencies. This operation is the equivalent of the homomorphic filter described earlier. The division is implemented with an inverse table and multiplier as shown in Fig. 13-6.

Shading in images refers to very low spatial frequencies that are unwanted. Removal of shading at real-time rates is difficult unless the shading source is fixed with time. Sometimes it is possible to measure the additive and multiplicative shading components of a sensor directly and store them in memories, where they can then be used to continuously correct the incoming image. It is also of interest to adaptively compensate for the shading components of any image by filtration. However, this requires a much larger kernel than the 15 × 15 hardware limit to filter very low shading frequencies from an image. The solution is to recursively convolve the filtered image with the kernel, effectively increasing the impulse response slope. (See Fig. 13-3.) The intermediate recursions are stored in a memory. Since the original image is continuously available, the memory is made to store the low-pass version of the filtration, and the final result is generated with an

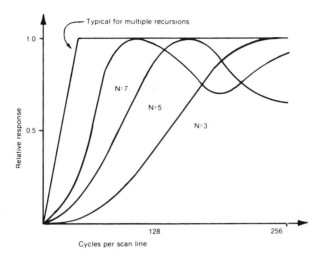

Figure 13-3 Impulse response of linear filter. Courtesy of SPIE.

-1	-1	-1	-1	-1	-1	-1
-1	-1	-1	-1	-1	-1	-1
-1	-1	-1	-1	-1	-1	-1
-1	-1	-1	+48	-1	-1	-1
-1	-1	-1	-1	-1	-1	-1
-1	-1	-1	-1	-1	-1	-1
-1	-1	-1	-1	-1	-1	-1

Figure 13-4 Weighting coefficients for 7 × 7 kernel. Courtesy of SPIE.

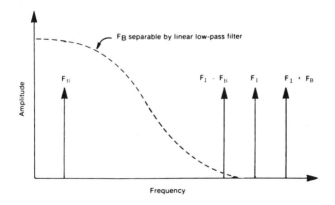

Figure 13-5 Frequency distribution for modulation. Courtesy of SPIE.

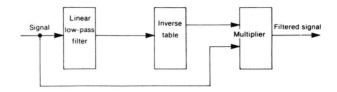

Figure 13-6 Homomorphic equivalent filter. Courtesy of SPIE.

inverse table and multiplier as in the homomorphic equivalent filter. The implementation is shown in Fig. 13-7.

An advantage to storing only low-pass images in the memories is that their bulk can be reduced by delta modulation coding to one bit per pixel. The memories are loadable directly from input or from recursive filtration, enabling them to be used in any of the modes previously discussed. By means of various switching paths (not shown in Fig. 13-7 for clarity), the user can have shading correction and/or filtering to an extremely flexible degree.

13-6   COMPUTED TOMOGRAPHY IMAGING*

Computed tomography has acquired many names. In common use are computerized transverse axial tomography (CTAT), computerized axial tomography or computer-aided tomography (CAT), reconstructive tomography (RT), computerized reconstruction, and computerized tomography of computed tomograph (CT). Each name refers to at least one aspect of the procedure. The most limiting term is CTAT because it pertains to the reconstruction by computer of those cross-sectional images that are transverse to the patient's long axis. The most general term is computerized reconstruction, which may be applied to non-medical as well as medical situations, and to reconstructions in three as well as two dimensions. The name used in this series is computed tomography (CT), to conform with the usage established by *Radiology,* and the numbers used to characterize x-ray absorption are called CT numbers.

Computed tomography is the reconstruction by computer of a tomographic plane of an object (a slice). It is developed from multiple x-ray absorption measurements made around the object's periphery (a scan). The fidelity of the image will depend upon the nature of the x-ray source and the detectors, the number and speed of the measurements

*Section 13-6 from *Introduction to Computed Tomograph,* General Electric Medical Products Division, © 1976 by General Electric Co. Reprinted courtesy of the General Electric Medical Products Division.

made, the details of the reconstruction technique (an algorithm), the machine characteristics, and the methods of data display and interpretation.

Historically, attempts have been made to use the computer to analyze images. In computed tomography, the computer is used to *synthesize* images. The basic unit of synthesis is the volume element. The CT slice is composed of many volume elements, each with its own characteristic absorption, that are displayed as a two-dimensional image array (matrix) of picture elements (pixels). Although the pixel of the display is two-dimensional, it represents a three-dimensional volume element having a thickness equal to that of the tomographic slice. Pixels may be displayed as a hard copy, computer printout of numerical values (*CT numbers*) that are proportional to the volume element absorption characteristics, or as a gray-scale presentation on a cathode ray tube or display monitor where each pixel element is assigned a particular shade of gray depending on its CT number.

As early as 1917, mathematical investigations applicable to the theory of reconstruction were conducted by Radon. Practical techniques were first developed in 1956 by Bracewell, who wished to identify those regions of the sun that emit microwave radiation. At the time, available microwave antennas could not focus on points. However, the total radiation from a ribbon-like strip could be measured. By using a series of these "strip-sums" in different directions, Bracewell was able to reconstruct a map of the microwave emissions. Somewhat similar techniques were developed for electron microscopy of extremely small and complex biological specimens.

Early investigations of image reconstruction for medical applications were carried out independently by Oldendorf in 1961, Kuhl and

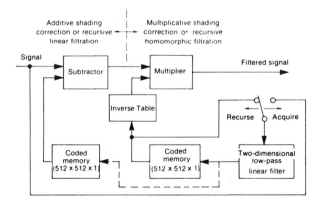

Figure 13-7 Filter as a shading compensator. Courtesy of SPIE.

Edwards in 1963, and Cormack in 1963. Kuhl built a number of tomographic image scanners for radionuclide imaging at the University of Pennsylvania that used very elementary reconstruction schemes (back projection and summation) and hence produced highly blurred images. A mathematically accurate method of reconstructing images from x-ray projections was developed by Cormack at Tufts University. Other early workers applying reconstruction techniques to radiological imaging included Tretiak and his co-workers, and Bates and Peters.

The current equipment for CT scanning (Fig. 13-8) consists of a patient handling table, a scanning gantry containing the collimated x-ray source and detectors, the data acquisition electronics, the x-ray generator, a computer, and the operator and viewing consoles.

Computer capabilities vary and may be supplemented by specialized equipment to speed the execution of the algorithm calculations. Data acquisition and image reconstruction by the computer can proceed simultaneously by using the time-sharing capabilities of the computer. Operator and viewing functions may be separated (as shown in Fig. 13-9) so that clinical examination of the scan data may proceed concurrently with data acquisition pertaining to the patient and computation. The viewing console incorporates a video display monitor with controls to vary the range of CT numbers displayed. A separate CRT may be used for photographic recording, as may a high-speed

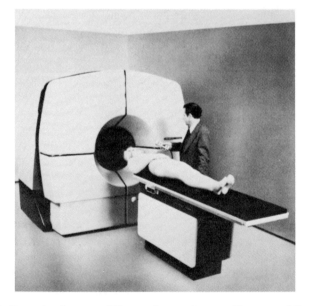

Figure 13-8 Example of current CT scanning equipment. Courtesy of General Electric Medical Products Division.

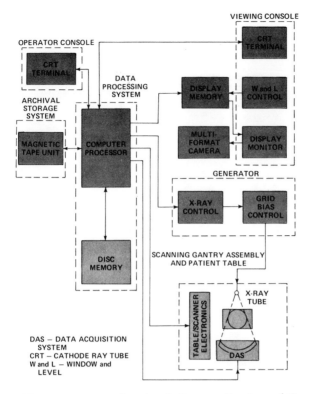

Figure 13-9 CT scanner system functional diagram. Courtesy of General Electric Medical Products Division.

printer for recording numerical data. A magnetic tape unit or floppy disk system may be incorporated for archival storage and retrieval of images and data.

CT system performance is evaluated using various *phantoms*. The phantom shown in Fig. 13-10 is composed of various sized Lexan® polycarbonate rods in nylon. A conventional x-ray of this phantom is shown in Fig. 13-11. Because the linear absorption coefficients of Lexan® polycarbonate and nylon differ by approximately one percent, the low contrast of the x-ray film does not differentiate the rods. However, the Lexan® polycarbonate rods can be clearly seen in the CT image shown in Fig. 13-12 because an absorption coefficient difference of one percent is within the capabilities of the CT system.

Figure 13-13 shows a computer tomography image of a bladder tumor. The advantage of such an imaging system is that an exact image of the bones, tumors, or other disorders can be distinguished by the physician.

Figure 13-10 Top view (a) and side view (b) of CT Phantom*. *CT Phantom provided by E. C. McCullough, Mayo Clinic and J. T. Payne, University of Minnesota. Courtesy of General Electric Medical Products Division.

Figure 13-11 Conventional x-ray of CT Phantom. Courtesy of General Electric Medical Products Division.

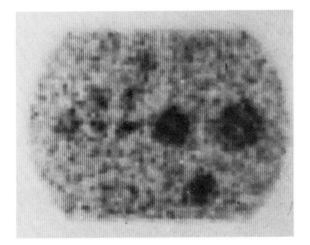

Figure 13-12 CT image of Phantom. Courtesy of General Electric Medical Products Division.

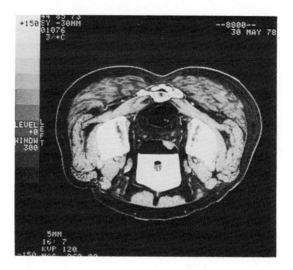

Figure 13-13 The bladder tumor is quickly referenced to the external anatomical landmark. In the upper left corner of the image format, "SY-30 MM" tells the surgeon or therapist that the tumor is located 30 mm cephalad of the pubic symphysis. Courtesy of General Electric Medical Products Division.

13-7   DIGITAL SUBTRACTION FLUOROSCOPIC SYSTEM WITH TANDEM VIDEO PROCESSING UNITS*

Digital subtraction fluoroscopic systems for visualizing arterial structures following the intravenous injection of radio-opaque agents or dyes (contrast media) are rapidly becoming widespread in diagnostic radiology. While existing digital fluoroscopic systems differ greatly in their design, imaging capabilities, and cost, most acquire images by pulsing the x-ray equipment several times per second at high currents, requiring sophisticated x-ray equipment and interfacing to the digital hardware. A digital fluoroscopic system that could utilize routine fluoroscopic equipment of the kind that exists in any radiology department, without the necessity of elaborate interfacing hardware, would be highly desirable. Let us consider such a system, capable of producing high-quality subtraction images at standard video rates.

Figure 13-14 shows a block diagram of the complete system, including the x-ray generator. This system differs from others that have

*Section 13-7 from Robert G. Gould, Martin J. Lipton, Paul E. Mengers, and Roger Dahlbert, "Digital subtraction fluoroscopic system with tandem video processing units." Society of Photo-Optical Instrumentation Engineers, Vol. 273, Application of Optical Instrumentation in Medicine IX, © 1981. Reprinted with courtesy of SPIE.

been described in the literature in that it is operated in the continuous fluoro mode rather than in a high-current pulsed mode. By using two video processors operating in tandem, a continuous, noise-reduced difference image can be displayed that shows the dynamics of the flow of the contrast agent through the field of view. The radiation dose to the patient is similar to that received with pulsed systems. The continuous output video of the intensified fluoroscopic image is recorded on videotape for possible reprocessing and sent to the video processors.

The first processor, a Quantex Corporation Model DS–30, is simultaneously placed in the averaging and differencing mode. This causes the output to be the difference between the most recent input video frame and the exponentially weighted average of preceding frames. Image differences due to the arrival of radio-opaque contrast media in the field of view are normally only a few percent of the maximum signal level and are comparable to the rms noise level. Prior to reconversion to analog form, the difference signal is amplified and the pedestal subtracted by means of the programmable digital lookup table.

The second processor is a Model DS–20 that redigitizes the difference image and then performs an exponentially weighted average that increases the signal-to-noise ratio and allows low-contrast imagery to be observed. After reconversion to analog form, the output is recorded on an Eigen video disk recorder and displayed on a standard TV monitor. Hard copy can be obtained with a multiformat camera receiving images from the video disk or from either of the two processors.

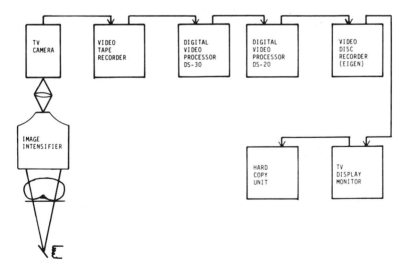

Figure 13-14 System block diagram. Courtesy of SPIE.

The block diagram of Fig. 13-15 shows the general organization of the processors. Both are available with an 8-bit A/D converter having a 10 MHz sampling rate and can digitize a 525-line composite video frame into a 512 × 512 pixel matrix at a rate of 30 frames per second. Each processor has a single memory of dimensions 512 × 512 and a depth of up to 12 bits. Fig. 13-16 shows the organization of the real-time arithmetic unit of the DS–30. The shaded pathway shows the signal flow when the unit is simultaneously in the averaging and differencing mode.

The averaging algorithm consists of dividing new data from the A/D converter by N (N restricted to 2^k, $k = 0, 1, \ldots, 7$) and adding this result to $(N-1)/N$ times the data in memory. N is referred to as the averaging parameter or averaging time constant. Implementation of this algorithm is achieved by subtracting memory data from A/D converter data, dividing this difference by N (right shift of k places), and adding the result to memory data. This result then replaces the previous contents of memory.

For a stationary image, the result of this process is to increase the signal-to-noise ratio of the image in memory by a factor of $\sqrt{2N-1}$. Fig. 13-17 shows the time required to achieve a given improvement factor assuming that the process begins with the input to memory of a single, nonshifted frame. Also shown is the time dependence for the SNR improvement factor for an equally weighted sequence of frames.

The advantage of averaging as defined above is that a noise-reduced normalized image of the most recent input period is continuously available. The disadvantage of the technique relative to linear

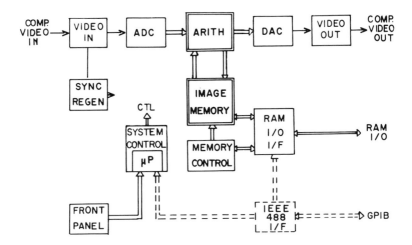

Figure 13-15 Digital video processor block diagram of Quantex Models DS–20 and DS–30. Courtesy of SPIE.

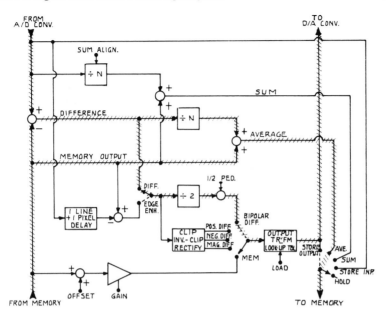

Figure 13-16 Signal flow diagram of DS–30 arithmetic unit. Courtesy of SPIE.

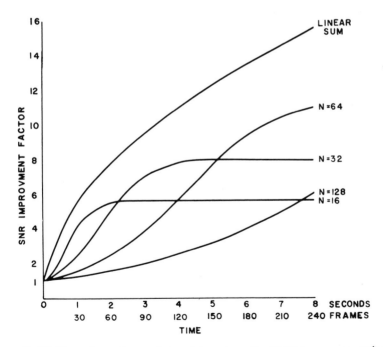

Figure 13-17 Time dependence of signal-to-noise ratio (SNR) improvement factor. Courtesy of SPIE.

(equally weighted) summation is that (1) a longer time interval, and therefore a greater dose, is required to achieve a given SNR improvement factor, and (2) response to an image change is slower. A partial compromise that is easily implemented is to perform a linear summation of $N = 2^k$ frames, with each frame shifted k places to the right, followed by averaging with an averaging parameter N. With the DS–30, the amount of shift is selected with a rotary switch labeled "sum alignment" and may be preprogrammed using the auto-sequence features.

The images obtained to date have been of anesthetized mongreal dogs averaging 20 kg in size. Injections of contrast media containing 400 mg/ml of iodine (Conray 400) were made into a femoral or iliac vein through a #7 French catheter using a power injector. Just prior to the injection, respiration was stopped. Injection rates and total volumes were noted. The most common rate was 6 ml/s, and total volume was in the 12–24 ml range, or about 1 ml/kg of body weight.

Fig. 13-18 illustrates the time history of a typical sequence. The first line indicates the injection interval and the subsequent increase and decrease of contrast media concentration in the field of view. In experiments with dogs, the x-ray generator was turned on coincidently with or shortly after injection. To reduce dose, however, it is desirable and feasible to delay exposure until two to four seconds before arrival of the contrast agent.

Coincident with initiation of radiation exposure, the first processor begins summing video frames into memory. Most often, 128 frames were summed, requiring slightly over four seconds. Following summation, the unit is immediately switched to the continuous averaging mode using an averaging parameter of $N = 128$. As the contrast agent

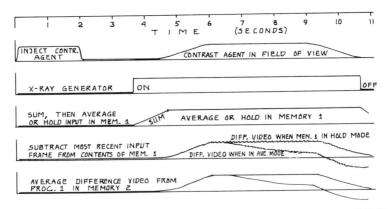

Figure 13-18 Time history of signal processing procedure. Courtesy of SPIE.

arrives in the field of view, a difference image is produced as indicated on Fig. 13-18.

Typically, a bolus (round mass) of contrast agent will traverse a field such as the carotid artery area in four to five seconds. If the x-ray generator is left on after the bolus has exited the field of view, a contrast reversal occurs, since the memory contents or mask image has been modified to be an image darkened by the presence of contrast agent. Subtraction of this image from one without a contrast agent creates a positive image of the arterial system. It it often possible simultaneously to observe the venous return of the contrast agent appearing in negative contrast. Figure 13-18 diagrams the contrast changes that occur in the continuous subtraction image.

A modification of the procedure just described can also be used to process the injection sequence. In this method, the averaging process of the initial processor is terminated just prior to the arrival of a contrast agent in the field of view, thereby freezing the current mask image in memory. Processing of the raw data stored on videotape facilitates this technique, since the best time to freeze the mask can be established. As shown in Fig. 13-18, freezing the mask results in a larger difference image. However, one of the benefits of the moving mask tandem processor operation is that it can proceed without operator intervention. Thus, there are no time-critical operations that need attention.

An example, of an image produced is shown in Fig. 13-19. In the figure, image A is a frozen average of four unsubtracted video frames acquired while the contrast agent was within the field of view and is similar to the unprocessed image viewed on a monitor. The subtracted images B were obtained using a moving average mask with an averaging parameter of $N-128$. These images are a frozen, exponentially weighted average of subtracted video frames with an averaging parameter of $N-64$. It should be noted that a continuous, real-time subtraction sequence can be observed on the TV monitor and is recorded on the video disk. The B image of Fig. 13-19 is equivalent to a single video frame of this sequence. Such static images can be viewed on the monitor or photographed with the multiformat camera using the disk recorder.

In temporal subtraction angiography, the signal can be defined as the difference in the x-ray transmission of an object (a blood vessel) with time. In the absence of object motion, this signal is created by the transient presence of iodine within the object. The ability of a system to image the difference depends on the signal-to-noise ratio, where the signal is a function of the sampling in the time interval during which the difference exists, and the noise consists of electronic noise σ_E introduced by the video chain and quantum mottle σ_Q. The signal depends

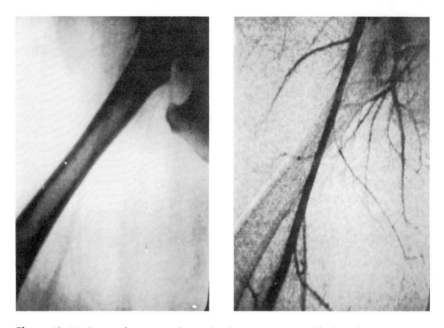

Figure 13-19 Femoral arteries of a 19-kg dog using a 24-ml bolus of contrast agent injected at 8 cc/sec. Courtesy of SPIE.

on the sample, since the concentration of iodine changes continuously as the bolus of contrast media flows through the vessel. In digital imaging systems, noise also results from digitizing the video image into a finite number of gray levels. In the tandem processor system, the SNR depends on the averaging parameters of the processors and the x-ray flux rate to the image intensifier.

Noise in a subtraction image σ_S is caused by noise in the mask σ_M and in the presubtraction image σ_P and is given by $\sigma_S = \sqrt{\sigma_M^2 + \sigma_P^2}$. Both σ_M and σ_P have electronic and quantum components $\sigma_M = \sqrt{\sigma_{EM}^2 + \sigma_{QM}^2}$ and $\sigma_P = \sqrt{\sigma_{EP}^2 + \sigma_{QP}^2}$, as discussed. For a given x-ray flux rate, σ_M is a function of the number of frames averaged to form the mask, decreasing proportionally to a factor that approaches the limit $1/\sqrt{2N_I - 1}$, where N_I is the averaging parameter of the initial processor. Because of contrast considerations, N_I is always large, usually 64 or 128. The presubtraction images are single video frames input to the first processor. σ_P is unaffected by N_I and much larger than σ_M.

The second processor averages subtracted video frames from the first unit and reduces both M and P by the same factor, which approaches the limit $1/\sqrt{2N_2 - 1}$, where N_2 is the averaging parameter of the second processor. However, the improvement in the SNR of the subtraction image is due almost entirely to a reduction in σ_P, since σ_P dominates the noise in video frames coming into the second processor. Thus, in this digital fluoroscopy system, the averaging parameter of the second processor is normally the most critical in reducing image noise. Fig. 13-20 shows the effect of the averaging parameter N_2 on subtraction images. N_1 is 64, and gain and output transform conditions are the same in all images.

Contrast is the magnitude of the difference in x-ray transmission of the object between the time of formation of the mask image and that of the presubtraction image. By using a large averaging parameter in the first processor, the image in memory is slow to change in response to the relatively abrupt change at the input due to the entrance of the contrast agent in the field of view. The larger N_1, the slower the change and the larger the difference image. A step contrast change of C^1 will diminish to $0.37\,C^1 N_1$ frames after the change, as shown in somewhat idealized form in Fig. 13-21.

Fig. 13-22 shows the effect of the averaging parameter N_1 on the subtraction image. N_2 is 64, and gain and output transform conditions are the same in both images. Note that the noise in the two images appears comparable.

If the patient moves between the mask and the presubtraction image, structured noise appears in the subtraction image. This occurs regardless of the design of the digital fluoroscopic system, and the tandem processor system is no more or less sensitive to patient motion than other systems. If the patient moves just as the contrast media enter the field of view and then remains stationary, the reversal image occurring just after the contrast media leave the field can be used for diagnosis (Fig. 13-17).

13-8 FUTURE DIRECTIONS IN DIGITAL FLUOROGRAPHY*

Digital fluorography (Fig. 13-23) using temporal subtraction techniques is becoming a strategic tool in the armamentarium of diagnostic radiology. There are, however, limitations that should be addressed and other areas to be explored if the full potential of this exciting new modality is to be realized. Significant new developments are required

*Sections 13-8, 13-9, and 13-10 from *Digital Fluorography: A Technology Update,* © 1981, General Electric Co. Courtesy of the General Electric Medical products Division.

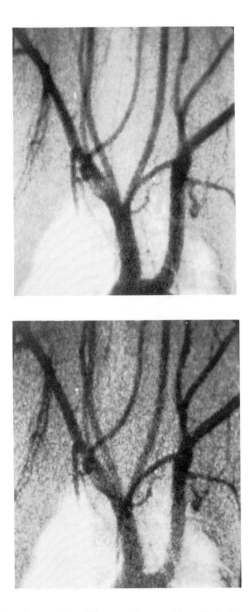

Figure 13-20   Effect of averaging difference image. $N_2 = 32$ in image A; $N_2 = 16$ in image B. Courtesy of SPIE.

in digital fluorography (DF) to remove these restrictions and to further extend the utility of this technology.

Digital subtractive angiographic fluoroscopy is also useful in exercise testing of patients with cardiac heart disease or coronary bypass surgery as well as in the diagnosis of the detection of heart diseases.

13-9 MOTION OF PATIENTS

Clinical studies have demonstrated that motion of patients is the primary limitation to vascular imaging using temporal subtraction methods. Movement may be either voluntary, such as breathing and displacement of the extremities, or involuntary, as in peristalsis, cardiac motion, swallowing, and arterial pulsations.

Several methods have been developed to deal with misregistration, to varying degrees of success. Remasking, the retrospective selection of an alternative mask, often reduces misregistration artifacts. In practice, 30 to 60 percent of temporal subtraction studies can be either improved or salvaged by remasking. However, alternative masks can contain some iodine, so this procedure can involve a tradeoff between

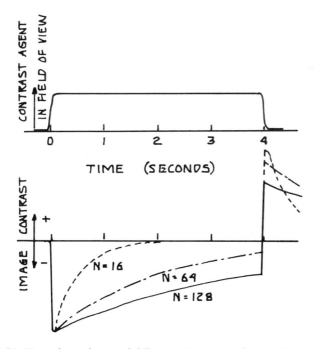

Figure 13-21 Time dependence of difference image amplitude. Courtesy of SPIE.

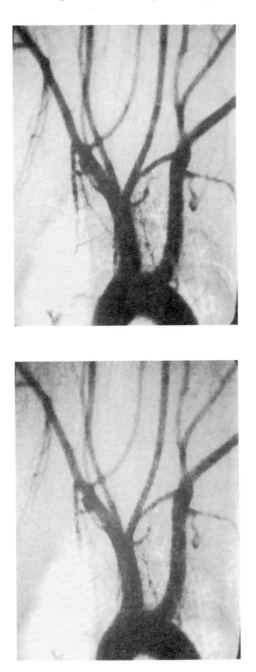

Figure 13-22 Effect of the mask image on contrast. $N_1 = 128$ in image A; $N_1 = 64$ in image B. Courtesy of SPIE.

contrast and artifacts. Using digital processing techniques to correct misregistration errors due to shimming and warping of image data prior to subtraction is either ineffective because of the complexity of the patient's motion or inefficient due to the computational power required to implement the fitting algorithms. Cooperation of the patient is a critical ingredient of most exams, and restraint procedures and devices have also been developed to minimize motion. These techniques, combined with remasking, allow excellent images to be obtained with minimal artifacts due to voluntary motion.

Artifacts caused by involuntary motion, usually of soft tissue, are much more difficult to suppress. Nonionic contrast agents and alternate injection techniques are being tried to eliminate swallowing artifacts in carotid procedures. Compression bands and intravenous administration of glucagon are used to reduce peristaltic motion of bowel gas, and ECG gating has been applied in studies of the aortic arch and pulmonary arteries to minimize pulsatile motion artifacts.

Dual-energy subtraction can be relatively insensitive to the patient's motion if the required low- and high-energy x-ray images are obtained close together in time. In principle, they can be acquired within a few milliseconds of each other. However, dual-energy imaging is not a panacea, since there are other factors that limit the effectiveness of energy subtraction for vascular imaging. First, an analysis of dual-energy subtraction shows that only one material can be cancelled in a given image. The implication for digital angiography is that processed images contain iodine plus either bone or soft tissue shadows. In practice, the iodine signal is optimized by subtracting the effects of soft tissue, so that images consist of iodine plus residual bone shadows. Second, in DF configurations, a significant fraction of the detected video signal is due to scattered x-rays and light scatter (veiling glare) in the image intensifier. Both of these effects lead to artifacts more severe in energy subtractions than in temporal subtractions. Other phenomena that can cause difficulties for energy subtraction include the transfer characteristics of the TV camera and beam hardening. Thus, while dual-energy imaging eliminates the soft tissue motion problem of temporal subtraction, a host of other factors conspire together to potentially limit its utility in DF.

13-10 HYBRID SUBTRACTION

Hybrid subtraction is a second-order technique that combines the advantages of temporal and dual-energy subtraction. The image acquisition sequence for hybrid subtraction is compared with those for tem-

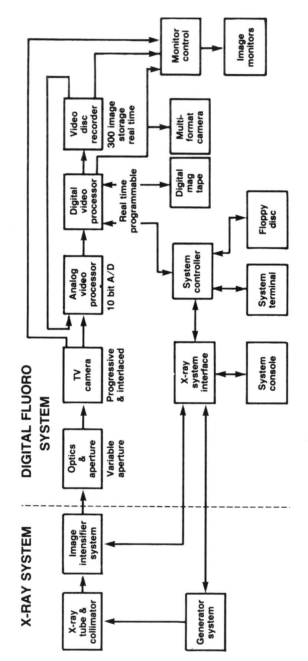

Figure 13-23 Functional block diagram of the General Electric Digital Fluoicon™ 3000 imaging system.

426

poral and energy subtraction in Fig. 13-24. A pair of images is obtained at low and high x-ray energies prior to the arrival of the opaquing agent into the region of interest. These two images are combined using energy subtraction techniques to eliminate soft tissue components and leave only the skeletal structures as a precontrast mask. A series of low- and high-energy image pairs is then acquired as the contrast bolus flows through the region of interest. Each of these pairs is processed to suppress soft tissue components and to yield a post-contrast image of iodinated vessels plus bone residuals. Finally, a temporal subtraction of the dual-energy mask and post-contrast images removes the bone structures and successfully isolates the iodine-filled vasculature. The hybrid image processing sequence is outlined in Fig. 13-25.

The advantage of hybrid subtraction over temporal subtraction is that it eliminates artifacts caused by soft tissue motion. The only tissue artifacts that remain are those due to motion during the short time interval (50–100 ms) from the start of the low x-ray energy exposure to the end of the high-energy exposure in a given image pair. Artifacts produced by misregistration of bones are also reduced, because the tissue subtraction process diminishes contrast due to bone.

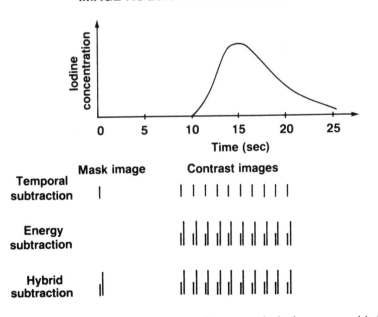

IMAGE ACQUISITION SEQUENCE

Figure 13-24 Image acquisition sequences for temporal, dual-energy, and hybrid subtraction techniques. Courtesy of General Electric Medical Products Division.

IMAGE PROCESSING
FOR HYBRID SUBTRACTION

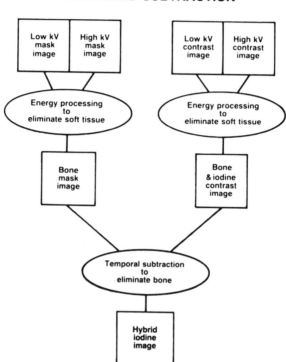

Figure 13-25 Image processing sequence for hybrid subtraction. Courtesy of General Electric Medical Products Division.

The principal advantages of hybrid subtraction over simple dual-energy imaging are, first, the simultaneous elimination of both soft tissue and skeletal structures and, second, greater immunity to detected scatter and veiling glare. The latter advantage derives from the fact that these errors are approximately equal in the pre- and post-contrast energy subtracted pairs and are cancelled by the temporal subtraction.

13-11   NUCLEAR MAGNETIC
RESONANCE IMAGING

The newest body-imaging tool is called nuclear magnetic resonance, abbreviated NMR. NMR tomography uses the behavior of simulated atoms within the body in the form of radio waves plus a strong electro-magnetic field. NMR is capable of showing the process and function rather than the image structure.

13-12　A DIGITAL PROCESSING OSCILLOSCOPE* ————————————————

With the continuing trend towards predominantly digital communications networks, many laboratories use efficient digital coding schemes for transmitting both voice and image signals. Initial studies of signal transmission schemes almost invariably take the form of a computer simulation that provides, among other things, an assessment of the fidelity of the proposed scheme. In the case of image transmission, an obvious and frequently used measure of the quality of the "received" image is the mean square error calculated on a pixel-by-pixel basis over an entire frame or series of frames.

While a vanishingly small mean square error is a sure sign of a nondegraded image, this easily calculated, objective measure of system performance is rather less useful when a small degree of degradation can be tolerated or when transmission errors become significant. At either stage it becomes necessary to view the image and subjectively assess the effect of such imperfections. Thus, an immediate requirement for any computer study of image processing schemes is the ability to digitize a typical image and then, after processing, reconstruct the image for subjective evaluation.

The cost of existing video equipment designed to perform these tasks while providing good linearity, fine resolution, and high-quality images is by no means insignificant. A low-cost alternative solution is, however, readily available to laboratories currently using, or proposing to use, what is rapidly becoming a general-purpose laboratory instrument, namely, the Digital Processing Oscilloscope (DPO).

The images reproduced by the DPO in this section, while not of studio quality, are adequate for many of the subjective evaluations that characterize the initial stages of image processing investigations. For example, it is possible to identify inadvertent errors that give rise to large mean square errors through no fault of the signal processing algorithm (Fig. 13-26b and 13-26c), and some feeling can be obtained

*Section 13-12 from M. C. Cavenor, J. F. Arnold, and G. A. Moyle, "Using a Digital Processing Oscilloscope in Image Processing Simulations," *Handshake Fall,* © 1980, Tektronix, Inc. Reprinted courtesy of Tektronix, Inc., Beaverton, Oregon. All rights reserved.

(a)

(b)

(c)

(d)

Figure 13-26 (a-e)

(e)

Figure 13-26 Examples of images reproduced by the Digital Processing Oscilloscope showing large, readily identified errors. (a) Original image; (b) inverted video signal; (c) lack of line synchronism; (d) transmission errors restricted to pixel in which they occur; (e) errors averaged over a block of pixels. Courtesy of Tektronix, Inc., Beaverton, Oregon.

for the way in which transmission errors manifest themselves with different processing schemes (Figs. 13-26d and 13-26e).

With only minor modifications, fully described in this chapter, the versatile DPO provides a useful facility for both image coding and restoration.

Images are encoded by using the DPO as a flying spot scanner. A photographic negative of approximately 100×80 mm of the scene to be digitized is attached to the face of the cathode ray tube (CRT), and, under program control, a sequence of constant-intensity spots appear on the CRT screen in a 256×256 matrix. A photomultiplier is mounted in front of the DPO screen as shown in Fig. 13-27 for measuring the intensity of light transmitted by the negative in the immediate vicinity of the spot.

The voltage developed across the anode load resistor of the photomultiplier is applied to the acquisition unit of the DPO for sampling at a time corresponding to peak intensity. Analog-to-digital conversion by the DPO results in a matrix of picture transmissions corresponding to the area of the negative scanned by the spot. This matrix of data is then

Figure 13-27 Tektronix WP1000 Digital Processing Oscilloscope and photomultiplier house. Courtesy of Tektronix, Inc., Beaverton, Oregon.

passed to the computer (a Digital Equipment Corporation PDP 11/10) for storage and processing.

Virtually any photomultiplier with good spectral responsiveness in the region of 500–550 nm can satisfy the far from stringent requirements of detecting the light transmitted through a photographic negative by a bright, well-focused spot on the DPO cathode ray tube. The relatively large and sensitive area of an end window photocathode was restricted by attaching a 1-mm diameter iris to the end of the tube before mounting it in front of the CRT. This reduces the solid angle for collection of light and therefore improves the resolution of the simple optical system.

The Tektronix WP1000 (Fig. 13-27) normally samples and digitizes signals on a pseudorandom basis, with a new sample taken every

6.5 microseconds. Thus, except for very slow waveforms, the input signal has to be repetitive. The DPO stores the information in the correct position within the 512-word storage array by digitizing both the vertical (i.e., voltage) and horizontal (i.e., time) positional information and using the latter as an address in the DPO memory at which the vertical information is to be stored.

In this application, however, only one point on the input signal waveform is of interest, namely, the peak. Therefore, it becomes necessary to disable the normally free-running Sample and Hold and then generate a signal to instruct the DPO to sample the input when it reaches its peak value. The hardware modifications needed to achieve this result are shown in Fig. 13-28. The lower printed circuit board

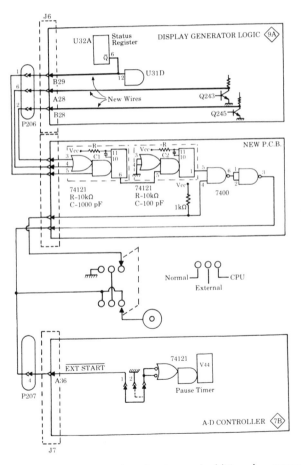

Figure 13-28 Modifications to existing circuitry and additional components needed to achieve image coding.

(PCB) is the A–D controller board, on which a link needs to be repositioned so that the Sample and Hold circuit will accept an EXTERNAL START pulse applied to pin A36 on socket J7. A connection already exists from this pin on the edge connector to the plug P207, thereby providing a convenient means of access.

The upper printed circuit board shown in Fig. 13–28 is the Display Controller board, to which three additional wires need to be added. A signal appearing at the Q output of the STATUS flip-flop signifies that the display controller is in the X–Y mode during the time the voltage at the collector of transistor Q243 or Q245 rises upon receipt of the command to display a spot.

With only limited spatial resolution and gray scale, the DPO cannot match the performance of specialized video equipment in providing an image coding and restoration facility. It does, however, allow simulations of image processing schemes to be initiated with an instrument that exists in several laboratories. Furthermore, its performance is more than adequate for many of the subjective evaluations that characterize the early stages of image processing investigations.

———————————————— **PROBLEMS** ————————————————

13-1 Discuss the meaning of image processing.

13-2 Define real time.

13-3 Discuss computer tomography.

13-4 Discuss digital subtractive fluoroscopy.

13-5 Go to the library. Make a project to get information on product inspection or scientific research. Do a term paper on real-time digital imaging in one of these fields.

14

SPEECH SYNTHESIS

14-0 INTRODUCTION

The increased use of digital equipment in the form of microprocessor and minicomputer technology has fostered a new era that combines analog and digital design techniques to produce devices like computers, games, appliances, and automobiles with synthetic speech capabilities. Speech synthesis technology focuses on applications spanning from aircraft instrumentation, banking systems, computer database access, to consumer/electronic products that may incorporate intelligible human-like voice responses. Although analog waveform decomposition into digital signals is not a new concept, the fusion of digital technology with the most complex of analog signals, the human voice, offers the greatest challenge to digital-to-analog conversion techniques.

At one end of the spectrum lies digital systems, perhaps microprocessor based, capable of storing and manipulating large quantities of information in seconds. At the opposite end lies an analog signal that is so complex, that we human beings, even with our vast information handling capabilities, frequently have difficulty deciphering a speech transmission spoken by another native speaker of the language, either in person, on the telephone, or in a room full of noise, simply because we "misunderstood" the spoken words, having mistaken them for similar-sounding words. The focal point in speech synthesis technology, then, is to generate the correct frequencies of sound that humans perceive as words in their language.

This chapter provides background information on the production of human speech sounds necessary for the design decision on which components best describe those sounds. It surveys the most widely used methods in speech synthesis and outlines some difficulties with each. General designs currently available in the form of semiconductor chips are also discussed.

14-1 PRODUCTION OF SPEECH SOUNDS*

Human speech is produced by the combined action of the vocal cords and the vocal tract, which consists of the throat, mouth, and nose resonance cavities. The vocal tract and vocal cord configuration govern how speech sounds differ. Sounds may differ from one another in three ways: loudness, pitch, and quality. Regulation of the vocal cord vibration rate (which changes the pitch) is, for the most part, determined by the individual and a product of age, sex, and other individual characteristics. Regulation of the volume of a resonance cavity is similar and, in addition, may be controlled voluntarily by the speech sound that is being produced.

Vocal cord vibration rate varies from 60-70/Hz for the lowest male voice to 1200-1300/Hz for the upper limit of a soprano. The average for a male speaker is approximately 100-150/Hz, that for a female speaker from 200-300 Hz. Vibrating vocal cords produce a buzz when air is forced through them that consists of brief pulses at a rate of 100 or more per second. Each pulse contains energy at many frequency levels. These pulses in turn excite the air in the resonance cavities, which may be tuned to different frequencies merely by changing the shape of the tongue, jaw, cheeks, and lips. The resulting sound wave contains a particular group of frequencies over 100/Hz.

The waveform for voiced sounds is regular and gives a good sensation of pitch; in voiceless sounds, variations in air pressure (produced by air flowing through the very narrow channel between the vocal cords) produce a much higher frequency. A female voice approximates 400 Hz for a voiced sound, a male voice hovering between 80 and 200 Hz. Predominant frequencies in unvoiced sounds are typically above 2000 Hz.

*Chapter 14 was developed by Ruth Palaszewski, M.A. in Linguistics, Professor of Computer Science at Boston College.

The frequency of a speech sound corresponds with its pitch; acoustic intensity is the measure corresponding to loudness (dB). The intensity of a sound segment will depend upon a number of factors, such as the degree of stress placed on each word in the sentence, the position of the segment in the sentences, and the individual characteristics of the speaker. Vowels generally have the highest intensity, and voiced sounds have a higher intensity than unvoiced sounds. A high-pass filter separates the high-frequency voiceless sounds from other sounds, passing them without any reduction and blocking out the low-frequency sounds. This method enables the average intensity of the speech segments to be determined.

Although Hz and dB are used to describe frequency and intensity of speech sounds, we must note that both measurements cannot be considered valid unless the measurements are related to how human beings perceive frequency and pitch of speech sounds. This perception of various speech sounds not only plays a pivotal role in the manner in which people are able to understand sounds in their native language and conversations with other native speakers, but also critically determines the intelligibility threshold in a synthetic speech device.

Speech sounds also differ from one another in quality. Vowels, all of which may be described as having the same pitch and loudness, are differentiated in terms of quality. Actually, a vowel contains a number of pitches simultaneously, which is referred to as its overtone structure. There is the one pitch at which the vowel is spoken and then the several other pitches that also occur. We differentiate one vowel from another by differences in the audible overtones. Try saying the words "heed, hid, head, had, hod, hawed, hood, who'd" to illustrate the differences in vowel quality. When these words are said in a normal tone of voice, the vocal cords vibrate at a particular frequency, giving us the characteristic pitch of the words. When the words are said in a whisper, a curious event occurs. Since the vocal cords are not vibrating in a whispered voice, there is no regular pitch. However, the whispered words form a series of sounds in a continuously descending pitch. We are actually hearing one of the overtones that characterize individual vowels.

Although there are many possible tones to a given vowel, only two specific pitches concern us here. The first characteristic pitch, or formant, is discernible in the vowels in the words given previously and goes downward through the series. The second formant goes up for the first four vowels in the series and then down through the last vowels. A third formant is also present in vowels, but its pitch is difficult to determine precisely. Fig. 14-1 illustrates the first three formant frequencies for the eight American vowels present in the series.

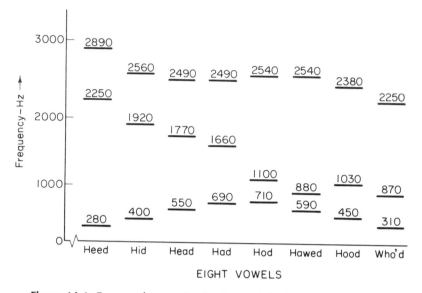

Figure 14-1 Formant frequencies for 8 vowels in American English.

It can be seen from the figure that the first formant frequency increases as one moves from the high vowel in "heed" to the low vowel in "had." In the same progression, the second formant decreases as the transition from the front vowel in "heed" to the back vowel in "who'd" occurs. The first formant is inversely related to vowel height, and although the second formant illustrates a relationship to the degree of backness of the vowel, the correlation is not as strong as between the first formant and vowel height. That is, the second formant steadily decreases through the progression of vowels, even though some of the vowels are not fully back, as in "head" and "had." The degree of lip rounding also affects the frequencies of the formants: generally, as sounds become more rounded, the higher formants show decreasing frequencies.

The acoustic properties of consonants are usually more complicated than those of vowels. Whereas vowels may be described in terms of quality using charts that indicate formants, consonants are conditioned according to the preceding or following vowel. Each of the stop sounds, for instance, conveys its quality depending on the adjacent vowel. At a release or formation moment in the articulation of any word containing stop consonants, the vocal tract will be in a different configuration, evidenced in different formant frequencies. The actual locus or origin of the formant will be a function of the adjacent vowels. Nasal consonants have a formant structure similar to that of vowels, with the exception that the particular frequency locations are in a position that is dependent on the particular nasal cavity resonances. The first formant for nasals is at about 250 Hz, the second at about 2500 Hz, and the third at over 3000 Hz. The differences between each of the nasals m, n, ng, then, is marked by the different formant transitions that occur at the end of each vowel.

The highest frequencies observed in speech occur with the fricative sounds, particularly the s sound, the random noise extending beyond the device limits used to record and visually illustrate the speech sounds.

14-2 METHODS OF SPEECH SYNTHESIS

The smallest units of sound recognizable by contrast with their environment are called *phonemes*. Stop consonants previously defined in terms of their voicing characteristics, like /p/ and /b/ /g/, are also phonemes, as are /t/, /p/, /k/. However, the sound for a particular phoneme may be subject to environmental influences. The /p/ in "pin," as contrasted with the /p/ in "spin," is a different variation of the phoneme, since the /p/ in "spin" is followed by a puff of air, whereas the /p/ in "pin" is not. The subcategorization of /p/ breaks into two allophones, one which is the unaspirated /p/ in "pin," and the other the aspirated allophone in "spin," which is better characterized as /ph/.

The constructive synthesis method of speech synthesis uses a phoneme-based system to generate synthetic speech by storing pre-encoded digital parameters corresponding to the phonemes in a word or sentence string. A phoneme-stringing system records a number of phonemes, often as many as 70, that are the basic sound elements, and, through the use of a synthesizer, strings the phonemes together according to a preprogrammed set of rules for the speech sounds. The advantage of a phoneme-stringing system is that almost an infinite vocabulary may be stored within a very small memory space, perhaps no greater than 6 kilobits of Read Only Memory (ROM). The major disadvantage is the poor speech quality—that is, speech that sounds like a computer. The difficulty lies in the absence of stress and intonation, two characteristic components of the manner in which human beings pronounce certain words in their language.

Allophone stringing, an improved version of phoneme stringing, operates in much the same fashion, but with an increased intelligibility. Recent experiments concerning the concatenation of words previously spoken in isolation indicate that the adjustment of the fundamental frequency is of paramount importance in terms of intelligibility. Olive and Nakatani showed that when telephone numbers were synthesized by splicing together prerecorded numbers, adjustments in the amplitude and duration and between word concatenation were not nearly as important as were adjustments in the fundamental frequency.

Both methods derive their vocabularies from precoded segments that may be combined in a variety of ways. An allophonic speech synthesizer offers a large vocabulary in a relatively small memory storage. In addition, the rules necessary for concatenating the allophonic segments must be stored because the transitions between allophone strings cause the resulting segment or word to sound mechanical and computer-like. The two solutions most commonly implemented to solve this problem are (1) the inclusion of rules that provide an algorithm through which different allophonic or phoneme sequences are assigned a sound, and (2) the addition of another part of speech called a diphone.

Dipones are sounds that extend from the middle of one phoneme to the middle of the next, thereby covering the transition area. Diphones alleviate much of the choppy transition problems, but an additional storage area is required to hold the over 2500 diphones that are applicable in the English language. In addition, English contains numerous instances in which an allophonic variation is attributed to both the preceding and succeeding sounds in the segment. The storage requirements for this type of high-quality speech synthesis necessitate that it take place on a mainframe computer rather than on a simple microprocessor. The diphone storage alone on a machine of this type is in excess of 240K bytes of memory.

Another method of digitizing speech is analysis/synthesis. Analysis/synthesis derives its entire vocabulary, whether in words, phrases, or sentences, from human speakers rather than the close approximations of these sounds used in the allophone/phoneme stringing method. The actual speech waveform is sampled, and data are extracted from it and encoded in the now popular Linear Predictive Code (LPC), which permits the waveform to be reconstructed at another time and place. The storage requirements for analysis/synthesis are exceedingly large, severely constraining the size of the vocabulary. However, the speech quality is exceptional.

Linear predictive coding (LPC) is only one of the methods used to sample the speech waveform. Pulse code modulation (PCM) techniques sample the amplitudes of an analog signal and convert these into wideband binary numbers. That is, rather than registering the exact amplitude of each sample, an approximation to the amplitude of each is made in the form of a group of 0 and 1 pulses. The speech waveform is generated with a relatively high degree of intelligibility when the maximum amplitude is divided into a minimum of 128 levels. The exact amplitude is then converted (quantized) to one level from these 128 levels that is nearly the same in amplitude. The quantizing error is the difference between the actual sample value and the quantized value.

Quantized speech uses a 7-bit code, so that 128 levels may be used. Each speech sample has a value ranging from a minimum of binary 0 (0000000) to a maximum of binary 127 (1111111), plus a synchronization bit, which yields 8 bits per sample. These 8 bits must be sent in 1/6000 second, the time between samples. Thus, 20.8 microseconds, (1/8 of 1/6000) are needed to send each bit, a rate of 48,000 bits per second.

Since the advent of very large scale integrated circuit (VLSI) technology, more than twenty-five manufacturing firms have been established that produce speech synthesis chips for more than a dozen products. The major synthesis chip companies include Texas Instrument, Inc.; National Semiconductor Corp.; Votrax; ITT Semiconductor; General Instruments Corp.; Centigram Corp.; Nippon Electric Co. U.S.A.; Hitachi Ltd.; and Matsushita Electric Corp. In the sections that follow, we shall analyze speech synthesizer systems; digital signal processor chips will be discussed in detail in the next chapter.

The reader interested in digital signal processors in the audio and television fields should consult the manufacturers and societies involved in this new area. The topic is beyond the scope of the text.

14-3   THE INTEL 2920 SIGNAL PROCESSOR*

The recently introduced 2920 Analog Signal Processor from Intel Corporation is an example of a VLSI device having the computational power to implement speech algorithms. The device, which consists of an EPROM programmed digital microprocessor that has been combined with A/D and D/A conversion for input and output, is capable of simulating networks of digital filters as well as a variety of other signal processing functions such as oscillators, modulators, and nonlinear transformations. In what follows, we show how to use the 2920 to realize a formant-based speech synthesizer. (See Fig. 11-44.)

---

*Sections 14-3 and 14-4 from Wallace H. Li and M. E. Hoff, Jr., "A General Purpose Formant Speech Synthesizer Module Using the Intel 2920 Signal Processor," pp. 1–6, Application Note, AP–111, © October 30, 1980. Courtesy of Intel Corporation. All rights reserved.

There are many approaches to the synthesis of human speech, but almost all are based on the basic model shown in Fig. 14-2. In this model, two basic sound sources are passed through a time-variable filter network to produce speech-like sounds. Each of the blocks in Fig. 14-2 has its counterpart in the human anatomy. The time-variable filter network represents the vocal tract, i.e., the cavities of the mouth, nose, and throat, which act as resonators. Their characteristics are time variable because they are influenced by the position of the lips, tongue, and jaw. One of the sound sources that excite the time-variable filter network consists of a buzz generator tht is representative of the air turbulence as it flows over the tongue, lips, and teeth. The typical speech synthesizer includes models for each source and for the filter network and provides for the appropriate modulation of the parameters of each block.

Three different approaches, illustrated in Fig. 14-3, have been commonly used to model the time-variable filter network. Two of them, the lattice filter and the multistage recursive digital filter approach, derive their parameters using LPC—that is, linear predictive coding. The third approach is based on models of speech formants, i.e., the resonance characteristics of the speech tract. In general, the formant models allow lower bit rates for synthesis than LPC, although derivation of operating parameters for formant synthesizers from human speech is more difficult than LPC analysis. Fig. 14-3a shows a lattice filter synthesizer configuration. A typical synthesizer will use some ten coefficients, labeled K_1 through K_{10}. Fig. 14-3b shows a multistage recursive digital filter implementation, which also typically uses ten coefficients, labeled in the diagram A_1 through A_{10}. Although the recursive filter may at first seem computationally simpler, the parameters are more sensitive to computation errors than the k parameters

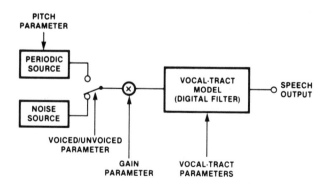

Figure 14-2 Basic speech model. Courtesy of Intel Corporation.

of the lattice filter network, and injudicious choices of the parameters can lead to instability. The lattice filter will be stable if the k_i, $i = 1, \ldots, 10$ are all of magnitude less than unity. Fig. 14-3c represents a formant synthesizer. The typical vocal tract has several resonances, usually referred to as formants. Adequate speech synthesis can usually be done by modeling the three most important formants, although some special treatment may be needed for certain nasal sounds. In general, the behavior of the formant filters is less sensitive to parameter variations than are the structures of Fig. 14-3a and 14-3b. The bandwidths of the formant resonances are relatively unimportant, and formant-to-formant frequency transitions are usually fairly smooth and well behaved. All of these characteristics serve to reduce the bit rate needed to drive the formant synthesizer.

The two sound sources that excite the filter stages represent air turbulence noise and pitch pulses. The noise generator is usually implemented as a pseudorandom number generator. The vocal cord impulses may be modeled by a pulse generator. The pulses may be shaped to correspond to the pulses produced by the human vocal tract. Because pulse waveforms are broadband signals, care must be taken in digital simulations to avoid alias-distortion effects.

Speech consists of periods in which either or both sound sources are excited, mixed with periods of silence. When the vocal cords are active, the speech is said to be voiced. When only air turbulence is exciting the tract, the speech is said to be unvoiced. Whispered speech can be simulated by using only noise excitation of the vocal tract.

Human speech can be thought of as consisting of sequences of basic sound segments, usually referred to as phonemes. Various students of speech have catalogued the number of distinct phonemes, usually listed for English at about 60. Synthesizers have been built on the basis of producing words by playing sequences of phonemes. However, an unnatural sound can result because a human speaker modifies each phoneme as a function of preceding and following phonemes. A number of researchers have investigated rules for phoneme-phoneme transitions. Both formant frequency and vocal cord pitch must be properly controlled through the transitions for a natural sound to result. However, a successful implementation of a set of rules could allow very low bit rate speech synthesis, perhaps under 200 bits/second.

The implementation in Fig. 14-4 shows the utilization of an Intel 2920 for the main part of the speech synthesizer under the control of an Intel microprocessor. The 2920 performs a simulation of the basic blocks of the synthesizer as shown in Fig. 14-5. Input control parameters to the 2920 are digital signals delivered from an adjacent (conventional) microprocessor. The control program within the 2920

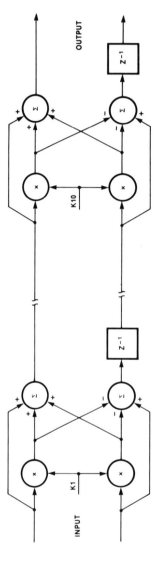

(a) Lattice Filter Synthesizer

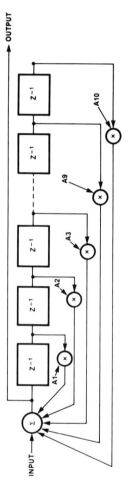

(b) Multi-stage Recursive Filter Synthesizer

Figure 14-3 (a—b)

444

(c) Formant Synthesizer

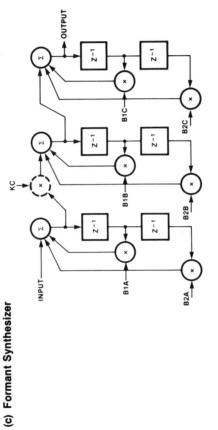

Figure 14-3 Time-variable filter models. Courtesy of Intel Corporation.

445

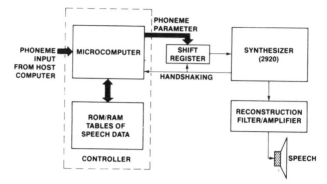

Figure 14-4 2920 Speech synthesizer module block diagram. Courtesy of Intel Corporation.

accepts these input parameters and distributes them to the various modules of the simulation. The 2920 generates the analog output signal representing the modeled speech.

The intermediate processor (Fig. 14-4) provides the functions of a table lookup of phoneme values and performs interpolations on those values to deliver data to the 2920 in synchrony with the 2920 sample rate. It may also accept external commands from a host processor and interpret them to select phonemes or words from its local dictionary tables.

14-4 FUNCTIONS OF THE SYNTHESIZER

A serial filter stage formant synthesizer architecture has been used for the 2920 application. The synthesizer portion is realized by a single 2920 chip as shown in Fig. 14-5. In order to produce speech of telephone network quality, an 8 kHz sample frequency has been used.

In the speech model of Fig. 14-5, there are two sources of excitation: a pitch oscillator and a noise generator. Either or both of these may be used to excite the formant filter network. The propagation control block determines the choice of the excitation sources via the control work CTRL. To generate voiced speech, the pitch oscillator output is propagated to the formant filters after it has been properly modified by the shaping network. The effect of this network is to introduce an approximately 20 dB per decade high-frequency rolloff.

To generate whispered speech, the noise generator output is propagated to the formant filters after it is shaped by the noise-shaping filter. This filter has characteristics similar to those of the pitch pulse

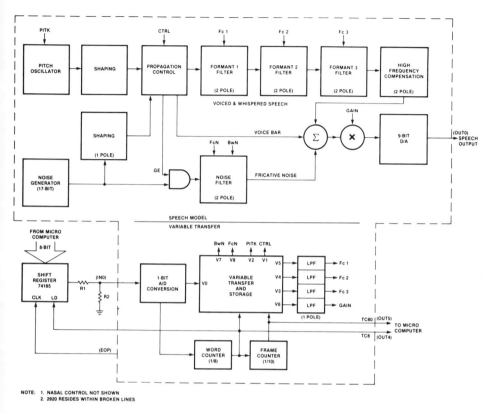

Figure 14-5 2920 Synthesizer block diagram. Courtesy of Intel Corporation.

shaping network. To generate voiceless fricative (e.g., f, s) or the unvoiced component of voiced fricatives (e.g., z, v), the noise generator output is gated to the noise filter under control of the signal labelled GE. For a voiceless fricative, the GE signal is constantly enabled. For the unvoiced component of voiced fricatives, the GE signal is a square wave synchronized with the output of formant filter 1. Another specialized waveform needed for natural-sounding speech is a voice bar. A voice bar is the quasiperiodic low-frequency energy radiated from the region of the vocal cords during the closure interval of voiced stop consonants. During this interval the vocal cords are vibrating, thus acting as the source of energy for the voice bar, but do not excite the normal vocal tract resonance. To simulate this effect, the pitch pulse is propagated directly to the adder. The voice bar feature can also be used as a tone source. Because the synthesizer realizes only the lowest three formants, a high-frequency compensation filter is placed following formant filter 3 to compensate for missing higher formants in order to produce a more natural-sounding voice spectrum. The adder combines the voiced or whispered speech, the fricative noise, and the voice bar signals. Then the overall signal is scaled through a multiplier to establish the desired amplitude level. The digital composite voice signal is then converted to analog at the 2920 output.

The lower half of the block diagram in Fig. 14-5 illustrates how the synthesizer control parameters are transferred from the controller to the 2920. As the figure shows, these parameters are transmitted in frames, with each frame containing one value for each of the ten parameters. Each parameter value is eight bits in width. The current version of the synthesizer uses only eight parameters for the speech model, as follows.

> CTRL: signal propagation control
>
> PITK: pitch frequency control
>
> Fc3: center frequency control for formant filter 3
>
> Fc2: center frequency control for formant filter 2
>
> Fc1: center frequency control for formant filter 1
>
> GAIN: overall gain control
>
> BwN: bandwidth control for the noise filter
>
> FcN: center frequency control for the noise filter

14-5   THE NSC SPEECH PROCESSOR
CHIP (SPC)* _____

The National Semiconductor speech synthesis system consists of the SPC device plus the speech memory (ROM) required to assemble a complete DIGITALKER™ kit. To this kit, a clock input signal or the necessary oscillator components, an audio filter and amplifier, and the control circuit function must be added. This would represent the minimum configuration shown in Fig. 14-6. The maximum amount of directly addressable speech memory accessible by the SPC is 128K bits, but external page addressing by the control circuit function can increase this ROM field as required.

The SPC utilizes the speech compression synthesis technique, which reduces the amount of memory needed to store electronic speech

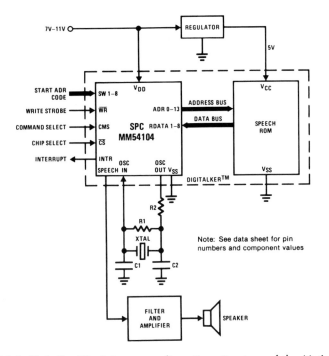

Figure 14-6 Digitalker™ minimum configuration. Courtesy of the National Semiconductor Corp.

by removing the excess of redundant data from the speech signal. The four main techniques to perform that task are

1. Elimination of redundant pitch periods
2. Adaptive delta modulation coding to minimize bandwidth and memory requirements
3. Phase angle adjustments to create mirror-image symmetry
4. Replacement of the low-level portion of a pitch period with silence (half-period zeroing)

Figure 14-7 contains a block diagram of the MM54104 SPC. The eight-bit start address bus allows up to 256 separately defined sounds or expressions to be stored in the speech ROM. The control interface to the start address port can take the form of decoding logic, a Microbus™ port, or mechanical switches.

When the $\overline{WR}$ goes high, the start address code is loaded into the control word address register. The SPC uses the control address to fetch the control word from ROM for the first block of speech data. The

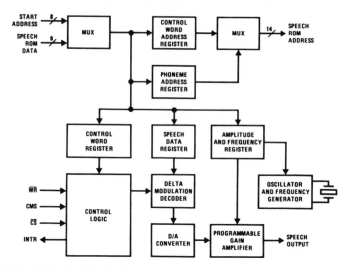

Figure 14-7 MM54104 block diagram. Courtesy of the National Semiconductor Corp.

control word contains waveform information, repeat information, and the address of the speech data. The latter is loaded into the phoneme address register and is used to fetch the speech data used to recreate the speech waveform. Before the synthesis takes place, the waveform data must be decoded to provide information such as male or female, voiced or unvoiced, half-period zeroed or not half-period zeroed, and whether silence is to occur.

As an example of how the overall frequency response of a particular application can minimize the need for extra filtering, consider the Digitalker™ to be voice announcement circuit in a telephone system.

In this case, the telephone network provides a natural attenuation to high frequencies that balances the SPC high-frequency pre-emphasis. As a result, the low-pass filter previously mentioned can be eliminated. However, because signal frequencies above 3 kHz must be attenuated before they are allowed to pass into the telephone network, a cutoff filter of 3400 Hz may be required in place of the 200 Hz low-pass filter. A good filter for this application is the National Semiconductor AF–133 active filter.

In addition to the 200 Hz-to-3400 Hz low-pass filter, an extra stage of filtering can be used for frequencies above 7 kHz. This filter is optional and is normally used only to further reduce sampling noise. Most systems can omit it, especially if the overall system bandwidth is not very wide. A second optional high-pass filter, which would normally cutoff below 200 Hz (adjusted to match the 200 Hz low-pass if provided), can be included to limit the overall low-frequency response of the system. If system characteristics do not require limiting low-frequency noise, however, the high-pass filter can usually be omitted. A circuit having the full frequency response characteristic is shown in Fig. 14-8. Figure 14-9 shows the recommended overall speech synthesis system frequency response.

While there is a wide variety of synthetic speech applications, the actual implementation in any single application is usually limited to one of the techniques, (1) single channel, hardware control logic; (2) single channel, software control logic; and (3) multichannel, hardware or software control logic.

Each of these approaches to circuitry for the SPC will be discussed in this section. Particular emphasis will be placed on items (2) and (3), however, because of the broad application possibilities for these two techniques.

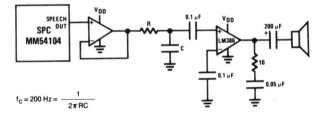

$$f_c = 200 \text{ Hz} = \frac{1}{2\pi RC}$$

(a) Minimum Low-Pass Filter/Amplifier

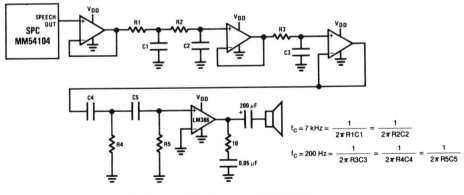

$$f_c = 7 \text{ kHz} = \frac{1}{2\pi R1C1} = \frac{1}{2\pi R2C2}$$

$$f_c = 200 \text{ Hz} = \frac{1}{2\pi R3C3} = \frac{1}{2\pi R4C4} = \frac{1}{2\pi R5C5}$$

(b) Maximum Filter Response Configuration

Figure 14-8 SPC filter and amplifier. Courtesy of the National Semiconductor Corp.

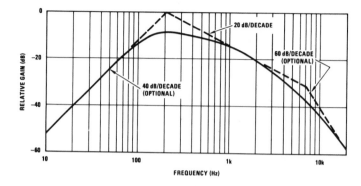

Figure 14-9 Recommended frequency response of entire audio system for MM-54104 SPC. Courtesy of the National Semiconductor Corp.

Certain applications require a relatively small number of sentences or announcements with very little similarity between the different sentences. An example of this might be a talking elevator controller, whose messages are brief and nonredundant (e.g., "going up," "first floor," "second floor," etc.). Here, certain words are used repeatedly, but the number of messages is limited and the length of each message is short. This application, and others just like it, does not require the assembly of short phrases into complete sentences, nor does it require a dynamic message structure, as would be required with an automatic bank teller (e.g., "your change is ten dollars"), where a monetary amount may change from message to message. This fixed-message application, therefore, may require only the minimum control circuit, as shown in Fig. 14-9.

In the figure, the SPC receives, through the SW 1–8 port, a separate coded input for each complete sentence or message that is synthesized. The circuit shown uses a mechanical switch group to interface the SPC and a hardware logic controller to input the coded message control data.

14-6   THE TEXAS INSTRUMENTS TMS5110A
SPEECH SYNTHESIZER* _____

The Texas Instruments TMS5100 voice-synthesis processor (VSP) has improved coding and decoding tables that allow it to offer twice the pitch range of, and higher quality synthesized speech than, the TMS-5100.

*Section 14-6 courtesy of Texas Instruments Incorporated.

The TMS5100A processes synthesized-speech data under the direction of any standard 4-bit microcomputer (e.g., the TMS1000). It can receive speech data from the TMS6100 128K bit voice-synthesis memory (VSM) and the TMS6125 32K bit VSM. A cost-effective minimum configuration can be designed using just three chips: the TMS-5110A VSP, the TMS6100 or TMS6125 VSM, and a TMS1000 microcomputer.

On-chip features of the TMS5110A include an 8-bit, digital-to-analog converter and a push-pull amplifier that provides 36 milliwatts to drive an external speaker directly.

Fabricated using reliable PMOS technology, the TMS5110A requires a single +5V power supply (±10%) and is packaged in a standard 16-pin, dual-in-line plastic package. Operating temperature of the device is 0 to 70 degrees C.

14-7   TELESENSORY SPEECH SYNTHESIZER SYSTEMS*

The SPEECH 1000 synthesizer board (Fig. 14-10) uses the stored vocabulary speech response unit. It contains an 8085A microcomputer, control program in ROM, Telesensory's Programmable Digital Signal Processor (PDSP™), 10-bit digital-to-analog converter, 7-pole anti-aliasing low-pass filter, 2-watt audio amplifier, three alternative interface I/O ports, and seven memory sockets for vocabulary storage. Almost any computer can command it to enunciate the stored words, phrases, or sentences as required.

The SPEECH 1000 synthesizer board is controlled by the host computer through the use of commands and word pointers. Commands are used to instruct the SPEECH 1000 board, for instance, to "stop talking immediately," to "repeat previous utterance," or "increase speaking rate." Word pointers specify which utterance should be spoken. By arranging commands and word pointers in a desired sequence and downloading them into RAM buffer on the SPEECH 1000 board, the host system's need for polling or interrupt handling is reduced.

Once the commands and word pointers are loaded onto the SPEECH 1000 board, the microcontroller retrieves the necessary encoded parametric speech data from the vocabulary memory, processes it, and presents it to the PDSP circuits for synthesis. The vocabulary memory may be as large as 458 kilobits or as small as 16 kilobits,

*Section 14-7 reprinted with permission of Telesensory Speech Systems.

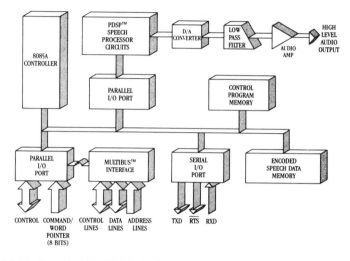

Figure 14-10 Speech 1000™ block diagram. Courtesy of the Telesensory Speech Systems.

because the memory configuration has been designed to accommodate 16K, 32K, or 64K ROM, or 32K or 64K EPROM.

Structured as a 12-pole lattice filter, the PDSP circuits perform thousands of multiply and add operations per second to decode the greatly compressed speech data and generate the digital representation of the original speech waveform with 10,000 10-bit samples per second. The D/A converter transforms the digital representation into its analog counterpart for amplification. The "on-board" amplifier supplies up to two watts into an 8 ohm speaker. Volume control can be accomplished either by the "on-board" potentiometer, by connecting an external potentiometer, or by using the downloadable software command, "attenuate amplitude."

The PROSE 2000 text-to-speech converter (Fig. 14-11) provides an easy and flexible way of synthesizing almost any voice message. Simply send it English words or whole sentences in standard computer code, and the PROSE 2000 does the rest. Using sophisticated text-to-speech conversion rules, it processes the incoming text to produce immediately intelligible speech output with human-like intonation.

The features of the PROSE 2000 include

1. Speech output from arbitrary English text input.
2. Programming to automatically convert abbreviations, numbers, and symbols to colloquial speech.
3. Production of human-like inflection based on content and punctuation.

Figure 14-11 The Prose 2000™ text to speech converter. Courtesy of the Telesensory Speech Systems.

4. Acceptance of ASCII-coded phoneme codes for nonstandard words and names.

5. Extensive user control of voice characteristics and timing.

6. Synchronization of voice output with other events.

7. Multibus™ compatibility, including an RS-232-C serial port.

8. Two-watt on-board audio amplifier.

Figure 14-12 shows the following systems:

1. Text Normalization. The text normalizer is responsible for expanding abbreviations to their full word form, expanding numbers and monetary amounts, handling punctuation and other nonalphabetic input characters, in putting phonemes, and dealing with special pronunciation modes. An example of the operation is the translation of "Jan. 22nd at 346 Fox St., St. Louis" to "JANUARY TWENTY SECOND AT THREE FORTY SIX FOX STREET, SAINT LOUIS."

2. Phonemics. The incoming word is looked up in a lexicon of about 1500 special words. If the search succeeds, the associated phoneme string is retrieved and passed directly to the allophonic process. If the lexicon search fails, the word is assigned a phoneme string and a stress pattern by a set of about 300 context-sensitive rules.

3. Allophonics. By assigning allophones (variants of a specific phoneme based on surrounding speech sounds), PROSE 2000 is able to

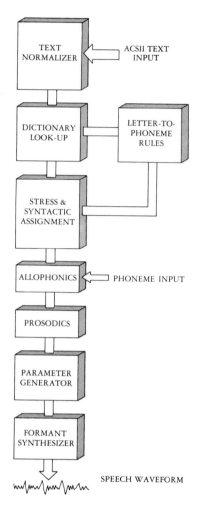

Figure 14-12 Software architecture linguistic processing. Courtesy of the Telesensory Speech Systems.

accurately represent the required pronunciation. The process is sensitive to the syntactic structure and stress pattern of the sentence, as well as the speech rate and prosody mode selected.

4. Prosodics. Prosodic rules determine the sound durations and fundamental frequency patterns of the words to be spoken. The resultant intonation contour gives the sentences the rhythm and melody of a human speaker. The rules are sensitive to phonetic form, the part of speech of the words in a sentence, and punctuation, as well as the prosody mode and speech rate selected by the user.

5. Parameter Generation. The parameter generator accepts the fully specific phonemes and produces as output a set of 18 time-varying speech parameters, using a "constructive synthesis" algorithm. Using this algorithm instead of pieces of prestored speech results in a good model of the human vocal tract and highly intelligible speech. The parameters control Telesensory's proprietary PDSP speech synthesizer IC in the generation of the speech waveform.

14-8 VOTAN SPEECH SYNTHESIS TECHNOLOGY*

Speech technology is still considered a relatively new field. While a number of companies have entered it in recent years, not one has developed the full range of technology.

Votan, for the first time, has developed an integrated solution to word recognition and speech generation in a cost-effective, all-digital implementation suitable for board products and VLSI. Major applications are seen in information processing, office automation, telecommunications, and instrumentation and control.

The standard Votan voice technology system consists of an analog-to-digital converter for transforming incoming audio signals to digital form; a digital voice processor for performing speaker-dependent recognition, speaker-independent recognition, voice response, voice store and forward, vocoding, and speaker verification; random access memory; an external control microprocessor; and a digital-to-analog converter for converting to analog audio output.

Voice processing is achieved with an A/D converter, a digital voice processor, an external control microprocessor, and a D/A for converting to analog audio output. Four 2901 bit-slice microprocessors are used to implement the voice processor. Depending on the application, the voice processor can perform functions for speaker-dependent recognition, voice response, voice store and forward, or combinations of recognition and response.

The primary function of the processor is to convert the input signal from the time domain to the frequency domain. The company's proprietary spectral transform yields 128 spectral coefficients in a system passband of 0 to 4 kHz.

*Section 14-8 courtesy of Votan, Hayward, California.

The task of converting voice signals from the time domain to the frequency domain has created a stumbling block for a number of companies that have attempted to enter the speech technology field. The Votan transform technique is unique in that it accomplishes the transformation without the need for multiplication or division. The transform calculations are extremely fast, exceeding real-time requirements by a large factor.

The new technique provides a spectral filtering capability greatly exceeding the capabilities of analog filter banks typically used in voice recognition. Each of the 128 spectral coefficients is equivalent to a very precise filter of about 30 Hz bandwidth. The equivalent analog filter would require 128 channels of up to 128 poles each.

This all-digital approach completely eliminates the requirement for precision analog filter components and provides significant flexibility in selecting spectral data for specific applications. The transform also provides a voice generation capability that is not readily obtainable with analog filter banks. Since the transform is invertible, spectral data may be reconverted to audio signal data.

Since there is substantial redundancy in the voice spectral data that may be removed without compromising voice quality, Votan uses psychoacoustic grading of the voice data in the encoding strategy it employs for voice data compression.

Raw spectral data is provided from the transform at a rate of 80,000 bits per second (bps). For voice response or transmission purposes, the encoding process provides excellent reproduction quality at 9600 bps, and a graded reduction in quality at lower bit rates.

Compared at a given bit rate to a number of other systems on today's market, the Votan products consistently deliver higher reproduction quality at significantly lower costs. Consider the following examples:

1. At 14,400 bits per second, the voice reproduction is of high quality, equal to the sound of the human voice over a telephone line.

2. At 9600 bps, the voice reproduction is of communications quality, roughly equivalent to the sound of the human voice over a telephone line.

3. At 4800 bps, the speaker's identity, mood, and emphasis are easily discernible.

An essential function in the word recognition or speaker verification mode is voiceprint pattern matching. Votan has implemented the dynamic programming pattern matching technique, which effectively accounts for normal variations in the voice print.

The V5000 (Fig. 14-13) integrates, in one compact system, two

Figure 14-13 The Votan Model V5000. Courtesy of Votan, Hayward, California.

major speech technologies: speaker-dependent recognition, and speech generation (voice response, vocoding, and voice store and forward).

Another unique feature of Votan's technology is its ability to record and play back the sounds of any language, since it is not based on a particular linguistic model of speech, as are phoneme-based systems. This digital approach contrasts to the rigid set of 60 seconds used by phoneme encoders to reproduce the English language. With phoneme-based systems, a different set of phonemes is required for each foreign language, speaker identification is not possible, and considerable skill is required to achieve acceptable results.

With all of Votan's speech generation products, the speaker's identity and intonations are clearly identifiable when the digitized voice is played back at all but the lowest bit rates. The user balances reproduction quality with storage or transmission rate requirements to select a bit rate, ranging from 4800 to 14,400 bits per second. Good communications quality is achieved at a range of 8000 bps or above. The selection is easily made by pressing two keys on a control panel.

14-9 ADAPTING A SPEECH SYNTHESIZER FOR ROBOTICS* _____

Voice output from computers has long been desirable, mainly because of its natural machine-to-human communication application. In recent years a number of speech synthesis products for consumers has appeared on department store shelves, and not long ago the first voice output peripheral became available to the personal computer owner. One of these, the Radio Shack TRS–80 Voice Synthesizer, manufactured by Votrax, uses phoneme reconstruction to actually synthesize human speech. Being an unlimited vocabulary machine, the Votrax unit can be used in output applications where standard predefined vocabularies from other synthesizer vendors do not exist. One such specialized field is robotics.

In performing extensive research on robot communications, it is necessary to interface this synthesizer to the TRS–80 Color Computer. Unfortunately, the Model I and the color do not share the same interface. The TRS–80 Color Computer has a unique expansion connector. Both connectors being different, the universal alternative is the RS–232C serial I/O.

In what follows, the reader will learn both how to interface the TRS–80 speech synthesizer to any serial port, and the details of an interface and vocabulary builder program for the Color Computer. First, let's take a look at the synthesizer as purchased.

Figure 14-14 is a partial schematic—that is, it shows the portion of the board that is discernible. The rest is either sealed or unmarked. The 74S133, a 13-input NAND gate that is wired as an address decoder, looks for an address of decimal 16352 or higher. With the serial interface, we have no use for this gate. Examining further, we see two 40105 IC's that are FIFO (first in/first out) registers that store 32 phoneme codes. The entire writing circuit is gated on and off by the 7474 shown in the upper right. This flip-flop is triggered on when a question mark

*Section 14-9 from Mark Robillard, "Adapting A Speech Synthesizer," *Robotics Age* © July/August 1982. Material reprinted courtesy of *Robotic Age*, 174 Concord Street, Strand Building, Peterborough, NH 03458.

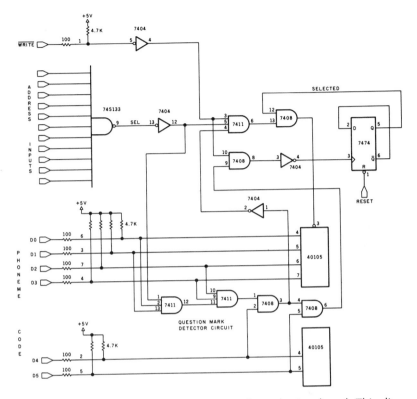

Figure 14-14 Partial schematic of Votrax speech synthesizer board. This diagram shows only the entry portion of the speech circuit. Courtesy of *Robotic Age.*

is received, and gated off when another one arrives. What you see in this partial schematic is all you need to see.

When the back of the unit is opened, the volume knob removed, and the select LED pressed in, the circuit board can be removed from the rear. It will go only as far as the speaker cable will allow. The following modifications may be performed on the board.

1. Remove the 40-pin ribbon cable.
2. Cut pin 9 of 74S133.
3. Add circuit to pin 1 of 7474 (Fig. 14-15).

This is all the modification necessary to the basic unit. Now on to the new circuit. Figure 14-16 depicts the serial interface. The 6402 is a CMOS UART (universal asynchronous receiver/transmitter) and is

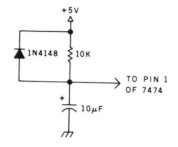

Figure 14-15 Power-up reset circuit to be added to 7474. Courtesy of *Robotic Age*.

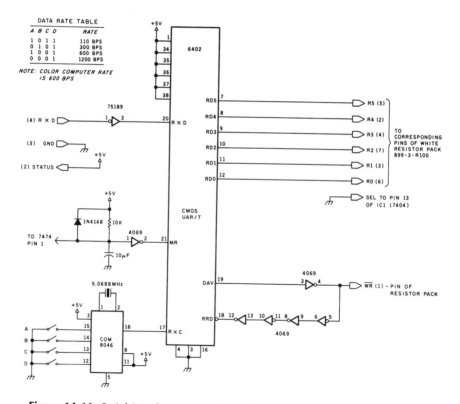

Figure 14-16 Serial interface to speech synthesizer. Courtesy of *Robotic Age*.

widely available. The 75189, 4069, and 8046 are also readily available. The received data output lines go to pins marked on the resistor pack located beside the ribbon connector. Five-volt power and ground can be picked up at any TTL chip on the board.

The Votrax synthesizer is a phoneme-based machine. Large amounts of words can be stored in the computer with relatively little memory. Table 14-1 lists the 64 phoneme sounds available with the synthesizer and the ASCII characters used to represent them.

Interfacing to the TRS–80 Color Computer cartridge port would require a special circuit mounted in a box and unique poke assignments

Table 14-1
Relationship between Votrax phoneme sounds and ASCII characters used to produce them.*

VOTRAX	ASCII	DECIMAL	VOTRAX	ASCII	DECIMAL
PA1*	SPACE	32	A1	@	64
I2	!	33	AH2	A	65
I	"	34	B	B	66
I3	#	35	CH	C	67
OO	$	36	D	D	68
OO1	%	37	E1	E	69
Y	&	38	F	F	70
U	'	39	G	G	71
IU	(	40	H	H	72
A2	)	41	I1	I	73
AY	*	42	J	J	74
NG	+	43	K	K	75
AW	,	44	L	L	76
O DEC.	—	45	M	M	77
E	.	46	N	N	78
ER	/	47	O1	O	79
PAO*	O	48	P	P	80
AW1	1	49	DT	Q	81
AW2	2	50	R	R	82
EH1	3	51	S	S	83
EH2	4	52	T	T	84
EH3	5	53	U1	U	85
UH1	6	54	V	V	86
UH2	7	55	W	W	87
UH3	8	56	ZH	X	88
AE1	9	57	Y1	Y	89
AE	:	58	Z	Z	90
AH1	;	59	O2	[	91
THV	v	60	O	/	92
TH	=	61	AH	]	93
SH	v	62	A	v	94
SELECT	?	63	NULL	—	95

*Courtesy of *Robotic Age*.

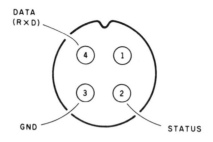

Figure 14-17 TRS–80 Color Computer serial port connections for printer. Courtesy of *Robotic Age*.

that would not be as easy to use as a print statement. After all, we are basically replacing the printed output with a voice.

The TRS–80 Color Computer has a serial RS–232C printer port built into the standard unit. The pin connections for this port are shown in Fig. 14-17. When the serial port is hooked up to the synthesizer, we can talk to the synthesizer with simple line-printer commands (PRINT #−2). Remember that a "?" turns the unit on, and then another turns it off. After sending out phoneme strings by hand for a while, you will wish you had some sort of vocabulary editor.

_____ **PROBLEMS** _____

14-1 Discuss the meaning of a speech synthesizer in a digital signal processor.

14-2 List five uses of a speech synthesizer.

14-3 Go to the library. Construct a project to generate a voice synthesizer for a robot, and work on it at home.

14-4 Discuss how a speech synthesizer can be used to monitor telephone calls in an automobile.

15

THE DIGITAL SIGNAL PROCESSING CHIP

15-0 INTRODUCTION*

The technology of integrated circuits and semiconductors has increased the potential of digital signal processing (DSP) chips [one through fifteen] used today. The Intel 2920 variety (Fig. 11-44) was one of the first DSP chips used in speech synthesizers, modems, and other applications. DSP chip evolution has paralleled the first Intel microprocessor family, viz., the 8008 followed by the 8080, which was an 8-bit general-purpose microprocessor. In this chapter, we will discuss the applications of the Texas Instruments TMS 320 DSP chip, the Intel 2920 DSP chip, and the NEC MPD7720 DSP chip. Besides these the following DSP chips are available: American Microsystems S2811, Bell Laboratories, Rockwell International, IBM, and other manufacturers who have associated microprocessors. The key difference between a DSP chip and ordinary microprocessors is that the DSP chip devotes a large rectangular or square area to the combinational array that performs such operations as carry look-aheads, needed for the execution of a multiplication in a single instruction cycle. Typically, this logic performs some varient of Booth's algorithm.

The DSP chips are small, requiring little space, have power

---

*Section 15-0 reprinted in part from EDN, July 1982 © Cahner's Publishing Co.

capabilities, are easy to program, and have higher bandwidth and the highest operating speed.

The Texas Instruments TMS 320 discussed in Section 15-1 is the first oriented chip to have an interrupt capability. This chip could use its general-purpose microprocessor capabilities to perform various managerial tasks in the background mode, and then, upon interrupt, could handle the time-critical DSP tasks in the foreground.

15-1 THE TEXAS INSTRUMENTS TMS320 DSP CHIP*

The TMS 320 family of VLSI processors utilizes 20 MHz NMOS speed, superior 32-bit microcomputer internal architecture, and 16-bit parallel I/O with transfer rates up to 40 Mbits per second. TMS320's comprehensive instruction set was designed to support a wide range of computation-intensive, high-speed applications, such as digital filtering, speech recognition, signal handling for telecommunications modems, data compression for linear predictive-code speech analysis and synthesis, graphics, image processing, spectral analysis, correlations, and fast-Fourier transforms. Specific instructions have been targeted to optimize the TMS320 for the digital signal processing and telecommunications markets. Separate data and program buses combine with a 32-bit ALU, a 16×16-bit parallel multiplier, a 0-through-15-bit barrel shifter, and a 32-bit accumulator to achieve a 200 ns execution time for 90 percent of the instructions. As a single-chip, high-performance microcomputer, the TMS320 is a cost-effective alternative to multichip bit-slice processors and I.C.'s dedicated only to digital signal processing.

Key features of the TMS 320 include

1. 200 ns instruction cycle for maximum clock of 20 MHz.
2. 16-bit instruction/data word.
3. 3K bytes of program ROM.
4. External program memory expansion capability to 8K bytes.
5. 288 bytes of data RAM.
6. 16-bit parallel I/O with transfer rates up to 40M bits per second.
7. Signed two's complement fixed-point arithmetic.

---

*Section 15-1 from 32010 and TMS 320 M10 High-Performance 16/32 Bit Microcomputers, Microcomputer Series Preliminary Data Manual, Texas Instruments Incorporated, © June 1982. Reprinted courtesy of Texas Instruments Incorporated, Houston, Texas. All rights reserved.

8. 16×16-bit parallel multiplier incorporated as hardware.

9. 0-through-15-bit barrel shifter.

10. 32-bit ALU.

11. 32-bit accumulator.

12. Eight parallel I/O ports.

13. Interrupt with full context saving.

14. Self-emulation capability.

15. Test modes to aid production and yield analysis.

16. Microcomputer/microprocessor mode option for TMS320M10.

17. Microprocessor-only version of TMS320 with TMS32010.

18. 40-pin dual-in-line package.

The 320 is not only a specialized device that can perform like a digital signal processing chip, but also a general-purpose micro-computer chip with a very fast and powerful ALU and multiplier. Beside speech and image processing, it can perform spectral analysis, correlations, digital filtering, high-speed modem operations, and DSP algorithms at high speeds for robot applications.

A block diagram of the internal architecture of the TMS320 is shown in Fig. 15-1. The hardware is optimized around a two-bus system: a 16-bit program bus (P-Bus) and a 16-bit data bus (D-Bus).

The TMS320 architecture is a single-accumulator Harvard type that has been modified for increased flexibility and arithmetic speed. Unlike a strict Harvard architecture, however, it allows crossovers between the separate program and data memories to facilitate program branches based on data manipulation instructions and data values embedded in program segments. As an example of the TSM320's flexibility, data tables can reside within program space so that a system designer can make tradeoffs between the amount of table and program space needed for a specific application. High performance is achieved by the 32-bit ALU, the 16×16-bit parallel multiplier, the 0-through-15-bit barrel shifter, and the 32-bit accumulator. A special-purpose operation, "data move," has been defined within the data memory to further enhance performance in convolution operations.

Two modes of operation are available on the TMS320: a microcomputer mode that can expand its 1.5K 16-bit words of on-chip ROM to 4K total words, and a microprocessor mode where all 4K words of program memory are external. A self-emulation mode that utilizes both the microcomputer and microprocessor capabilities of the TMS320 is available for program development.

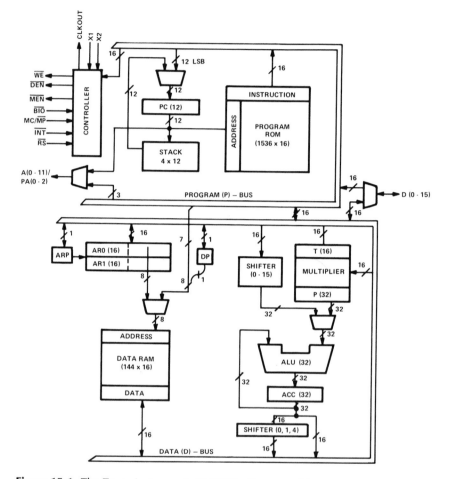

Figure 15-1 The Texas Instruments TMS320. Courtesy of Texas Instruments, Incorporated.

The on-chip ROM could be used to store those routines which are both heavily used and invariant over many applications. The user's external memory could then be reserved for specific information. One example of how to use this storage flexibility is in automotive applications: program and data for different engines are stored in external ROMs, while the algorithm for manipulating any engine is placed in the on-chip ROM. The TMS320's simple, yet comprehensive, instruction set, eight I/O ports and single-level interrupt provide the design engineer with a wide range of application options.

15-2   EXAMPLES OF APPLICATIONS USING
THE INTEL 2920 PROCESSOR* _____

As an example of using digital processing techniques to implement a typical analog circuit, consider the development of a sweeping local oscillator (SLO). This circuit is made up of three building blocks: (1) a sawtooth wave sweep rate generator (SRG); (2) a voltage-controlled oscillator (VCO); and (3) a waveform modifier (to reduce harmonic content of the VCO).

The sweep rate generator subsystem controls the minimum frequency, the frequency range, and the rate of change of frequency of the VCO. It does this by producing a sawtooth wave whose slope determines the rate of change, whose voltage excursion is proportional to the frequency range, and whose offset represents the minimum of that range.

The sawtooth wave is simple to generate: continuous decrementing of a register by a fixed value produces a linear negative slope. When the register voltage changes sign (crosses zero), a constant equal to the desired peak amplitude of the sawtooth is added. A load (LDA) instruction accomplishes the task.

The first step is to generate the slope constant. Suppose that four sweeps per second are desired. The resulting calculations are given in Fig. 15-2.

The VCO is developed similarly, except that the decrement value is not a constant, but rather, is determined by a scaled version of the SRG input waveform. Assuming a sweep from dc to 1.3 KHz, an offset would be determined by the low frequency, and the scaling factor by the high frequency. The net result would be a sawtooth wave with a period varying as a function of time.

This high-frequency sawtooth wave (dc to 1.3k Hz) has significant harmonic content, which will be reflected by the sampling frequency harmonics and will cause aliasing distortion of the SLO output. Digital filters cannot be used to compensate for this because they are also susceptible to the aliasing components.

Some method must therefore be found to reduce the harmonic content of this signal. One approach is to filter the VCO output by means of an external filter. This, however, would involve additional hardware, plus many extra instructions for I/O and A/D conversion.

---

*Section 15-2 from the *2920 Analog Signal Processor Design Handbook,* Chapt. 7, pp. 7–1 to 7–4, August 1980. Reprinted by permission of Intel Corporation, Copyright 1980.

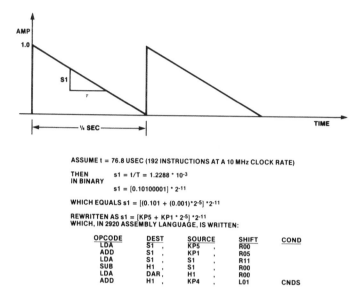

ASSUME t = 76.8 USEC (192 INSTRUCTIONS AT A 10 MHz CLOCK RATE)

THEN   s1 = t/T = 1.2288 * 10⁻³
IN BINARY
               s1 = [0.10100001] * 2⁻¹¹

WHICH EQUALS s1 = [(0.101 + (0.001)*2⁻⁵] *2⁻¹¹

REWRITTEN AS s1 = [KP5 + KP1 * 2⁻⁵] *2⁻¹¹
WHICH, IN 2920 ASSEMBLY LANGUAGE, IS WRITTEN:

OPCODE	DEST	SOURCE	SHIFT	COND
LDA	S1 ,	KP5 ,	R00	
ADD	S1 ,	KP1 ,	R05	
LDA	S1 ,	S1 ,	R11	
SUB	H1 ,	S1 ,	R00	
LDA	DAR,	H1 ,	R00	
ADD	H1 ,	KP4 ,	L01	CNDS

Figure 15-2 Sawtooth sweep rate generator. Courtesy of Intel Corporation.

An alternative is to shape the waveform in the time domain to look more like the desired sinusoid.

Investigation of the Fourier transforms of various symmetric waveforms reveals that a trapezoidal waveform can be adjusted so that even harmonics are eliminated and the first odd harmonic is the fifth. This adjustment is done by selecting the top of the trapezoid to be two-thirds of the peak of a corresponding triangular wave. The flow diagram to accomplish the transformation is shown in Fig. 15-3.

The final, correctly assembled, 2920 program is shown in Fig. 15-4, which gives the correct assembly code with comments, the hexadecimal object code, a symbol table with a list of errors or warnings, and RAM/ROM sizes. The program requires 18 instructions and 5 RAM locations.

Another example of an application that uses the 2920 is the piecewise linear logarithmic amplifier. The purpose of the logarithmic amplifier is to amplify low-level signals with a higher gain than high-level signals to reduce the overall output dynamic range. As an additional feature, the particular log amplifier described below provides an example of the use of 2920 code to implement a piecewise linear approximation of a general function. The input dynamic range of the amplifier is 50 dB, with an error of less than 1 dB for signal levels to −30 dB. The transfer characteristic is shown in Fig. 15-5.

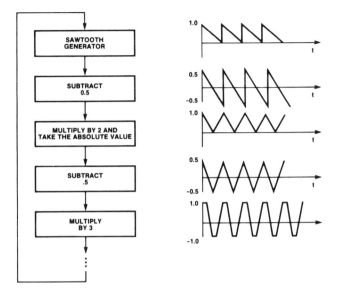

Figure 15-3 Waveform shaper. Courtesy of Intel Corporation.

```
LINE  LOC OBJECT  SOURCE STATEMENT

   1    0 48BAEF  LDA  S1, KP5, ROO         ;SET SWEEP RATE FOR SLO = 4HZ
   2    1 40BA8C  ADD  S1, KP1, RO5
   3    2 40004F  LDA  S1, S1, R11
   4    3 4000FB  SUB  H1, S1, ROO          ;SWEEP RATE GENERATOR IS H1
   5    4 404CEF  LDA  DAR, H1, ROO
   6    5 78B2DD  ADD  H1, KP4, LO1, CNDS   ;RESET H1 IF < 0
   7    6 44086E  LDA  H2, H1, RO4          ;H2 IS SCALED SWEEP WAVEFORM WHICH
   8    7 44088C  ADD  H2, H1, RO5          ; DRIVES VCO, RESULTING IN SLO MAX
   9    8 46006E  LDA  H2, H2, RO4          ; FREQUENCY OF 1.3KHZ
  10    9 44086D  ADD  H2, H1, R12
  11   10 4600FB  SUB  VCO, H2, ROO         ;VOLTAGE CONTROLLED OSCILLATOR
  12   11 424CEF  LDA  DAR, VCO, ROO
  13   12 7CB2DD  ADD  VCO, KP4, LO1, CNDS  ;RESET VCO IF < 0
  14   13 421BEF  LDA  OSC, VCO, ROO        ;WAVESHAPING WILL BE DONE IN RAM LOCATION OSC
  15   14 4892EB  SUB  OSC, KP4, ROO        ;CENTER SAWTOOTH ABOUT ZERO
  16   15 4810C7  ABS  OSC, OSC, LO1        ;DOUBLE AND TAKE ABSOLUTE VALUE
  17   16 4892EB  SUB  OSC, KP4, ROO        ;CENTER TRIANGLE WAVE ABOUT ZERO
  18   17 4810CD  ADD  OSC, OSC, LO1        ;MULTIPLY BY THREE. WAVEFORM IS CLIPPED TO
  19                                        ; BECOME TRAPAZOIDAL. RESULT IS IN OSC


SYMBOL:                 VALUE:

S1                         0
H1                         1
H2                         2
VCO                        3
OSC                        4


ASSEMBLY COMPLETE
ERRORS    =    0
WARNINGS  =    0
RAMSIZE   =    5
ROMSIZE   =   18
```

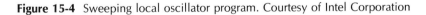

Figure 15-4 Sweeping local oscillator program. Courtesy of Intel Corporation

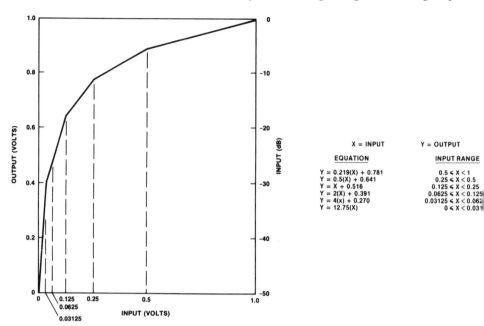

Figure 15-5 Log amplifier piecewise linear approximation transfer characteristics. Courtesy of Intel Corporation.

Six linear sections are used to approximate the log amplifier. The equations for these sections and the range of inputs for which each equation is used are given in Fig. 15-5. The equations were obtained graphically and then adjusted for coding efficiency. The input for the log amplifier must be positive and less than or equal to 1 V. To simplify matters, the endpoints for the linear sections were chosen as powers of two. This way, only one bit of the number to be processed need be checked to determine whether that number falls within an input range. The constant multipliers (slopes) of the linear sections were chosen to minimize error and still allow the multiplications to be efficiently handled in 2920 code.

The outputs for the amplifier are also less than or equal to 1 V, and positive. An output of 1 V corresponds to 0 dB, 0.8 V to −10 dB, 0.6 V to −20 dB, and so on. An output of 0 V corresponds to −50 dB or below. Thus, for a device with a maximum output of 1 V, an output of 0.7 V indicates a signal level of −15 dB. Regardless of V_{REF}, a 2920 output that is 70 percent of full scale represents −15 dB. Any dc offset that may exist at the output of the part should be taken into account when interpreting the output in dB.

The equations used in the log amplifier program are shown in Fig. 15-5, and the assembly code is given in Fig. 15-6. The first linear section of the amplifier to be implemented is the sixth section, which corresponds to inputs less than 1/32 V. However, all input signals, regardless of amplitude, are processed by the equation for this section initially. The original signal is then placed in the DAR. All subsequent operations are conditional, performed only if the tested bit of the DAR is a "one." Otherwise, a NOP is performed. Each bit of the DAR is tested, starting with bit 3 and progressing to bit 7. When a "one" is located, the multiplier and offset correeesponding to the indicated range of the output are used to compute the result, which replaces any previously computed result. If no "ones" are encountered, the input is less than 1/32 V, and only NOP's are performed. The value computed for the sixth section then remains unmodified. Since the program starts out by checking for small signals and then progresses to large signals, the computed value that corresponds to the signal range into which the input signal falls will be the final result.

If the input to the log amplifier has an offset error, it will show up at the output as an error that increased with decreasing input signal

```
***LOG AMP*****

ABS XO, XO, ROO              ;PREVENT PROCESSING OF NEGATIVE NUMBERS

;   SECTION 6
LDA LOUT, XO, LO2            ;LOUT = 12.75(XO)  ,   0 < XO < 0.03125
ADD LOUT, XO, LO2
ADD LOUT, XO, LO2
ADD LOUT, XO, RO1
ADD LOUT, XO, RO2

LDA DAR, XO, ROO             ;TRANSFER INPUT TO DAR TO DO CONDITIONAL ARITHMETIC

;   SECTION 5
LDA LOUT, XO, LO2, CND3      ;LOUT = 4(XO) + 0.270  ,   0.03125 < XO < 0.0625
ADD LOUT, KP2, ROO, CND3
ADD LOUT, KP5, RO5, CND3

;   SECTION 4
LDA LOUT, XO, LO1, CND4      ;LOUT = 2(XO) + 0.391  ,   0.0625 < XO < 0.125
ADD LOUT, KP3, ROO, CND4
ADD LOUT, KP2, RO4, CND4

;   SECTION 3
LDA LOUT, XO, ROO, CND5      ;LOUT = XO + 0.516  ,   0.125 < XO < 0.25
ADD LOUT, KP4, ROO, CND5
ADD LOUT, KP2, RO4, CND5

;   SECTION 2
LDA LOUT, XO, RO1, CND6      ;LOUT = 0.5(XO) + 0.641  ,   0.25 < XO < 0.5
ADD LOUT, KP5, ROO, CND6
ADD LOUT, KP2, RO4, CND6

;   SECTION 1
LDA LOUT, XO, RO3, CND7      ;LOUT = 0.219(XO) + 0.781  ,   0.5 < XO < 1
ADD LOUT, XO, RO4, CND7
ADD LOUT, XO, RO5, CND7
ADD LOUT, KP6, ROO, CND7
ADD LOUT, KP4, RO4, CND7

LDA DAR, LOUT, ROO           ;TRANSFER RESULT TO DAR TO OUTPUT OR OTHER
                             ;REGISTER FOR FURTHER PROCESSING
```

Figure 15-6 Piecewise linear log amplifier program. Courtesy of Intel Corporation.

Table 15-1
Pole/Zero Locations.*

Singularity	Normalized (1rps)	Denormalized (1 KHz)
Simple Pole	$\sigma_0 = 0.83124$ $\omega_0 = 0$	$\sigma_0 = -5222$ rps
Complex Pole Pair	$\sigma_1 \ \sigma \ -0.31128$ $\omega_1 = \pm 1.09399$	$\sigma_1 = -1955.8$ rps $\omega_1 = \pm 6873.7$ rps
Complex Zero Pair	$\sigma_2 = 0$ $\omega_2 = \pm 2.2701$	$\sigma_2 = 0$ rps $\omega_2 = 14263$ rps

*Copyright Intel Corporation, 1980.

strength. An input offset equal to 2^{-8} causes an error of about 2.5 dB in the approximation for the sixth section of the amplifier. If input offset should be a problem, it can be compensated for by adding a constant to the input before processing.

A third example of the 2920 processor make use of the digital filter. A multifrequency receiver requires a low-pass filter that can pass frequencies in the band from dc to 1k Hz with less than 1 dB ripple and that can provide at least 25 dB of rejection for frequencies above 2k Hz. A study of filter curves* shows that an elliptic function filter with 3 poles, 2 zeros, and a 25% reflection coefficient can meet these requirements. The filter pole/zero values are found normalized to 1 rad/sec bandwidth.† The normalized and denormalized values are listed in Table 15-1 for the filter selected.

The corresponding gain vs. frequency and s-plane plots are shown in Figs. 15-7 and 15-8, respectively.

Now that the poles and zeros are identified, the basic block diagram of the digital filter can be drawn, and the coefficients calculated. The three poles will require three delay elements, two of which can be used to implement the two zeros. The cascaded structure not only simplifies the calculations, but also realizes a digital filter structure that requires less coefficient accuracy than a direct (noncascaded) implementation would. The block diagram is shown in Fig. 15-9, along with the variable names that will be used in the 2920 program.

*See the nomographs in A. I. Zverev, *Handbook of Filter Synthesis*, Wiley & Sons, N.Y., pp. 140–143.
†Zverev, p. 178.

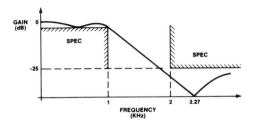

Figure 15-7 Filter characteristics. Courtesy of Intel Corporation.

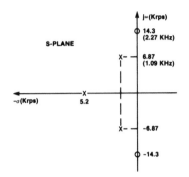

Figure 15-8 Pole and zero plot in the s-plane. Courtesy of Intel Corporation.

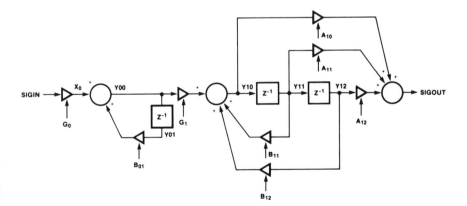

Figure 15-9 Block diagram of complex 3-pole 2-zero elliptical digital filter. Courtesy of Intel Corporation.

For the purposes of this example, assume a sample rate of 10kHz, or a period of 100 microseconds. Further, suppose that coefficient accuracies of $\pm 1\%$ or better are required. Then we have the following calculations.

1. Simple-pole calculations (Courtesy of Intel Corporation).

$$B_{01} = e^{-\sigma T} = \exp\left[-(5222)(0.0001)\right]$$
$$= 0.593214$$

$$B_{01} + 1\% = 0.10011001011 \text{ (in binary)}$$

$$B_{01} = 0.10010111110$$

$$B_{01} - 1\% = 0.10010110010$$

A value in this range can be represented as

$$V = 2^{-1} + 2^{-4} + 2^{-5} - 1^{-10}$$

$$\text{dc gain} = 1/1 - B_{01} = 2.4583$$

Complex-pole calculation (Courtesy of Intel Corporation).

$$B_{11} = 2e^{-\sigma T} \cos \omega t$$
$$= 2\exp\left[-(1955.8)(0.0001)\right]$$
$$\cos\left[(6873.7)(0.0001)\right]$$
$$= 1.271229$$

$$B_{11} + 1\% = 1.01001000101 \text{ (in binary)}$$

$$B_{11} = 1.01000101011$$
$$= 2^0 + 2^{-2} + 2^{-6}$$

$$B_{11} - 1\% = 1.010000\pm 000\pm$$

$$B_{12} = -e^{2\sigma T} = \exp\left[-(2)(1955.8)(0.0001)\right]$$
$$= 0.67627194$$

$$B_{12} + 1\% = 0.10101110110$$

$$B_{12} = 0.10101101001$$

$$B_{12} - 1\% = \left[(1+B_2)\sqrt{1+(B_1{}^2/4B_2)}\right]^{-1}$$

Complex-zero calculation (Courtesy of Intel Corporation).

$$A_{10} = 1$$

$$A_{11} = -(2)(A_{01})\,e^{-\sigma 2T}\,\cos\omega_2 T$$
$$= -0.28798805$$
$$= 0.01001001101 \text{ (in binary)}$$
$$= -2^{-2} - 2^{-5} - 2^{-8}$$

$$A_{12} = A_{01}e^{-2\sigma 2T}$$
$$= (1)\exp(0)$$
$$= 1.0$$

Figure 15-10 gives the complex filter program.

15-3 AN EXAMPLE OF A MODEM THAT USES THE INTEL 2920 PROCESSOR*

As an example of how the Intel 2920 processor can be used in modem applications, the design of a Bell 202 type, 1200 bps, FSK modem using the 2920 is discussed in this section. This standard modem can operate in half-duplex mode over two-wire lines and in full-duplex mode over four-wire lines. The 202 transmits and receives asynchronously, with frequencies of 1200 Hz (mark, or logic "one") and 2200 Hz (space, or logic "zero"). In addition, a 900 Hz tone is transmitted to signal the end of transmission.

The modem functions implemented by the 2920 are shown in Fig. 15-11. The 2920 performs both the transmit and receive functions, at a sample rate of 8 kHz, common in telephony applications. A 2912 switched-capacitor filter implements the antialiasing and reconstruction filters as well as the transmitting filter and part of the receiving filter.

The transmitter consists of a phase-coherent oscillator, wave-shaping circuit, and gate logic. The oscillator frequency is controlled by the request-to-send (RTS) and DATA signals. With RTS active, the DATA input is used to key the oscillator, generating the appropriate mark and space frequencies. The resulting signal is shaped to approximate a sinusoid before being outputted by the 2920. Logic that monitors the two oscillator control signals is used to turn the oscillator output off after transmission is completed. A clear-to-send (CTS) logic signal is also generated by the transmitter in response to the RTS signal. There is a 180 ms delay before CTS goes active.

---

*Section 15-3 from "Using the 2920 Processor in Modem Application," AP-117 by John Rittenhouse, © June 1981 by the Intel Corporation. Reprinted by Permission of Intel Corporation. Copyright 1981.

```
ISIS-II 2920 ASSEMBLER X102                                    PAGE    1

ASSEMBLER INVOKED BY  AS2920 FILTER

Three Pole Two Zero Elliptical Low-pass Filter

  LINE  LOC OBJECT SOURCE STATEMENT

     1                 $TITLE ('Three Pole Two Zero Elliptical Low-Pass Filter')
     2
     3                 Y12     EQU   YO1
     4                 SIGOUT  EQU   Y12
     5
     6                         , POLE 1
     7
     8    0 400BEF LDA YO1, YOO              , YO1=YOO
     9    1 40223E LDA YOO, DAR, R2          , YOO=GO*XO  (INPUT SCALED DOWN BY 4)
    10    2 40001C ADD YOO, YO1, R1
    11    3 40007C ADD YOO, YO1, R4
    12    4 40009C ADD YOO, YO1, R5
    13    5 40003B SUB YOO, YO1, R10         , -YOO= GO*XO + BO1*YO1
    14
    15                         , POLE 2 & 3
    16
    17    6 4200EF LDA Y12, Y11              , Y12 = Y11
    18    7 460BEF LDA Y11, Y10              , Y11 = Y10
    19    8 440B5E LDA Y10, YOO, R3          , Y10 = G1*YOO (STAGE PROPAGATION SCALED DOWN BY 8)
    20    9 4600BC ADD Y10, Y11, R6
    21   10 4600FD ADD Y10, Y11, RO
    22   11 46003C ADD Y10, Y11, R2          , Y10 = B11*Y11
    23   12 44001A SUB Y10, Y12, R1
    24   13 44005A SUB Y10, Y12, R3
    25   14 44009A SUB Y10, Y12, R5
    26   15 4400BA SUB Y10, Y12, R6          , Y10 = B11*Y11 + B22*Y12 + G1*YOO
    27
    28                         , ZERO 1 & 2
    29
    30   16 4208ED ADD SIGOUT, Y10           , SIGOUT = A10*Y10 + A12*Y12
    31   17 42002A SUB SIGOUT, Y11, R2
    32   18 42008A SUB SIGOUT, Y11, R5
    33   19 4200EA SUB SIGOUT, Y11, R8       , SIGOUT = A10*Y10 + A11*Y11 + A12*Y12
    34
    35
    36   20 4044CF LDA DAR, SIGOUT, L1       , OUTPUT SCALED UP BY 2
    37
    38
    39                 END


  SYMBOL:                    VALUE

  Y12                          0
  YO1                          0
  SIGOUT                       0
  YOO                          1
  Y11                          2
  Y10                          3

ASSEMBLY COMPLETE
```

Figure 15-10 Complex digital filter program. Courtesy of Intel Corporation.

The receiving section of the modem consists of a receiving filter, automatic level control (ALC), delay line discriminator, and carrier detector. The first operation performed by the receiver is to filter the incoming signal to remove out-of-band noise. Then the signal is passed through the ALC to produce a constant-amplitude signal at the detector input. The detector is a delay line discriminator, consisting of a delay, multiply, and low-pass filter. The voltage level at the output of the low-pass filter varies with the frequency of the received signal. By comparing this signal to a threshold, a decision can be made as to whether a mark or space frequency has been received. To prevent noise from being interpreted as valid data, a carrier-detect function is implemented which turns the modem output off if the signal energy in the passband of the receive filter drops too low. A soft carrier turnoff in response to the 900 Hz end-of-message tone.

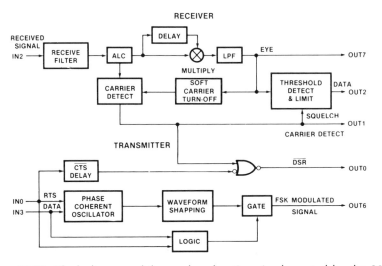

Figure 15-11 Block diagram of the modem functions implemented by the 2920. Courtesy of Intel Corporation.

The modem uses phase-coherent, frequency-shift-keyed (FSK) modulation. The FSK generator is based upon a simple voltage-controlled relaxation oscillator, implemented in the 2920 by subtracting a value (step size) from a memory location (the oscillator) once each sample period. When the result of the subtraction is negative, the oscillator is reset by adding one to it. The step size of the oscillator determines the frequency of the oscillation and can be computed from the relation $K = f_0/f_s$, where f_0 is the desired frequency of the oscillator, f_s is the sample rate, and K is the step size as seen in Fig. 15-12. Varying the step size on the basis of external conditions varies the frequency of the oscillator. Because only the step size of the oscillator is changed, and the oscillator continues from its previous sample value, the oscillator is phase coherent.

The oscillator for this modem must generate four frequencies, corresponding to mark, space, end of message, and off. Using two input channels and a one-bit A/D conversion for each channel, two control bits are read by the 2920 and used to key the oscillator as shown in Fig. 15-13.

With RTS active (high), the DATA input controls mark and space frequencies. If both inputs are low, the oscillator outputs a steady zero level. A flow chart for the modulator is shown in Fig. 15-14. Initially, the step size is calculated to given a 1900 Hz oscillation. Then, one of the control bits (RTS) is read from input channel zero. The frequency

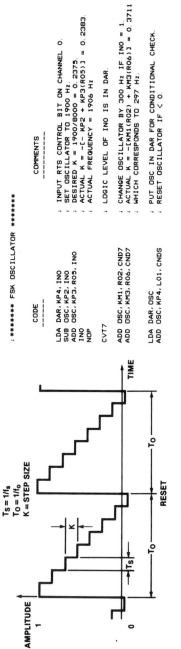

; ******** FSK OSCILLATOR ********

```
        CODE                      COMMENTS
        ----                      --------

LDA DAR, KP4, INO       ; INPUT RTS CONTROL BIT ON CHANNEL 0.
SUB OSC, KP2, INO       ; SET OSCILLATOR TO 1900 Hz.
ADD OSC, KP3, RO5, INO  ; DESIRED K = 1900/8000 = 0.2375.
INO                     ; ACTUAL K = -[- KP2 + KP3(RO5)] = 0.2383.
NOP                     ; ACTUAL FREQUENCY = 1906 Hz

CVT7                    ; LOGIC LEVEL OF INO IS IN DAR.

ADD OSC, KM1, RO2, CND7 ; CHANGE OSCILLATOR BY 300 Hz IF INO = 1
ADD OSC, KM3, RO6, CND7 ; ACTUAL K = -[KM1(RO2) + KM3(RO6)] = 0.3711
                        ; WHICH CORRESPONDS TO 297 Hz.

LDA DAR, OSC            ; PUT OSC IN DAR FOR CONDITIONAL CHECK.
ADD OSC, KP4, LO1, CNDS ; RESET OSCILLATOR IF < 0.
```

$T_S = 1/f_s$
$T_0 = 1/f_0$
K = STEP SIZE

AMPLITUDE
1

0

T_0 RESET T_0

TIME

Figure 15-12 Implementing an FSK oscillator. Courtesy of Intel Corporation.

480

IN0(RTS)	IN3(DATA)	DESIRED FREQUENCY
0	0	0 Hz
0	1	900 Hz
1	1	1200 Hz
1	0	2200 Hz

Figure 15-13 Modulator control. Courtesy of Intel Corporation.

of the oscillator is increased by 300 Hz if this bit is a "one"; otherwise, it is left unchanged. The second control bit (DATA) is then read from channel three, causing the frequency to be reduced by 1000 Hz if it is a one. If the bit is a zero, the frequency is not modified. Thus, using the two control bits, it is possible to produce 900 Hz, 1200 Hz, and 2200 Hz tones. The actual frequencies generated by the 2920 are 906 Hz, 1203 Hz, and 2203 Hz. The sawtooth output waveform of the relaxation oscillator is then transformed using piecewise-linear techniques to approximate a sinusoid. To provide for the OFF state (both inputs bits equal to zero), the contents of a register are ANDed with the output of the oscillator to gate it on and off. This gate register, initially filled with zeros, is loaded with ones only if one of the control bits is a one. Thus, the oscillator output will be clamped to zero if both control bits are zero.

The receiving filter improves the signal-to-noise ratio by passing the desired frequency components of the received FSK signal and rejecting out-of-band noise. If the filter bandwidth is too wide, noise will interfere with the performance of the demodulator. If the filter bandwidth is too narrow, significant sidebands of the received FSK signal may be lost, thereby reducing modem performance.

The effect of the receiving filter on the signal spectrum can most easily be evaluated by observing the demodulator output. If randomly keyed data is received and the level transitions of a one-bit period are observed at the demodulator output over a period of time with an oscilloscope, a pattern like that of Fig. 15-15 will be seen. This EYE pattern provides a useful means of evaluating modem performance. If significant sidebands are removed from the signal spectrum by the receiving filter, the EYE pattern will begin to collapse, or become unsymmetrical. This will make the detection operation of the demodulator more susceptible to noise and transmission line distortion.

The spectrum of a randomly keyed FSK signal for a 202 type modem is shown in Fig. 15-16. As the figure shows, the frequency range from approximately 1100 Hz to 2300 Hz is the most critical, although sidebands are present outside this range. A rule of thumb for binary

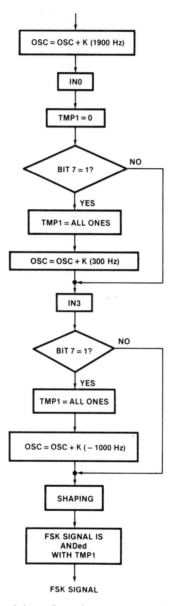

Figure 15-14 FSK modulator flow chart. Courtesy of Intel Corporation.

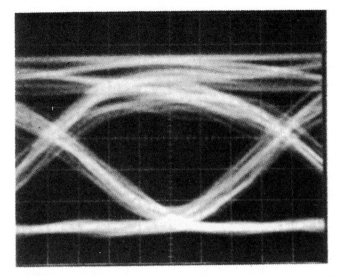

Figure 15-15 Reconstructed EYE pattern from the demodulator output. Courtesy of Intel Corporation.

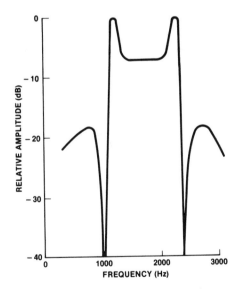

Figure 15-16 Sketch of the spectrum of a randomly keyed FSK signal for a 202 type modem. Courtesy of Intel Corporation.

FSK is that in excess of 1 Hz of bandwidth is required for each 1 bps of transmission rate. Therefore, at least a 1200 Hz bandwidth centered halfway between the two FSK frequencies is required for this modem application. This is the 1100 Hz to 2300 Hz frequency band just identified as significant in the figure. Frequency components in this range should be passed by the receiving filter with a minimum of amplitude and phase distortion.

The receiving filter used in this modem was designed interactively using the SAPS20 applications compiler and has the gain characteristics shown in Figs. 15-17 and 15-18. The filter is realized with five cascaded second-order sections, as shown in Fig. 15-19. This section implements a complex-pole pair and a complex-zero pair. For a simple zero, B2 in the figure is zero. If only a pole is needed, both B1 and B2 are zero. The poles and zeros for the receiving filter are listed in Fig. 15-17. (These are s-plane locations before being moved to the z-plane, via the matched-Z transformation, for plotting and generation of 2920 code.) A zero was placed at dc to remove any dc component from the received signal that would adversely affect the demodulator. As can be seen from Fig. 15-18, the frequencies in the band from 1100 Hz to 2300 Hz are passed by this filter with little attenuation, the greatest being 1.72 dB at 1100 Hz. The passband ripple from 1200 Hz to 2200 Hz is 0.5 dB. On the other hand, the filter provides greater than 20 dB attenuation below 700 Hz and greater than 45 dB attenuation below 450 Hz. The rejection at 4000 Hz (half the sample rate) is 13 dB. The anti-aliasing function, performed externally to the 2920 by the 2912 filter, provides additional high-frequency rolloff (14 dB at 4000 Hz) to complete the band-pass characteristic of the receiving filter as shown in Fig. 15-20.

Because the receiving filter does not have a symmetrical frequency response with respect to gain or phase about the central frequency, there will be some distortion of the received FSK signal. This is reflected in the EYE pattern (Fig. 15-15), which is not symmetric. The top of the EYE pattern corresponds to frequencies less than the central frequency. If additional effort is applied to the design of the receiving filter, more symmetrical gain and phase characteristics can be obtained, resulting in a more symmetrical EYE pattern and a corresponding improvement in modem performance. The effect of the expected transmission line characteristics must also be included when designing the receiving filter to account for amplitude and phase distortion of the received signal.

Because the demodulator for this modem implementation is sensitive to the amplitude of the received signal, the receiving filter is followed by an automatic level control to maintain a constant signal

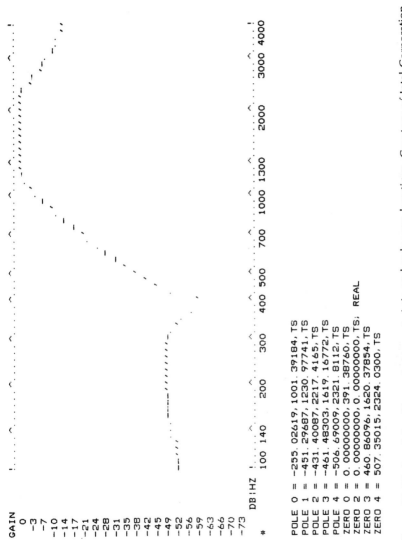

POLE 0 = -255.02619, 1001.39184, TS
POLE 1 = -451.29687, 1230.97741, TS
POLE 2 = -431.40087, 2217.4165, TS
POLE 3 = -461.48303, 1619.16772, TS
POLE 4 = -506.69009, 2321.8112, TS
ZERO 0 = 0.00000000, 391.38760, TS
ZERO 2 = 0.00000000, 0.00000000, TS; REAL
ZERO 3 = 460.86096, 1620.37854, TS
ZERO 4 = 507.35015, 2324.0300, TS

Figure 15-17 Receiving filter gain characteristic and pole-zero locations. Courtesy of Intel Corporation.

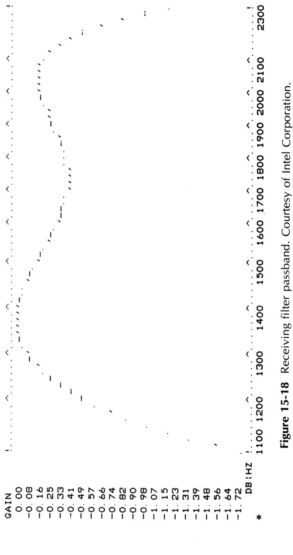

Figure 15-18 Receiving filter passband. Courtesy of Intel Corporation.

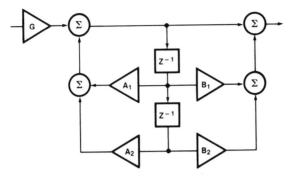

Figure 15-19 Diagram of a digital filter quadratic section. Courtesy of Intel Corporation.

amplitude for the demodulator. Continuous-time modem implementations frequently use a hard limiter to provide this level control function. Such an operation generates harmonics, which may be removed by a low-pass filter in a continuous-time system. However, in a sampled-data system, these harmonics are reflected about the sample rate (aliasing), interfering with the desired signal. It is therefore desirable to use a linear method of level control in a sampled system.

The automatic level control function is accomplished in this implementation as shown in Fig. 15-21. The received signal is divided by a level proportional to its amplitude. This level is derived from the signal by performing an envelope detection with a full-wave rectifier and a low-pass filter. The filter bandwidth must be narrow enough to reject the harmonics and aliasing terms generated by the full-wave rectifier. A one-pole filter with a bandwidth of 20 Hz is used in the current implementation. Because of the narrow bandwidth of the level control, it cannot follow a rapidly varying signal amplitude. If the envelope of the received signal is of a sufficiently high frequency that it is shifted in phase by the low-pass filter with respect to the received signal, distortion will result. With a low-pass bandwidth of 20 Hz, an amplitude modulation of up to approximately 2 Hz can be tolerated. The main function of the level control is to compensate for low signal levels and amplitude fades, rather than to remove higher frequency modulation.

Demodulation of the frequency shift keyed signal is accomplished with a delay line discriminator. Other techniques can be used, but this one is particularly simple and effective. Such a demodulator consists of a delay line, multiplier, and low-pass filter. The signal is multiplied by the delayed signal and low-pass filter. The level at the output of the low-pass filter depends on the frequency of the received signal.

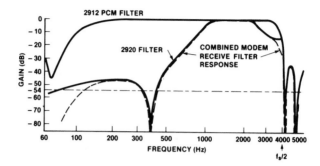

Figure 15-20 Combined 2912/2920 receiving filter response. Courtesy of Intel Corporation.

The delay line serves to implement a phase shift in the signal equal to ωT, where T is the delay. The delayed signal is then multiplied by the undelayed signal, generating sum and difference frequencies

$$A \cos (\omega t) \cdot A \cos (\omega t + \theta) = \frac{A^2}{2} \cos (\theta)$$
$$+ \frac{A^2}{2} \cos (2\omega t + \theta) \qquad (15\text{-}1)$$

where

$$\theta = \omega T$$

$$\omega = \text{signal frequency}$$

$$T = \text{delay}$$

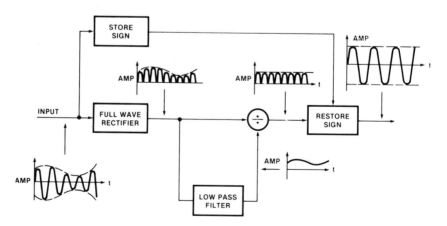

Figure 15-21 Automatic level control block diagram. Courtesy of Intel Corporation.

The frequency component at twice the original frequency is removed by the low-pass filter, leaving only the baseband component. Since $\theta = \omega T$, and T is fixed, the value of this baseband term is dependent only on the frequency and amplitude of the incoming signal. By holding the amplitude fixed with the automatic level control, the term becomes dependent only on the frequency of the received signal. Hence, the desired demodulation can be accomplished by comparing the value of this term with a threshold. Figure 15-22 shows the demodulator characteristic. If T is properly chosen, and the signal frequency variation is not too large, only the "linear" region of the demodulator is used.

For ease of implementation, T was chosen to be 125 μs (one sample delay at f=8k Hz). The region of the demodulation characteristic used for this delay is nearly linear. The "ideal" choice would have been T= 147 μs, which results in a 90° phase shift of the signal at 1700 Hz, the modem central frequency. This would center the operation on the demodulator characteristic, taking advantage of the most linear region and resulting in a decision threshold of zero. The decision threshold for the current implementation is nonzero. However, the automatic level control will ensure that this threshold does not change with varying received signal levels.

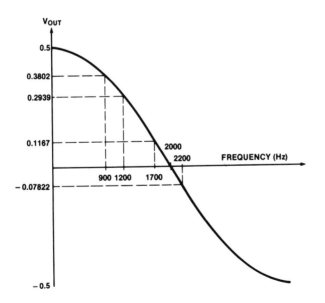

Figure 15-22 Demodulator transfer characteristic. Courtesy of Intel Corporation.

15-4 THE μPD7720 SIGNAL PROCESSING (SPI) SYSTEM*

Digital signal processing systems generally are made up of FIR/IIR filters and/or DFT/FFT processors.

Fabricated in high-speed NMOS, the μPD7720 signal processing interface (SPI) is a complete 16-bit microcomputer (Fig. 15-23) on a single chip. ROM space is provided for program and data/coefficient storage, while the on-chip RAM may be used for temporary data, coefficients, and results. Computational power is provided by a 16-bit Arithmetic/Logic Unit (ALU) and a separate 16 × 16-bit fully parallel multiplier. This combination allows the implementation of a "sum of products" operation in a single 250 ns instruction cycle. In addition, each arithmetic instruction provides for a number of data movement operations to further increase throughput. Two serial I/O ports are provided for interfacing to codecs and other serially oriented devices while a parallel port provides both data and status information to conventional μP for more sophisticated applications.

Applications of the μPD7720 chip includes

1. Speech synthesis and analysis.
2. Digital filtering.
3. Fast Fourier transforms (FFTs).
4. Dual-tone multifrequency (DTMF) transmitters/receivers.
5. High-speed data modems.
6. Equalizers.
7. Adaptive control.
8. Sonar/radar image processing.
9. Numerical processing (calculation-intensive applications).

Features of the μPD7720 include

1. Fast instruction execution: 250 ns/8 MHz clock.
2. 16-bit data word.
3. Multioperation instructions for optimizing program execution.
4. Large memory capacities.
5. Program ROM, 512 × 23 bits.
6. Data/coefficient ROM, 510 × 13 bits.

---

*Section 15-4 from *μPD7720 Signal Processing Interface (SPI) Technical Manual*. Reprinted by permission of NEC Electronics, U.S.A. Inc.,© 1982.

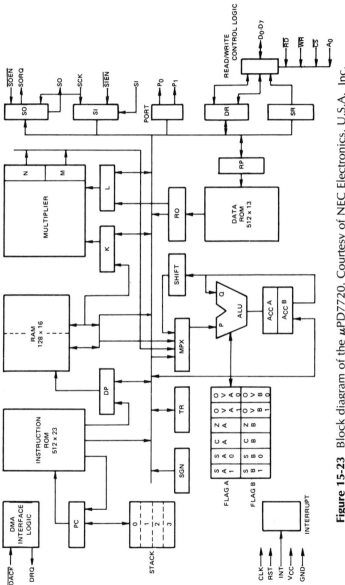

Figure 15-23 Block diagram of the μPD7720. Courtesy of NEC Electronics, U.S.A. Inc.

491

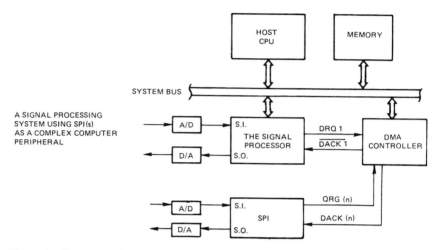

Figure 15-24 A signal processing system using the SPI(s) as a complex computer peripheral. Courtesy of NEC Electronics, U.S.A. Inc.

7. Data RAM, 128 × 16 bits.
8. Fast (250 ns/8 MHz) 16 × 16-bit parallel multiplier with 31-bit result.
9. Four-level subroutine stack for program efficiency.
10. Multiple I/O capabilities.

Handshake signals, including the Direct Memory Access (DMA) controls, allow the SPI to act as a sophisticated programmable peripheral as well as a stand-alone microcomputer as shown in Fig. 15-24.

The SPI has four (4) instructions. Two of these instructions, OP and RT,* are almost identical in that both execute the same operations, but RT also implements a subroutine/interrupt return when it completes its other operations.

OP and RT can perform the following operations in a single instruction: Implement an ALU operation on either accumulator, using an operator from one of the four inputs; modify the lower four bits and upper three bits of the data RAM pointer; decrement the data/coefficient ROM pointer; and move data from one register to another. While this is happening, the two 16-bit multiplier input registers are multiplied, and their 31-bit product is placed in the multiplier output registers.

*In the assembler, the RT instruction is treated as a variation of the OP instruction, not as a separate instruction.

Figure 15-24 also shows the input and output data of the μPD7720 serially as well as communicating on a microcomputer system bus.

Figure 15-25 shows two μPD7720's in a cascaded configuration. The SPI's could also be attached to a microcomputer bus if desired, but this is not shown in the example. This configuration is good for systems in which data rates exceed the capability of one SP∓ to process the allocated function completely within the available time.

Figure 15-26 shows an application of the SPI for spectral analysis.

15-5 THE ADAPTIVE TRANSVERSAL FILTER USING THE μPD7720* _____

Adaptive transversal filters have been used for channel equalization in high-speed modems for years. Without such a filter, high data rates over existing telephone lines would be nearly impossible. For this reason, telecommunications is one of the few industries that use DSP techniques in their products, having bitten the bullet on the cost of custom chips and expensive boards. The filter described in this section is a simplification of the type used in modems, functioning as a linear equalizer.

Figure 15-27 shows the algorithmic structure of the adaptive filter in question and the equations of the three basic parts into which it can be broken for calculational purposes.

Upon close examination of the figure, it can be seen that a multitude of multiply-add operations are necessary to implement the filter. The ability to do fast multiplies and adds is crucial to the use of any DSP component, the speed being directly related to the "bandwidth" of the real-time application involved. Another important aspect of the algorithm is that all the data and coefficients are variables and therefore must be kept in RAM. An efficient technique for accessing and addressing two variables for multiplication can be just as important to performance of the algorithm as is the speed of multiplication and addition.

The decision or detection part of the algorithm varies depending on the application and system and was left as a block in the diagram to highlight this point. Most modem equalizers output to a controlling processor (the transversal filter's output) that can detect the character, make a limit value decision, and send that decision back to the equali-

---

*Section 15-5 from Daniel Epstein, "An Adaptive Transversal Filter Using the μPD7720," National Electronics Conference, October 27, 1981. Reprinted courtesy of NEC Electronics, USA, Inc.

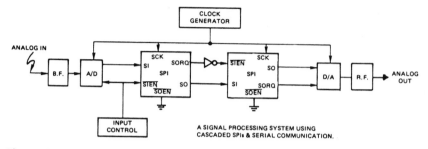

Figure 15-25 A signal processing system using SPI's and serial communication. Courtesy of NEC Electronics, U.S.A. Inc.

zer to calculate the filter error (ϵ_k). A detection algorithm, using a hard-limited four-state output ($0.7 \pm 0.7j$), fills out the algorithm of Fig. 15-27. The controlling processor only inputs data. No outputs are used in the system, but such an operation could easily be added.

To give some idea of the task at hand, counting individual operations, it takes four address manipulations, five data accesses, four multiplies, three adds, and one subtract to do the calculations necessary for just one of the taps in equation 1 using complex data and coefficients. In the filter of the example, 24 taps of complex data and coefficients are used.

The µPD7720 is specifically designed to implement DSP algorithms. Like other single-chip microcomputers, the 7720 contains instruction ROM (512 × 23), data RAM (128 × 16), program counter, stack (4 level), ALU, internal registers, and I/O and interrupt capability. To meet the needs of DSP computations, some additional features were incorporated, viz., a 16-bit data word, data ROM (512 × 13), a 16-bit pipeline multiplier, dual accumulators with flags, a primary bus (IDB), four special buses, effective memory addressing capability, a 250 ns multioperation instruction, and state-of-the-art architecture tying all the pieces together.

The µPD7720 has four major calculation-oriented functional blocks: dual data RAM (64 × 16 high and low), data ROM, multiplier,

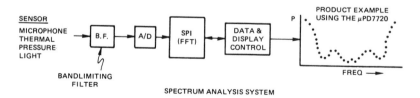

Figure 15-26 Spectrum Analysis System. Courtesy of NEC Electronics, U.S.A. Inc.

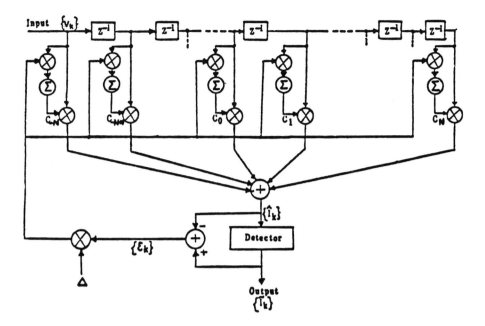

1) **Transversal Filter Equation**

$$\hat{I}_\kappa = \sum_{1=-N}^{N} C_1 V_{\kappa-1}$$

2) **Coefficient Adjustment**

$$C_{(\kappa+1)} = C_{\kappa 1} + \Delta\epsilon_\kappa V^*_{\kappa-1}$$

3) **Detection & Error**

$$\gamma_\kappa = \text{sgn}\ (\hat{I}_\kappa)$$

$$\epsilon_\kappa = \gamma_\kappa - \hat{I}_\kappa$$

$$\text{sgn}\ (x) = \begin{cases} 1 = -N, \ldots\ldots -1, \emptyset, 1, \ldots\ldots +N \\ +.7 + j.7, \quad R_e\ (x)\ >0, I_m(x)\ >0 \\ .7 - j.7, \quad R_e\ (x)\ >0, I_m(x)\ <0 \\ -.7 + j.7, \quad R_e\ (x)\ <0, I_m(x)\ >0 \\ -.7 - j.7, \quad R_e\ (x)\ <0, I_m(x)\ <0 \end{cases}$$

Figure 15-27 Adaptive transversal filter algorithmic structure. Courtesy of NEC Electronics, U.S.A. Inc.

and ALU. The key to the 7720 achieving a 250 ns load-multiply and add/sub is connecting all the blocks at the same time. This is handled in the SPI by the IDB and special buses.

The IDB may be used for memory, accumulator, and all register data transfers, except multiplier output. All of these locations can send data to either multiplier input register.

The special buses are included in the SPI to speed the throughput of the multiplier and ALU. Only two of the four special buses are used in the example filter's implementation. One bus connects the two multiplier output registers directly to one of four ALU multiplexed inputs, while the other bus makes a direct connection from high RAM to the K-multiplier input register.

Using all three buses in parallel, the K-register can receive data from high RAM. The L-multiplier input register receives data from the IDB, which could be the same value that went to K, a value from low RAM, or even a value from one of the registers. Finally, a multiplier output via its own bus can be operated on by the ALU. As long as multiplier and its registers are synced and buffered properly, all three exchanges can and do happen in the same instruction.

The multiplier in the SPI has two input and output registers. In each instruction cycle, the multiplier multiplies the values in the input registers and places the solution in the output registers, creating a one-instruction cycle pipeline. There is no multiply instruction.

The SPI's RAM is broken into two halves, each addressed by the low six bits of the same seven-bit pointer (DP). (See Fig. 15-28.) The MSB of the DP is not used for addressing, but decides which of the two memories interfaces to the IDB. In either case, on a read, the high RAM value is always made available for input to the K-register. This unique feature makes it possible for the same, or two different, RAM values to be sent to the multiplier in the same instruction. Of course, the two values must come from matching address locations in high and low RAM, as there is only one address pointer (DP).

The DP has unique features of its own. As part of the same instruction that can effect a load-multiply and add, two distinct parts of the DP can be modified in different ways. The high three bits are modified by being exclusive-Ored with three bits in the instruction word. The low four can be incremented, decremented, cleared, or not effected, depending on two other bits in the word. This partitioning of the DP gives the RAM a column/row structure in which the row address is defined by DPH (high three) and column by DPL (low four; row mobility is better than column). An additional feature gained by this partitioning is that by placing all the values for an individual calculation in the same column (or row), a subroutine for that calculation could

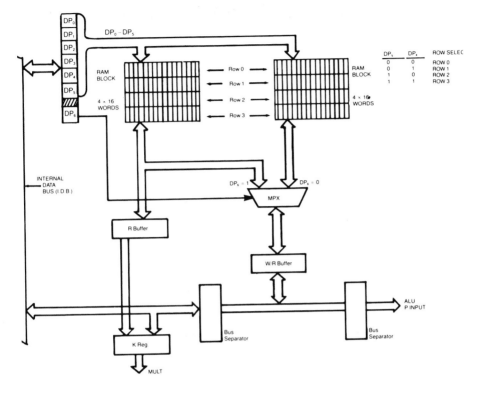

Figure 15-28 Block diagram of RAM, DP and peripherals. Courtesy of NEC Electronics, U.S.A. Inc.

be independent of column (row) position, and therefore, a whole array of values requiring the same calculation could use one or two basic subroutines.

PROBLEMS

15-1 Discuss the technology of the digital signal processing chip.

15-2 Go to the library and build or propose a digital signal processing chip for data communication, spectrum analysis, or physiological monitoring in cardiology.

15-3 Discuss a processor used in modem applications.

APPENDIX

The window functions given here are all assumed to be even functions of t with a width τ. However, only half of the function, corresponding to the range $0 \leqslant t/\tau \leqslant 0.5$ is shown in each case.

Let $w(t)$ represent the continuous-time form of any window function as given in the equations or as shown on the curves. The discrete-time window function is determined by replacing t by $n\,\mathrm{T}$ and evaluating the function for integer values of n.

Let $\mathrm{W}(f)$ represent the Fourier transform of $w(t)$, and let $\mathrm{W}(0)$ represent the dc value of the transform. The amplitude response for each window function in decibel form is defined by

$$\mathrm{W_{db}}(f) = 20 \, \mathrm{Log}_{10} \frac{|\mathrm{W}(f)|}{\mathrm{W}(0)} \qquad (A\text{-}1)$$

The amplitude response curves are presented as a function of f/F, where F is defined as

$$\mathrm{F} = \frac{1}{\tau} \qquad (A\text{-}2)$$

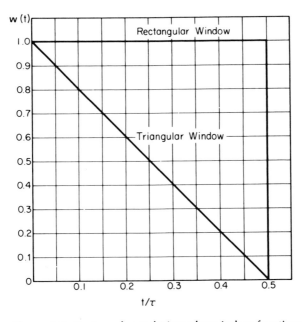

Figure A-1 Rectangular and triangular window functions.

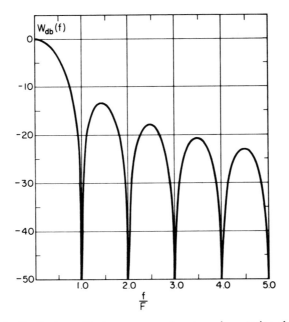

Figure A-2 Decibel amplitude response of rectangular window function.

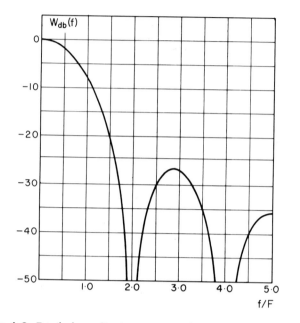

Figure A-3 Decibel amplitude response of triangular window function.

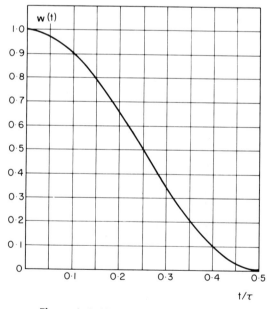

Figure A-4 Hanning window function.

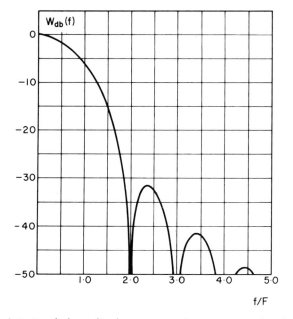

Figure A-5 Decibel amplitude response of Hanning window function.

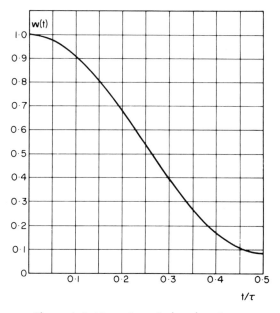

Figure A-6 Hamming window function.

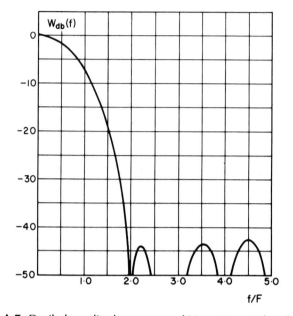

Figure A-7 Decibel amplitude response of Hamming window function.

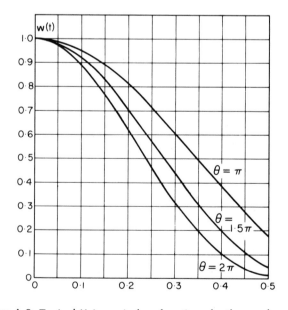

Figure A-8 Typical Kaiser window functions for three values of θ.

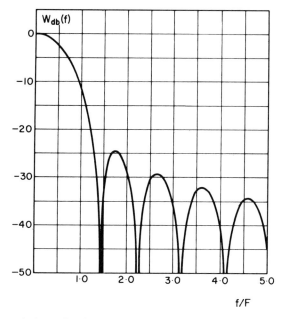

Figure A-9 Decibel amplitude response of Kaiser window function with $\theta = \pi$.

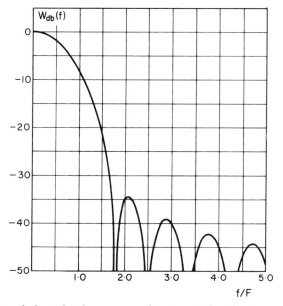

Figure A-10 Decibel amplitude response of Kaiser window function with $\theta = 1.5\pi$.

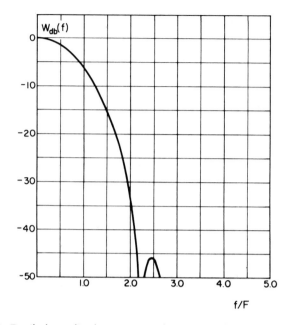

Figure A-11 Decibel amplitude response of Kaiser window function with $\theta = 2\pi$.

REFERENCES

_____ *PART I* _____

Antoniou, A. *Digital Filters: Analysis and Design.* New York: McGraw-Hill, 1979.

Blackman, R. B., and Tukey, J. W. *The Measurement of Power Spectra from the Point Of View of Communication Engineering.* New York: Dover, 1959.

Bogner, R. E., and Constantinides, A. G., eds. *Introduction to Digital Filtering.* New York: Wiley, 1975.

Brigham, O. *The Fast Fourier Transform.* Englewood Cliffs, N. J.: Prentice-Hall, 1974.

Cadzow, J. A., Martins, H. R. *Discrete-Time and Computer Control Systems.* Englewood Cliffs, N. J.: Prentice-Hall, 1970.

Castleman, K. R. *Digital Image Processing.* Englewood Cliffs, N. J.: Prentice-Hall, 1979.

Cooley, J. W., Tukey, J. W. "An Algorithm for the Machine Computation of Complex." *Math. Computation,* 19 (1965): 297-301.

Digital Signal Processing Committee. *Programs for Digital Signal Processing.* New York: IEEE Press, 1979.

Gold, B., and Rader, C. M. *Digital Processing of Signals*. New York: McGraw-Hill, 1969.

Hamming, R. W. *Digital Filters*. Englewood Cliffs, N. J.: Prentice-Hall, 1977.

Helms, H. D., Kaiser, J. F., and Rabiner, L. R., eds. *Literature in Digital Signal Processing*. New York: IEEE Press, 1975.

Hewlett-Packard, Inc. *Fourier Analyzer Training Manual,* Application Note 140-0.

Lam, H. *Analog and Digital Filters: Design and Realization*. Englewood Cliffs, N. J.: Prentice-Hall, 1979.

Oppenheim, A. V., ed. *Application of Digital Signal Processing*. Englewood Cliffs, N. J.: Prentice-Hall, 1978.

Oppenheim, A. V., and Schafer, R. W. *Digital Signal Processing*. Englewood Cliffs, N. J.: Prentice-Hall, 1975.

Peled, A., and Liu, B. *Digital Signal Processing*. New York: Wiley, 1976.

Rabiner, L. R., and Gold, B. *Theory and Application of Digital Signal Processing*. Englewood Cliffs, N. J.: Prentice-Hall, 1975.

Rabiner, L. R., and Rader, C. M., eds. *Digital Signal Processing*. New York: IEEE Press, 1972.

Rabiner, L. R., and Schafer, R. W. *Digital Processing of Speech Signals*. Englewood Cliffs, N. J.: Prentice-Hall, 1979.

Rader, C. M., McClellan, J. H. *Number Theory in Digital Signal Processing*. Englewood Cliffs, N. J.: Prentice-Hall, 1979.

Salazar, A. C., ed. *Digital Signal Computers and Processors*. New York: IEEE Press, 1977.

Schwartz, M. *Signal Processing: Discrete Spectral Analysis, Detection, and Estimation*. New York: McGraw-Hill, 1975.

Stearns, S. D. *Digital Signal Analysis*. Rochelle Park, N. J.: Hayden Book Co., 1976.

Terrell, T. J. *Introduction to Digital Filters*. New York: Wiley, 1980.

Tretter, S. A. *Introduction to Discrete-Time Signal Processing*. New York: Wiley, 1976.

Wait, J. V. "Digital Filters." In *Active Filters: Lumped, Distributed, Integrated, Digital, and Parametric,* edited by L. P. Huelsman. New York: McGraw-Hill, 1970.

_____ *PART II* _____

Aggarwal, J. K. *Digital Signal Processing*. North Hollywood, Calif.: Western Periodicals, 1979.

Antoniou, A. *Digital Filters: Analysis and Design*. New York: McGraw-Hill, 1979.

Application of Filters to Analog and Digital Signal Processing. 2nd edition. Wavetek Rockland, Inc.: Rockleigh, N. J., 1979.

Araseki, T., et al. "A Microprocessor Echo Canceller," *Proceedings of the 4th International Conference on Digital Satellite Communication*. 1979.

"Arithmetic Chips Assume Greater Importance as μC Users Demand Faster Response," *EDN*, April 14, 1982, p. 61.

Beauchamp, K. G., and Yuen, C. K. *Digital Methods for Signal Analysis*. London and Boston: George Allen & Unwin, 1979.

Bendat, J., and Piersol, A. *Engineering Applications of Correlation and Spectral Analysis*. New York: John Wiley & Sons, 1980.

Bjørnø, L. ed. *Underwater Acoustics and Signal Processing*. D. Reidel, 1981.

Broderson, R. W., Hewes, C. R., and Buss, D. D. "A 500-Stage CCD Transversal Filter for Spectral Analysis." *IEEE Journal of Solid-State Circuits*, SC-11 No. 1, February 1976, pp. 75-84.

Cappellini, V., and Constantinides, A. G., eds. *Digital Signal Processing*. London and New York: Academic Press, 1980.

Cappellini, V., Constantinides, A. G., and Emiliani, P., eds. *Digital Filters and Their Applications*. London and New York: Academic Press, 1978.

Cavenor, M. C., Arnold, J. F., and Moyle, G. A. "Using a Digital Processing Oscilloscope in Image Processing Simulations." HANDSHAKE FALL 1980, Tektronix, Inc., Beaverton, Oregon.

Chen, Chi-hau, ed. *Digital Waveform Processing and Recognition*. CRC Press: Boca Raton, Fla., 1982.

Chen, Chi-Tsong. *One-Dimensional Digital Signal Processing*. New York: Dekker, 1978.

Cushman, R. H. "ICS and semiconductor." *EDN*, July 16, 1982.

Dahlberg, R. C. "Real-Time Image Filtering and Shading Correction." *Society of Photo-Optical Instrumentation Engineers* 207 (1979).

Dixon, R. C. *Spread Spectrum Systems*. New York: John Wiley & Sons, 1977.

Dorsey, E., and Caldwell, J. "Application of the PDSP Set to LPC System." Palo Alto, California: Telesensory Systems Inc., CHIG10-5/81/0000-0382, IEEE 1981.

Durden-Smith, J. "Nuclear Magnetic Resonance." *Technology,* January/ February, 1982.

Epstein, D. "An Adaptive Transversal Filter Using the μP7720." National Electronic Conference, October 27, 1981.

EyeCom. *Handbook of Image Processing.* Spatial Data Systems, Inc., 1980.

General Electric Medical Products Division. *Digital Fluorography: A Technology Update.* 1981.

General Electric Medical Products Division. *Introduction to Computed Tomography.* 1976.

Gill, S. P. "Voice Technology: An Integrated Approach." Hayward, California: VOTAN, CHI 738-4/82/0000-0001, IEEE, 1982.

Golomb, S. "Shift Register Sequences." San Francisco: Holden-Day, Inc., 1965.

Gould, R. G., Lipton, M. J., and Dahlberg, R. "Investigation of a Video Frame Averaging Digital Subtraction Fluoroscopic System." Society of Photo-Optical Instrumentation Engineers, Conference on Digital Radiography, Vol. 314. September 14-16, 1981.

Huang, T. S., ed. Two-*Dimensional Digital Signal Processing.* Berlin and New York: Springer, 1981.

Hurst, S. L. *The Logical Processing of Digital Signals.* New York: Crane and Russak, 1978.

Institute of Electrical and Electronics Engineers. *Programs for Digital Signal Processing.* New York: IEEE Press, 1979.

Intel Corp. "High-Speed Digital Servos for Motor Control Using the 2920/21 Signal Processor." Application Note AP-124. Santa Clara, California: Intel Corp., January 1982.

Intel Corp. "Intel iSBX Bus Specification." Santa Clara, California: Intel Corp., 1980.

Intel Corp. *2920 Analog Signal Processor Design Handbook.* Santa Clara, California: Intel Corp., 1980.

Intel Corp. *2920 Signal Processor Data Sheet.* Santa Clara, California: Intel Corp., 1980.

Intel Corp. *2920 Signal Processing Applications Compiler User's Guide.* Santa Clara California: Intel Corp., 1980.

Karwoski, R. "The FFT and a Fast FFT Processor Design." TRW application note. 1980.

Kunt, M., and DeCoulon, F., eds. *Signal Processing: Theories and Applications.* New York: North Hollywood, 1980.

Lerner, E. T. "Products That Talk." *IEEE Spectrum,* July 1982, pp. 32-37.

Li, W. H., and Hoff, M. E., Jr. "A General Purpose Formant Speech Synthesizer Module Using the Intel 2920 Signal Processor." API-III, Intel Corporation Application Note, October 30, 1980.

Mandel, A., Eichler, K., and Sprangenberg, L. "Effective Voice-Output Design Calls for High Speed Quality." *EDN,* September 10, 1982.

Mazzarini, T. "Specify Low-Speed Modems Properly." Electronic Design 9, April 26, 1978, pp. 72-66.

McDonough, K., Caudel, E., Magar, S., and Leigh, A. "Microcomputer with 32 Bit Arithmetic Does High-Precision Number Crunching." *Electronics,* February 24, 1982, p. 105.

Mengers, P. E. "Real-Time Digital Signal Processing: Its Advantages and Applications." *Optical Spectra,* December, 1981, pp. 54-58.

Mengers, P. E. "Recent Developments in Medical Imaging." *Electro Optical Systems Design.* Cahners Publications, 1982.

Mitra, S. K., and Kastrom, M. P. *Two-Dimensional Digital Signal Processing.* Stroudsburg, Pa.: Dowden, Hutchinson & Ross, 1978.

NEC Electronics. μPD7720 *Signal Processing Interface (SPI) Technical Manual.* NEC Electronics, U.S.A. Inc., 7720TM–5–82–1/2K.

Oppenheim, A. V., ed. *Applications of Digital Signal Processing.* Englewood Cliffs, N. J.: Prentice-Hall, 1978.

Rabiner, L. R., and Gold, B. *Theory and Application of Digital Signal Processing.* Englewood Cliffs, N. J.: Prentice-Hall, 1975.

Rabiner, L. R., Schafer, R. W., and Rader, C. M. "The Chirp Z-Transform Algorithm." *IEEE Transactions Audio Electroacoustics* AU-17, 1969, pp. 86-92.

Ramirez, R. W. "The Fast Fourier Transform's Errors Are Predictable, Therefore Manageable." *Electronics,* Vol. 47, No. 12, June 13, 1974, pp. 96-102.

Robillard, M. "Adapting A Speech Synthesizer." *Robotics Age,* July/August 1982.

Roden, M. S. *Digital and Data Communication.* Englewood Cliffs, N. J.: Prentice-Hall, 1982.

Sawyer, G., Johnson, J., Jurasek, D., and Kassel, S. "Special-Function Modules Ride on Computer Board." *Electronics,* April 10, 1980, pp. 135-140.

Schirm, L. "Multiplier-Accumulator Applications Notes." TRW LSI Products, January 1980.

"Signal-Processing Design Awaits Digital Takeover." *EDN,* June 24, 1981, p. 119.

Spectrum Analysis-Theory Implementation and Application. Rockleigh, N. J.: Wavetek Rockland, Inc., 1977.

Stremler, F. *Introduction of Communication Systems*. Reading, Mass.: Addison-Wesley, 1977.

Terrell, T. J. *Introduction to Digital Filters*. New York: Wiley, 1980.

Texas Instruments, Inc. "TMS320 Preliminary Functional Specifications." Texas Instruments document TMS320 ISS2, Texas Instruments, Inc., February 23, 1982.

Texas Instruments, Inc. "TMS 32010 and TMS 320M10 High-Performance 16/32 Bit Microcomputers." *Microcomputer Series, Preliminary Data Manual,* Texas Instruments, Inc., June 1982.

Wickey, D. and Kane, L. "Match Vocabulary, Speech Quality to Your Voice-Output Application." *EDN,* September 1, 1982.

INDEX

511